Foundations
of
Experimental
Embryology

Foundations
of
Experimental
Embryology

Edited by

Benjamin H. Willier
Professor Emeritus of Biology
The Johns Hopkins University

and

Jane M. Oppenheimer
Professor of Biology
Bryn Mawr College

Prentice-Hall, Inc.
Englewood Cliffs, N.J.

PRENTICE-HALL INTERNATIONAL, INC., *London*
PRENTICE-HALL OF AUSTRALIA, PTY., LTD., *Sydney*
PRENTICE-HALL OF CANADA, LTD., *Toronto*
PRENTICE-HALL FRANCE, S.A.R.L., *Paris*
PRENTICE-HALL OF INDIA (PRIVATE) LTD., *New Delhi*
PRENTICE-HALL OF JAPAN, INC., *Tokyo*
PRENTICE-HALL DE MEXICO, S.A., *Mexico City*

Library of Congress Catalog Card Number: 64-12546

Printed in the United States of America
32985-C

Dedicated to the memory of
Ross Granville Harrison

Preface

It is the purpose of this collection of articles, already recorded elsewhere in the literature, to answer a need of those who are interested in the early history of experimental embryology, and to encourage respect for those investigators who blazed the trails we now follow in contemporary embryology. In achieving these aims we tried to abide by two basic criteria in choosing the selections. Foremost was our desire to include only articles of unusual excellence and of both pioneering and enduring quality, namely those that have had a definite influence on the rise of experimental embryology. Secondly, we wished to maintain a balance of areas among the selections. We hope this small volume reflects something of the variety of the ideas, discoveries, and method of some of the beginning experimentalists in embryology and developmental physiology.

Most readers who have delved at all into the older literature of experimental embryology will, in all likelihood, find old favorites absent from this work. Some articles were too long for inclusion in a volume of this size. Such works give place to what it is hoped will be happy new discoveries for some readers. Embryology has not moved forward in a straight line, and as in all anthologies, some of the choices have been arbitrary. If the readers feel, however, that the basic aims of the editors have been achieved on the whole, the time and work invested in the preparation of this book will have been well spent. The editors will be content if others find the reading of the book as rewarding and intellectually stimulating as they did during its assemblage.

All of the articles, save that of Driesch, are reproduced in full without abridgment in any way. The editors feel strongly that it is important for the student to see how various workers have attacked key problems in the past—how ideas led to technical ways of testing their validity—how the results were analyzed and interpreted.

We terminate this preface by an expression of our deep indebtedness to all of those devoted friends of the embryo who have translated or aided in the translation of the articles written in the German language. We are also indebted to John Spurbeck for his care and skill in preparing the photographic reproductions of the original illustrations. To these we have a special sense of gratitude since without their help this work would have been difficult if not impossible. The editors, however, are solely responsible for the text of *Editors' Comments* preceding each of the eleven articles reproduced.

Benjamin H. Willier
Jane M. Oppenheimer

Table of Contents

Foundations
of
Experimental
Embryology

PART ONE

1888

Contributions to the Developmental Mechanics of the Embryo. On the Artificial Production of Half-Embryos by Destruction of One of the First Two Blastomeres, and the Later Development (Postgeneration) of the Missing Half of the Body

by W. ROUX

from the Anatomical Institute of Breslau

Roux, W. 1888. Beiträge zur Entwickelungsmechanik des Embryo. Ueber die künstliche Hervorbringung halber Embryonen durch Zerstörung einer der beiden ersten Furchungskugeln, sowie über die Nachentwickelung (Postgeneration) der fehlenden Körperhälfte.* Virchows Arch. path. Anat. u. Physiol. u. kl. Med. 114: 113-153; Resultate 289-291. Tafel II und III. Translated by Hans Laufer and printed by permission of Springer-Verlag.

* The portion of the article dealing with postgeneration is omitted in this translation.

During the second half of the nineteenth century it became gradually apparent that descriptive and comparative approaches to the study of how an embryo develops were inadequate for explaining the role of causal factors in the developmental process. The chief and most influential advocate of a new approach by experiment was Wilhelm Roux (1850-1924), a German anatomist. He founded a new discipline, causal analytical embryology, which he called developmental mechanics (Entwicklungsmechanik in German). He drew up a program for procedure, and established the Archiv für Entwicklungsmechanik der Organismen, the first volume of which appeared in 1894-95. It was the first and for several decades the leading international journal for causal analytical embryology and still is important today.

Roux defined the over-all program of Entwicklungsmechanik as the resolution of developmental processes into simpler, but still complex, functional processes, and the analysis of these functional processes into really simple ones, which may be identical with those which underlie inorganic or physico-chemical processes.

With causal analysis his guiding motive, Roux performed a simple type of experiment on the frog's egg at the two- and four-celled stages of cleavage. If he injured one of the two first-formed blastomeres, the surviving blastomere developed a half-embryo; this is the work that is presented here. With a strong predilection for philosophical speculations concerning development, Roux interpreted the facts as suggesting that differentiation might be one of two types, namely self-differentiation (independent or mosaic development) or correlative dependent differentiation (interaction of cells or groups of cells). He felt that the fact that one cell at the two-cell stage develops a half-embryo suggests that each cell develops independently of its neighbor and thus that the total development represents the summation of partial mosaic developments.

These conclusions of Roux were later shown to be erroneous for the frog's egg (A. Brachet, 1905; McClendon, 1910). However, Roux's work on the production of half-embryos is significant for several reasons. It initiated a new trend in method of attack on embryogenesis and marked a major turning point in its study by shifting emphasis from descriptive to experimental embryology. It pointed to a new direction for embryological thought and theoretical interpretation. It opened the way for a new and experimental attack on the significance of interrelationships between tissues and thus led to new insights into old problems of epigenesis. It is safe to say that all the analytical embryology of the late nineteenth and of the twentieth century has built upon foundations laid by Roux.

CONTRIBUTIONS TO THE DEVELOPMENTAL MECHANICS OF THE EMBRYO. ON
THE ARTIFICIAL PRODUCTION OF HALF-EMBRYOS BY DESTRUCTION OF ONE
OF THE FIRST TWO BLASTOMERES, AND THE LATER DEVELOPMENT (POST-
GENERATION) OF THE MISSING HALF OF THE BODY

The investigations that will be recorded in this article are closely connected with my previous works on developmental mechanics and presuppose therefore a knowledge of their results, at least for full understanding.
Since I have noticed that my previous works have remained almost unknown even to many specialists in the field, it appears proper to preface
this treatise, meant for a larger circle of readers, with a brief review of
the pertinent results.

The following investigation represents an effort to solve the problem
of self-differentiation[1]—to determine whether, and if so how far, the fertilized egg is able to develop independently as a whole and in its individual
parts. Or whether, on the contrary, normal development can take place
only through direct formative influences of the environment on the
fertilized egg or through the differentiating interactions of the parts
of the egg separated from one another by cleavage.

For the egg as a whole I answered this question by rotating eggs in
a perpendicular plane in such a way that, while the centrifugal force
did not inhibit their development, the eggs continuously altered their
orientation with respect to gravitational force, to the magnetic meridian
and to the source of light and warmth. The result was that normal
development was neither suspended, altered, nor even retarded by this
process. We can conclude from this that the typical structures of the
developing egg and embryo do not need any formative influence by
such external agencies for their formation, and that in this sense the
morphological development of the fertilized egg may be considered as
self-differentiation. Nevertheless, several possibilities of external formative influence still remain that have not been tested by this experiment.
These are of a very general character, for example His[2] made the hypothesis that many cells have a tendency to move toward the direction
from which oxygen enters, thus enlarging the surface of the embryo.
It is also conceivable that the blastomeres lying on the surface of the
blastula and the gastrula gradually become flatter on their external sur-

[1] Cf. W. Roux, Beiträge zur Entwickelungsmechanik des Embryo. No. 1. Zeitschr. f.
Biologie. 1885. Bd. XXI.

[2] W. His, Untersuchungen über die Bildung des Knochenfischembryo (Salmen). Arch.
f. Anat. u. Physiol., anat. Abth. 1878, S. 220.

faces only because influences from outside cause their transformation into functional epithelia, thereby producing a mechanical tendency towards the densest concentration possible and toward the minimizing of the external surface, in contrast to the previous tendency towards the greatest possible sphericity for each individual cell. These speculations must still be checked against reality. The fact also must not be overlooked that the influence of external agencies may be a necessary condition for development, even though these influences may have no directly formative effect. For example, no development at all will take place without a certain amount of heat and also, later, of oxygen. But it cannot be deduced from this that such agencies determine which part of the egg produces the eyes, the blastopore, or the neural groove, or that they are the cause for the specific formation of the parts, despite the fact that abnormal formations result from an abnormal rise in temperature according to Panum, Dareste and Gerlach.

It has thus been shown that the development of the form of the fertilized egg, apart from that of several more general structures, occurs without external formative forces. We therefore have to look for the formative forces in the egg itself, which imposes a very pleasant limitation on further investigation.

As the result of this insight, it seems to me necessary to determine first of all whether all or many parts of the egg must collaborate if its structures are to form normally, or whether, on the contrary, the parts of the egg separated from one another by cleavage are able to develop independently of one another, and to show also, if possible, what share in the normal development each of the two principles has—that of differentiating interaction of the parts with one another, and that of self-differentiation of the parts.

As an argument for a certain independence in the development of the individual blastomeres, one could utilize, although not with certainty, the following fact about the egg of the frog, found by myself and shortly thereafter by Pflüger. This is that the first plane of cleavage of the egg represents the median plane of the future embryo, thus separating the material of the right and of the left half of the body, a fact which has been determined independently by van Beneden and Julin[3] for the ascidians. M.v.Kowalewski[4] later made observations that indicate similar conditions in the case of a teleost (*Carassius auratus*). At the same time I found a fact that we will use later on, that the cleavage plane perpendicular to the median plane of the future animal can be formed first

3 Ed. van Beneden et Ch. Julin, La segmentation chez les Ascidiens et ses rapports avec l'organisation de la larve. Arch. de Biologie. T.V. 1884.

4 Miecz. v. Kowalewski, Ueber die ersten Entwickelungsprozesse der Knochenfische. Zeitschr. für wissenschaftl. Zool. 1886.

although it normally appears second—and I later succeeded in producing this anachronism artificially.

In addition, it was already known to previous authors that the upper, black hemisphere of the frog's egg always corresponds to a definite side of the embryo, the dorsal side, according to these authors. This interpretation could no longer be considered correct, however, after my investigations and those of Pflüger. I recently have shown by means of certain localized defects on the cleaved egg that the middle portion of the black hemisphere of the frog's egg provides the material for the ventral surface of the embryo, in contrast to the previous view.[5]

I found moreover that the cephalic and caudal ends of the embryo are already determined at the stage of the first cleavage of the frog's egg and that in the case of *Rana esculenta,* the green or water frog, they are already recognizable by an oblique position of the axis of the egg, a condition which had already been determined independently by Van Beneden and Julin for the ascidians and later by M.v.Kowalewski for *Carassius* (although the latter author did not take the occasion to mention his predecessors as having observed this fundamental behavior in relatively closely related classes of animals). It is worth mentioning that observations pertinent to this matter had already been recorded in the posthumous papers of G. Newport, published in 1854. These aroused no notice at the time and were not discovered again until later. I showed furthermore[6] that the position of the cephalic and the caudal side of the embryo in the egg is normally determined by the union of the nucleus of the sperm and that of the ovum, the half of the egg penetrated by the male nucleus becoming the caudal half of the embryo, while the opposite half of the egg produces the cephalic half. It was possible to recognize the direct causal connection because I succeeded in fertilizing each egg from an arbitrarily chosen meridian and thereby determined the caudal side of the embryo of the egg at will. In the case of other animals where the side of the egg fertilized does indeed coincide with a definite side of the embryo, but where spermatozoa penetrate into the egg at a typical point, such a conclusion cannot be drawn with certainty but can at most be expressed as a conjecture.[7]

[5] Anatom. Anzeiger. 1888, No. 25. Ueber die Lagerung des Materiales des Medullarrohres im gefurchten Froschei.

[6] Beiträge zur Entwickelungsmechanik des Embryo. No. 4. Arch. für mikrosk. Anat. 1887. Bd. 29.

[7] According to my previous investigations the location of the following form changes are normally determined by the arbitrarily selected location of the region of fertilization.

(1) The spermatozoon takes a typically curved course in the vertical meridional plane which passes through the point of sperm entry: in the fertilization plane.

(2) The union of the two sexual nuclei takes place in the fertilization plane.

(3) In *Rana fusca,* on the side of the egg opposite the side of fertilization, the dark

Such is the case with the hen's egg, where it has long been known that the location of the embryo is determined with regard to the axis of the whole egg, even though the exact relation of the median plane to the first cleavage and the exact relation of this to the direction of the nuclear fusion has not been discovered. V. Kölliker[8] had already surmised that that portion of the blastodisc of the hen's egg that divides most rapidly develops later into the posterior part of the blastoderm, in which the first traces of the embryo originate; and His[9] has shown further that in the blastodisc of the hen's egg after it has been laid every region of the external germ layer corresponds to a definite part of the future animal. For the further development of these parts, however, His assumes—in contrast to possible self-differentiation of the individual regions—mechanical interactions of the region of origin with adjacent or more distant regions. For two of these structures, the neural tube and the intestinal tube, I was able to demonstrate,[10] by separation of their primordia from the parts lateral to them, that such interactions are not necessary, since in spite of their isolation the development of the primordia was completed, and even faster than normally. According to this we should look for the formative causes effective in the development of these tubes in the parts which compose the tube itself, while the neighboring regions even offer a resistance to the development of the tubes, which must gradually be overcome. But from these results we must not deduce that all organs acquire their form by self-differentiation of the complex of

---

hemisphere becomes lighter and takes the form of a gray crescent adjacent to the white hemisphere. This crescent is symmetrically oriented with respect to the meridian of fertilization. In the case of the green frog the pigment is likewise displaced, although perhaps in a somewhat different manner, so that the white portion reaches farther up on the same side.

(4) The first plane of division lies in the plane of the meridian of fertilization.

(5) The first appearance of the blastopore occurs in the meridian of fertilization, namely:

(6) On the half of the egg lying opposite to the side of fertilization, approximately at the border of the dark hemisphere and at the margin which subsequently becomes lighter (see No. 3).

(7) The lateral blastopore lips develop symmetrically with respect to this meridian.

(8) Both the neural ridges and the whole later embryo are located symmetrically with respect to the meridian of fertilization, that is to say, the plane of the meridian of fertilization becomes the median plane of the animal.

(9) The side of the egg that is fertilized becomes the caudal side of the animal.

In order to gain insight into the causal relationships upon which these multiple correlations are based, I have made an effort to produce artificial separations of these correlations and have frequently been successful. A further report on this matter will be forthcoming.

8 A. Kölliker, Entwickelungsgeschichte des Menschen und der höheren Thiere. Leipzig 1879.

9 His, Unsere Körperform und das physiologische Problem ihrer Entstehung. 1874.

10 Beitrag 1 zur Entwickelungsmechanik des Embryo. Zeitschrift für Biologie 1885.

parts of which they are composed. On the contrary, each case must be investigated individually, and for many structures it is beyond all doubt that they are produced by mechanical interactions with neighboring parts, for example the shape of the liver, the lungs (His, Braune), bones (A. Fick), paths of many vessels (G. Schwalbe), etc. In connection with this I have shown, by producing an artificial rhomboid fossa on the neural tube which survived the deforming effect, that the embryo possesses vital adaptability to passive deformation to a very high degree; thus the theoretical possibility of such an origin has been demonstrated for the normal rhomboid fossa, which would agree with His' assumption.

In addition, numerous facts of pathology also argue for the self-differentiation of the parts of the egg, for example dermoid encysted tumors, etc., facts which I have collected in the article last referred to. Yet only direct experimentation with the egg can clarify for us with perfect certainty the actual participation of self-differentiation of the parts of the egg in normal development. Years ago[11] I worked along these lines and verified, in general, that operations that produce an extrusion of material from the cleaving and cleaved egg do not prevent development or cause general malformation. The resulting embryos develop rather normally and have only a localized defect or a localized malformation.

In order to acquire more specialized knowledge, I used the portion of the spawning period in the spring of 1887 that remained, after the conclusion of time-consuming experiments, for pertinent investigations on which I will report in the present article.

Although, as will be seen, the results were very extensive, many important questions had to be left temporarily unanswered, questions that could have been easily answered by continuation and a slight variation of the experiments. This present study is therefore only one installment, as it were, of the theme treated, that of self-differentiation.

The plan of the experiments was as follows:

In the first experiment the eggs of the green frog, *Rana esculenta,* were placed individually in glass dishes, and the oblique position of the black hemisphere and the direction of cleavage were sketched during the formation of the first cleavage. Then one of the first two blastomeres was pricked once or more with a fine needle. The present position of the egg was then compared with the drawing. A new sketch was made if there was a difference, and the location of the puncture points was

[11] "Vorläufige Mittheilung über causal-autogenetische Experimente," Vortrag gehalten am 15. Febr. 1884. in der Schlesischen Gesellschaft für vaterländische Cultur. (Lecture delivered on February 15th, 1884 to the Silesian Society for Native Culture.) My neglect in sending in a review resulted in there being no notice of that lecture in the corresponding annual report of the Silesian Society. The report was first published in Beitrag 1 zur Entwickelungsmechanik, Zeitschrift für Biologie 1885.

indicated, along with the position of the egg material exuded through them, the exovates. Unfortunately most of these eggs in the first experiments either did not develop at all or developed normally, in spite of the fact that the punctured blastomere often discharged large amounts of material and became filled up again by a flow of substances from the neighboring cell. As a result, in addition to their loss, an extreme disorder of the egg substances must have been present. Therefore, after the destruction of a single blastomere I could observe the externally visible processes in a few eggs only. In many of the eggs, the unoperated control eggs as well as the experimental ones, occasional malformations were already occurring, as is customary toward the end of the spawning period. I have already described this effect briefly in a previous publication. Since ability of the eggs to develop normally might cease completely at any time, I operated after the formation of the first cleavage on great numbers of unisolated eggs lying together in clusters. After several hours, or the next day, I selected and placed in separate dishes those eggs in which the operated blastomere had not cleaved. Occasionally the second cleavage occurred during the operation on the first egg, and I then pierced two of the blastomeres lying next to one another, or perhaps only one of four.

Even after repeated puncture of a cell with a fine needle, and in spite of considerable exovation, the cell often developed normally. So, beginning on the third day, I heated the needle by holding it against a brass sphere for a heat supply, heating the sphere as necessary. In this case only a single puncture was made, but the needle was ordinarily left in the egg until an obvious light brown discoloration of the egg substance appeared in its vicinity. Some of this discolored material stuck to the needle when it was pulled out and formed a broad slightly protruding cone—a sign that it had become firmer and thus was partly coagulated. As a result of this, exovates no longer issued even out of the puncture points. I now had better results; they were as follows. In about 20% of the operated eggs only the undamaged cell survived the operation, while the majority were completely destroyed and a very few, where the needle had possibly already become too cold, developed normally. I thus developed and preserved over a hundred eggs with one of their halves destroyed, and, of these, 80 were sectioned completely. Eggs that were intended for the latter purpose were taken out and killed from time to time. More were taken from the early stages, those of the morula and the blastula, than from the later stages already provided with the rudiments of special organs.

In each experiment we likewise, although more rarely, observed in the unoperated control egg a failure of one of the two or four first blastomeres to develop as well as other malformations. These eggs were also preserved at various stages and sectioned for comparison with the operated eggs. The same was done with eggs which did not develop in spite of their having been placed in seminal fluid.

Since the treatment of the eggs with respect to preservation and staining is important for the findings in the nuclei, and since it offers many difficulties in itself, I will briefly report the essential facts about it and my experiences which depart somewhat from those of previous authors. In a slight variation of Born's modification of O. Hertwig's method, the eggs were killed by placing them in water of about 80° C. for several minutes; this not only kills the egg and makes it rather resistant due to coagulation, but suffices also to make it easy to cut off the periblast. Hardening and preservation were done by Born's method in 70% to 80% alcohol. Staining was done, according to O. Schultze's method, in borax carmine followed by differentiation in weak hydrochloric acid alcohol. Then, for the purpose of embedding, the eggs were transferred into absolute alcohol overnight, placed in toluene for several minutes and then for several hours, or days if preferred, in old thick resinous oil of turpentine. The eggs were placed on blotting paper and freed of excess turpentine with a brush dipped in toluene. The eggs, perfectly suited for sketching, were stored dry, but one must be careful not to use too much toluene in rinsing since otherwise not enough turpentine resin will remain in the specimen to keep it pliant. After the evaporation of the toluene the eggs become as hard as stone and are then correspondingly brittle when cut. This happened to me, unfortunately, with the majority of the preparations I demonstrated in Wiesbaden at the Naturalists' meeting, due to my efforts to clean the surface completely of turpentine. Should this happen, however, the eggs are still not completely lost. I softened them by placing them for two or three days in a 30% solution of potassium carbonate; then they were again dehydrated and saturated with turpentine. A portion of them remained undamaged and proved upon microscopic examination after sectioning to be well preserved internally also. Some however were already so softened on the outside, before the inside became sufficiently so, that their outer portions wore off during the following manipulations and I had only the remains to cut—which fortunately provided the most important regions anyway.

Using Spee's method, the eggs were embedded in boiled paraffin which melted at 50°. I found embedding overnight to be better than the shorter half-hour period, and I also observed no damage in increasing the temperature to 60° C. I found danger of the eggs becoming hard only in toluene, that evaporates completely, after which, as has been mentioned, the eggs become as hard as stone if another fluid or soft substance such as turpentine resin or paraffin does not penetrate them immediately.

The preservation and staining of the nuclei was quite good in many of the preparations and the mitotic structures were therefore easy to see. In other specimens that seemed to have been treated exactly the same way, but had perhaps been overheated in the process of killing, defined structural detail of the nuclei was no longer recognizable.

The information reported below on abnormal nuclear structure cannot, because of the latter's very nature, be attributed to possible changes due to the preparation of the eggs. Moreover, the abnormal nuclear structure was found also in preparations which showed well-preserved normal nuclei in other regions. In spite of good preservation of structure of interphase nuclei, so extraordinarily few mitotic figures were perceptible in many embryos that I had to assume, along with Flemming, that the majority of the mitotic figures (which certainly occur frequently in the process of continuous development) had either reverted to the interphase type during the heat-killing of the egg or had rapidly gone to completion.

The experiments themselves consisted, as has been noted, in altering by operation one of the two cells formed after the appearance of the first cleavage plane in the fertilized egg[12] and thus depriving it of its ability to develop. Coming now to the report of our experimental results, we will first present the processes which take place in the untreated egg-half after this crude interference.

In many cases no developmental phenomena were perceptible in this cell. More often the symptoms of death already described were apparent, gray discoloration and the formation of spots.[13] In other cases these blastomeres went through several further cleavages only to die likewise, as I have elsewhere described, with an accompanying maximal flattening

[12] J. Dewitz recently reported (Biolog. Centralbl. 1887. pg. 93) that unfertilized frogs' eggs can be stimulated to the point of cleavage by placing them in mercuric chloride solution. The more detailed report promised has not yet been published. Nevertheless, this assertion has been reported, unquestioned, in various periodicals. I attempted to check it by placing unfertilized frog eggs in a series of 24 dishes with mercuric chloride solutions of varying strengths (from 0.001-1.4 parts per hundred). In the weakest solution a clouding of the jelly coat and the egg water occurred, if at all, only after several hours. Somewhat stronger solutions caused more cloudiness of the jelly coat in a shorter time and flaky coagulation of the egg water. On the other hand, I noticed in 0.5% solution that the eggs often burst open along half or whole meridians. When this happened the edges of the rupture were either sharp, slightly serrated and granular as a result of the strong coagulation of the yolk; or, if the coagulation had not yet penetrated deeply enough at the time that the surface layer coagulated and shrank, fluid yolk forced its way in fine lines out of the split and then coagulated also. Occasionally such fissures were approximately perpendicular to each other and provided on casual observation an appearance similar to one of the first cleavages. In other cases the egg did not burst open along the great circles or even along circular lines at all but in irregular lines oblique to one another. One cannot, however, designate such coagulation phenomena as cleavages, and thus as vital processes of definite importance in developmental mechanics.

[13] Beitr. zur Entwickelungsmechanik No. 1. Zeitschr. f. Biologie. 1885.

of the cells against one another, occasionally leading to the disappearance of the externally visible cleavage planes. On the basis of the third type of behavior, about to be described, we can properly assume that in these first two cases the supposedly undamaged cells had actually been directly affected by the operation and died from its effects and not as a result of the failure of interaction with the other cells.

In the third type of development, which was achieved in approximately 20% of the treated eggs in the last experiments, the untreated cell continued to survive. Various results might have been expected from this: for example, abnormal processes might intervene which would lead to bizarre structures. Or the single half of the egg, which, after all, according to many authors, is a complete cell with a nucleus completely equivalent in quality to the first segmentation nucleus, might develop into a correspondingly small individual. These authors see in the mechanism of indirect nuclear segmentation, on my authority as it were, only a contrivance for qualitative halving. I have repeatedly and clearly opposed this opinion. But instead of the possible surprises as postulated above an even more amazing thing happened; the one cell developed in many cases into a half-embryo generally normal in structure, with small variations occurring only in the region of the immediate neighborhood of the treated half of the egg. These variations will be mentioned in the section on the behavior of this latter half.

By repeated cleavages of the undamaged half of the egg a structure was at first produced which deserves the name of a *semimorula verticalis,* since it is built substantially like the vertical half of a morula. I mean by this that it was a hemispherical structure which consisted, in its upper region, of tightly packed small pigmented cells, and in its lower region of larger unpigmented cells. One component, however, of the normal morula was not properly developed in the eleven *semimorulae verticales* that were sectioned. This was the segmentation cavity. It should have been represented by an approximately hemispherical cavity adjacent to the undeveloped half and delimited by closely packed cells. Instead of this, the internal cells are merely loosely arranged with interstices between them. Sometimes there is a larger but not sharply delimited cavity that is separated from the undeveloped half by a layer of cells. Occasionally there is no indication at all of the formation of the cavity, not even the loose arrangement of the cells.

The next stage, the blastula, is not distinctly separated from the morula stage, since the blastula develops from the morula mainly by a further diminution in size of the cells and an enlargement of the internal cavity. This latter results from a gradual thinning of the roof of the cavity, which can be extremely varied in different individuals.

I found several *semiblastulae verticales* corresponding to this stage and sectioned them. The interesting thing here is that at this stage the internal cavity proves to be well defined, bordered by densely packed cells in the majority of cases, so that in comparison with the condition in the semimorulae the cells must have subsequently rearranged themselves and approximated themselves closely together. The blastocoele thus formed sometimes lies completely enclosed in the developed half, i.e., it is separated from the undeveloped half by a single or multiple layer of cells (Plate II, Fig. 1). Sometimes it borders directly on the boundary surface, which is approximately flat. In one case, however, it extends into this half (Fig. 2) and has thus acquired approximately the shape of a complete blastocoele; this however was caused merely by an abnormally large secretion of fluid by the developing half. In another case there is no indication at all of the formation of a cavity; the cells lie tightly together at all points and therefore border directly on the undeveloped half.

I thought that I had preserved a very large number of half-embryos at the next stage of development, gastrulation. However, after they were sectioned, it turned out that the majority were still at the blastula stage and that, at the first superficial examination, beginning gastrulation has merely been simulated by a slight indentation of the semiblastula toward the operated half of the egg. In contrast, another group of eggs exhibited, on the thickened free edge, structures that actually characterize a still more advanced stage, so that I have among the sectioned eggs only three half-embryos which are really at the gastrula stage.

The median plane can already be clearly distinguished in the normal gastrula as a plane passing through the center of the whole spherical structure and dividing symmetrically both the horseshoe-shaped blastopore and, internally, the cavity of the archenteron that is continuous with it. The cavity of the archenteron is covered on the outside by a thin double layered sheet that is dark on the outside. The horseshoe-shaped rim of this sheet forms, together with the adjacent white yolk mass, the blastopore. The dark sheet develops into the dorsal half of the embryo and I have therefore designated it as the dorsal plate. The middle of the horseshoe-shaped rim represents the head region and the open part of the arc the tail region of the embyro. Later the two halves of the horseshoe-shaped edge of the dorsal plate approach one another, proceeding in the cephalocaudal direction, and then merge. Normally the horseshoe-shaped rim is divided symmetrically by the median plane of the embryo.

As has been mentioned, because of the turning in of the free edge of the living half it is extremely difficult in half-embryos to identify the pertinent structural features by superficial examination and to judge whether the semigastrula is a lateral or an anterior or a posterior one.

Figure 3 represents a rather advanced stage, where one would be inclined to identify the section as a median one through a *semigastrula*

Plates II and III

All these figures represent frog embryos (Rana fusca and esculenta).

F	Segmentation cavity	Ch	Chorda dorsalis (notochord)
Ec	Ectoderm (external germ layer)	Md	Neural fold
En	Endoderm (internal germ layer)	U	Gastrocoele; in Fig. 12 blastopore
Ms	Mesoderm (middle germ layer)	D	Yolk cells
		V	Vacuoles

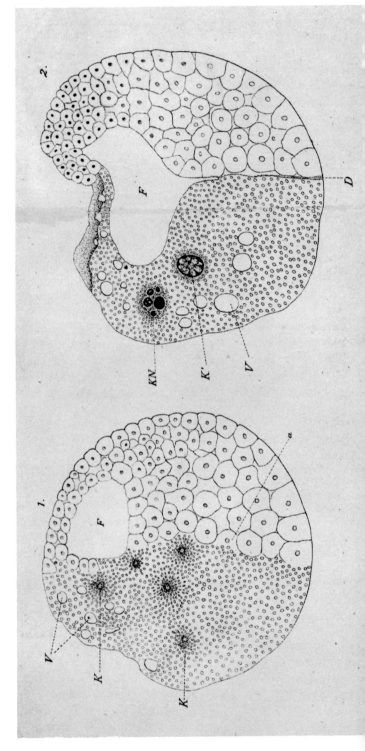

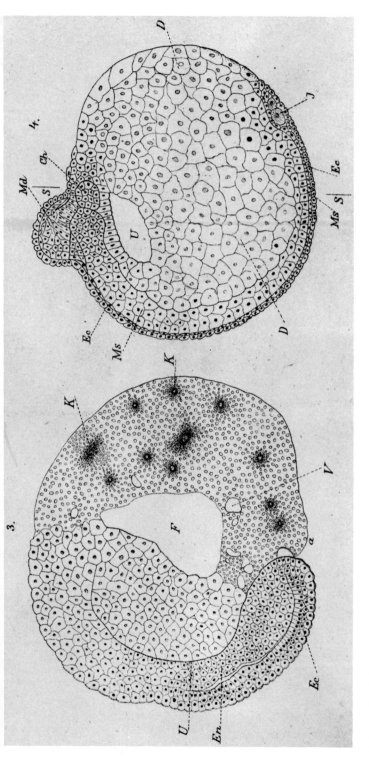

Fig. 1 *Semiblastula verticalis*, vertical meridianal section. The cells are sketched schematically. (a) a cell bounded only toward the developed side of the egg.   Fig. 2 *Semiblastula verticalis*, section of the same. Extension of the cleavage cavity into the undeveloped half of the egg. *KN* nuclear nest. *K'* a very large nucleus with reticular structure.   Fig. 3 *Semigastrula lateralis*, oblique longitudinal section.   Fig. 4 *Hemiembryo sinister*, cross section. *S-S* the median place. The right half of the egg is already completely cellular as a result of the post-generation of the germ layers which has begun. Notochord has already caught up in its development to the normal size of the cross section. *J* two yolk cells, which have remained young.

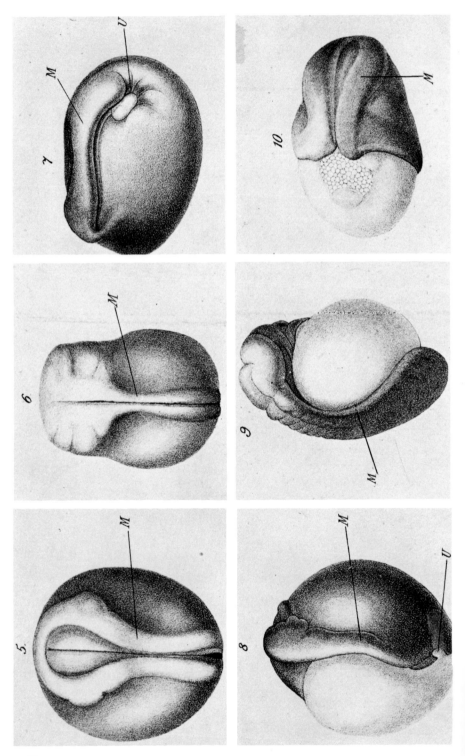

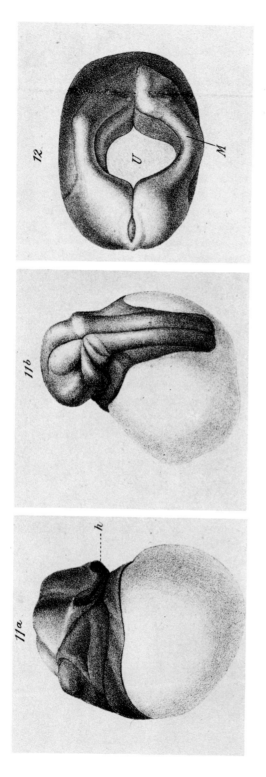

Fig. 5 Dorsal surface of a normal frog embryo with neural folds still separated. **Fig. 6** The same, with neural folds already united. **Fig. 7** *Hemiembryo dexter*, with postgeneration of the external germ layer already almost completed. **Fig. 8** The same, older, but with less post-generation. **Fig. 9** *Hemiembryo sinister*, still older, almost without post-generation. **Fig. 10** *Hemiembryo anterior*, already in the process of post-genera-tion. **Fig. 11** *Hemiembryo anterior*, older. (a) ventral side. (h) the adhesive gland. (b) dorsal side. Post-generation of the neural folds is already far advanced. **Fig. 12** Three-quarter embryo with *asyntaxia medullaris* (Roux). The left half of the head is not developed, the ectoderm is nevertheless already post-generated in its area. (U) a part of the blastopore that has re-mained open.

anterior. Since however the direction of the cut is not perpendicular to the surface separating the developed from the undeveloped half, but runs almost parallel to it, and since the dorsal plate is present in almost its entire length, the section figured proves to be one through a *semi-gastrula lateralis.* This diagnosis is easily and certainly confirmed if we mentally integrate the appearance of all the sections. The lumen of the archenteron is still only a slit in spite of its great length. The outer layer, the ectoderm, is clearly distinguishable from the inner layer, the endoderm. The blastula fluid and therefore the blastocoele also is still maintained, which is not normally the case at this time. The incorrectness of the view of previous authors, according to which the side of the egg adjacent to the blastocoele becomes the dorsal side of the embryo, is clearly evident in the more lateral sections where the blastocoele is located on the ventral side of the egg opposite to the dorsal plate. This is true in the developed as well as the undeveloped halves.

The next stage of development normally shows the first external rudiments of special organs, especially the primordium of the central nervous system in the form of a neural plate with both its lateral edges raised as the neural folds. The neural folds are separated from one another by a considerable distance in the cephalic region but gradually approach one another until they almost touch (Plate III, Figs. 5 and 6). The egg can already be called an embryo at this stage. We must now inquire what the unoperated half has formed that may correspond to this stage.

Figures 7 to 9 represent three of the most nearly normal specimens in various degrees of development. These as well as four other similar specimens that I possess all have a single neural fold only, which, however, is developed in its full length and normally shaped apart from inconsequential irregularities.

I must mention in this connection that even in normal embryos the shape of the folds at various ages is not always so constant and stereotyped as in the beautiful models by Ecker-Ziegler so frequently reproduced by later authors. On the contrary, rather high degrees of variation occur that have already been partially described by O. Hertwig[14] and myself.[15] Many of these variations seem to represent reversions to processes that are known in fishes, and that are caused primarily by anachronisms in differentiation and growth of the various parts. Such anachronisms are also evident in the relative delay or acceleration of the development of the individual germ layers. For example, many otherwise normal embryos possessing rather undifferentiated neural folds already show development within the mesoderm, the endoderm and in

14 O. Hertwig, Die Entwickelung des mittleren Keimblattes der Wirbelthiere. Jena 1883. Taf. V. Fig. 5.

15 Beitrag 1 zur Entwickelungsmechanik des Embryo. Zeitschr. f. Biol. 1885. Bd. XXI.

the chorda dorsalis that normally does not occur until nearly the time that the neural tube closes. In these cases there is an obvious retardation in the ectoderm as compared with the development of the two other germ layers. Such variations can easily lead to differences of opinion between observers should one of them attempt general deductions on the basis of insufficient material. The rates of development of the two lateral halves of the body also show variations of a lesser degree and provide the advantageous opportunity of permitting two stages of development to be observed in the same specimen.

Such variations, caused by inhibiting factors and the retardation of various processes, occur frequently toward the end of the spawning period, or as the result of an insufficient supply of air. Frequently, however, they are compensated for during the further course of development.

I sectioned six of the *hemiembryones laterales* that were obtained as a result of the above operation. Inspection of the cross-sections shows only half of the neural plate to be present. This is especially noticeable in the more advanced stages where the neural fold is already formed and typical in structure (Fig. 4). The typical arrangement of the cells of the more advanced neural tube is already nicely attained in many preparations but not so obvious in other places. The older embryos show the neural tissue in the cephalic region to be thickened and appropriately shaped. The originally lateral side of the ectoderm (the horny layer) had previously joined with the lateral edge of the neural plate, and in the course of the formation of the neural fold had been raised along with it to approach the midline. In the oldest embryo this horny layer had already separated from the neural part, although there is no opportunity here for it to merge with a similar layer of the other half. For the time being it projects unattached toward the other undeveloped half. This free edge, as well as the dorsal edge of the *semimedulla lateralis,* is curved ventrally, which also occurs in normal embryos.

The cavity of the archenteron has taken form only in the developed half and likewise extends only as far as the chorda. Its lumen is often too narrow and still slit-shaped. In other cases it has enlarged somewhat but is still constricted in the cephalic region by too great a concentration of yolk. The endoderm is normally constituted.

The formation of the mesoderm and the chorda dorsalis is normally a new feature of this phase. Our half-embryos also have formed these parts. I have no specimen in the very short phase in which we could gain clear insight into the origin of the mesoderm. In all the preparations it is already completely separated and in some cases it shows the normal cross-sectional appearance and the normal arrangement of the cells. In the older embryos the separation into lateral plate and somitic mesoderm is taking place or is already completed. In the oldest embryo the latter is already split up into somites. The lateral half of the mesoderm is thus normally developed (compare Fig. 4, Ms).

Since the chorda dorsalis is a median organ, it is of special interest to ascertain whether it is completely or only half formed. In order to judge this, a more exact discussion of its normal development is necessary. The complete separation of the chorda dorsalis from the three other layers takes place later posteriorly than anteriorly. It separates first from the ectoderm, then from the mesoderm, and finally from the endoderm.[16] Occasionally there is a stretch in the middle where it is not completely separated from the endoderm, while farther back it is already completely separate, and then farther posteriorly it again seems to be at an earlier stage of development[17]. Where it is completely separate it is round, oval or oblong in cross-section and is of quite variable thickness at different points along its length, generally decreasing in size from back to front. However very evident exceptions to this rule occur. Occasionally swellings are followed by constrictions in a regularly occurring fashion. Moreover the thickness varies considerably between chordas of different individuals at the same stage of development. The number of cells of approximately corresponding points may fluctuate almost by a factor of two.

Our half-embryos showed the chorda cell layer still connected with the intestinal endoderm in some places, and deflected dorsally as in the normal structure, but corresponding in its extent only to the lateral half of the anlage. Usually, however, the chorda is already completely separated and is round or slightly oval in cross-section. Thus we see that a half-oval has not been formed. The diameters seem to be somewhat smaller in size and number of the cells than is the case in whole embryos, but this could not be determined with certainty because of the normal variation in thickness. Therefore I wish only to mention that the periphery of its cross-section was formed by five cells at its thinnest point, whereas in apparently corresponding stages and regions of normal em-

16 I clearly saw matamerism in the separation of the *chorda dorsalis* from the mesoderm. For in each third or fourth section the separation was still hardly recognizable, while, in the sections lying between, the separation was already evident in the completed rearrangement of the cells. This is the case at the time when the chorda still is associated with the endoderm but already lies like a raised strand between the mesoderm halves on both sides, a strand which is still connected with the ectoderm only in a few places, i.e. the strand is not yet separated from the ectoderm by rearrangement of its cells.

17 At the same time it may be seen in this region, where separation from the endoderm has only just been completed, how the latter remedies the defect thus created in its continuity. At first this occurs exactly in the same way as at the beginning of the healing of a wound, by flattening of the epithelial cells at the edge and thus a covering over of the defect only. Subsequently, of course, the epithelial cells multiply and become taller.

bryos the whole chorda consists of eight to ten cells, although sometimes only six.

I wish to remark at this point, however, that I found several clearly recognizable half-chordas, *semichordae*, in preparations which I will describe later. This being so, the finding in the present instance of almost complete chordas must not be attributed to primary formation of the whole but rather to a very early postgeneration of the missing lateral side.

The median plane of the whole embryo, which in our half-embryos is defined only by the surface between the developed and undeveloped halves of the eggs, was represented in many cases by a straight line on the cross-section. That is to say, the dorsal and ventral edge of the *semimedulla,* the center of the chorda, the dorsal and ventral edge of the primitive intestinal cavity, or of the endoderm, and the ventral edge of the ectoderm lay approximately in a straight line. However, in the cephalocaudal direction, as we have said, the *semimedulla lateralis* was bent concavely toward the missing half.

Lateral displacement of the chorda dorsalis, which we observed once, was probably likewise a result of the disturbed mechanical correlation of materials, caused by a missing half. The dorsal part of the endoderm in this case remained against the median line between the semimedulla and the ventral parts. Nevertheless it is interesting that the axial parts can form and develop after such a considerable shift from their normal orientation.

There is a different reason for another phenomenon we also observed repeatedly, the absence of endoderm and archenteron when an approximately well-formed neural fold, chorda, and half of the mesoderm are present. This malformation, which I will call *anentoblastia* and from which an anenteric (gutless) condition will probably result at a more advanced state, cannot be directly related to our present experiments, since I have observed it not only in lateral hemiembryos but also in bilaterally symmetrical embryos, both operated and unoperated. I will describe these in greater detail at some other time. Here I only wish to mention a few points to which I shall refer later. In bilaterally symmetrical embryos the two neural folds are located far apart, occupying the lateral edges of the embryo which resembles an oval plate, almost flat. Under each neural ridge is found a well-differentiated *semichorda lateralis* which is round and easily distinguished in the cross-section by the three or four cells which compose it. A similar though lesser separation of the neural folds is often found confined only to certain regions, especially near the posterior half of the spinal cord. In such a case presence of the endoderm could be demonstrated in the sections. On the other hand, repeated observation of the living egg easily established that the large fissure between the two medullary folds represented the blastopore, at least the remains of it. Now according to other observations of mine, the half neural plate on each side is adjacent to the lateral lip of the blastopore, and the normal symmetrical shape of the neural plate is produced by the approach and fusion of these lips. Therefore if we wish to be exact we cannot designate the absence of fusion confirmed by these observations with the term *spina bifida,* which is customarily used to describe this condition repeatedly observed in higher animals. We must use instead the term *asyntaxia medullaris* (from ἀσυνταξία, non-union) or, simply indicating the result, *diastasis medullaris.* I prefer the first term since it suggests the actual phenomenon.

In cases of *asyntaxia medullaris* in the middle and caudal regions of the embryo I often saw in the course of time the neural folds approach each other caudally. As a result only a hole remained, midway along the length of the neural tube, that later completely closed. What has happened here therefore has only been a retardation of the growing downwards from the equator of the egg of the half dorsal plates from the two sides; qualitative differentiation was not inhibited and produced the neural folds before the fusion of the halves of the dorsal plates. An analogy between the formation of the embryonic anlagen in amphibians and in fishes is quite clearly illustrated by this form of *diastasis medullaris* and by the derivation of the archenteron from the blastopore. The *asyntaxia medullaris* can thus correspond to the "retardation in the joining of the halves of the germ ring to form the middle and posterior parts of the embryo" described by Rauber.[18] Rauber used the term dehiscence of the embryonic primordia to describe this condition, but for the reasons I have stated this does not seem as good a term as the one I have used. Likewise I consider the term *hemididymus* that he used to describe this retardation to have been appropriate only when it was necessary to contrast it with true twinning, which is no longer the case since von Recklinghausen's[19] basic treatment of the problem. Also von Recklinghausen's interpretation of *spina bifida* receives further support from explanation of the *diastasis medullaris* observed in the frog.

In addition to the lateral half-embryos I have now to describe several other imperfect embryos. Some of these also are produced by specimens treated after the first cleavage and are associated with a not infrequent variation in the temporal sequence of the cleavages, which, as we have seen, has a certain importance for the future embryo. Occasionally the actual second cleavage, separating head and tail ends, appears first[20] as I

18 A. Rauber, Formbildung und Formstörung in der Entwickelung von Wirbelthieren. Leipzig 1880. S. 35 und 123.

19 v. Recklinghausen, Untersuchungen über die Spina bifida. Berlin 1886, and this Archiv Bd. 105.

20 My view of this event, that the position of the median plane of the embryo does not coincide with the plane of the first cleavage, and is merely an anachronism,

have proved in opposition to Rauber and Pflüger. It was hoped that such eggs would produce half-embryos of a different character as a result of operations after this first cleavage, provided the untreated cell was capable of development. I tried to achieve the same thing after the second cleavage by puncturing both the two front or the two rear cells. I actually succeeded in this way in producing anterior and posterior half-embryos. One day I produced a substantial number of *semigastrulae anteriores* and set them aside for further development. Beautiful anterior half-embryos developed from these, *hemiembryones anteriores,* the great majority of which were lost during their further development due to an occurrence that I shall describe in the second part. At the present moment I have only four preserved anterior half-embryos. Figures 10 and 11 show the external appearance of two of these anterior hemi-embryos; the embryo shown in Fig. 10 has only the front half of the two neural folds. The two normal embryos shown in Figs. 5 and 6 can be examined for comparison, even though they are at a different stage of development. The cross-sections made frontally in the case of the embryo in Fig. 10 and approximately transversely in Fig. 14 reveal the normal internal structure of the neural plate with its neural folds, as well as of the chorda, the mesoderm, and the endoderm. However, this latter encloses only a slit-shaped archenteron cavity that is too narrow cephalically at this stage of development. In both cases the displacement of the yolk, which normally proceeds in a caudoventral direction, was impossible, due to the resistance of the undeveloped posterior half of the egg. The posterior half of the body is missing, just as if it had been cut off; in Fig. 11 we see the subsequent postgeneration of one part of it (see below).

I would like to mention further that the Anatomical Institute here recently received a calf foetus which was developed almost to full maturity. It represented a typical *hemitherium anterius* in its externally visible parts, the whole rump half being absent. The internal organs are at the moment still covered by a translucent membrane originating from the edge of the defect and thus do not permit a more exact judgement. This highly interesting malformation, which is so obviously similar to the experimental results just reported, will be described more exactly by one of my doctoral candidates.

---

gains support from other observations of anachronisms. For example, I have even observed, instead of the first horizontal cleavage, which usually appears as the third cleavage, a third vertical cleavage dividing the whole egg or one half only. Afterwards normal embryos were produced. The third and fourth vertical cleavages are very frequently exchanged, as can be easily established in the case of *Rana esculenta* by use of the cleavage plan which I have given, and this in turn often appears only in parts of an egg. In this year (1887) I caused, by artificial deformation of the egg, the cleavage which forms the median plane to be formed as the third one, and after the horizontal cleavage. This was without harmful effect on later development.

I have no definite example of the corresponding posterior half-embryo. One of the four preserved semigastrulae can perhaps be considered a posterior one, in view of the thickness and shortness of the blastopore lips.

I attempted in several of the eggs which I punctured after the second cleavage to kill only one of the four blastomeres present or to leave only one alive. The latter experiment resulted in several vertical quarter morulas and quarter blastulas, the former in several three-quarter blastulas and two three-quarter embryos. These embryos possess the rear half of the body and one lateral half of the front part. Before the time of the Naturalists' meeting in Wiesbaden I had only seen the embryos soaked with turpentine. Being interested in the first posterior half-embryos that had formed, I overlooked the continuation of one of the neural folds towards the front; moreover this was only slightly elevated. This continuation, after the embryo was completely dried, prepared, and sectioned, turned out to be a true front half of a neural fold. This was the reason that at that meeting both of these embryos were described only as posterior half-embryos.

One of these three-quarter embryos (Fig. 12) is well-developed, and as instructive for us as a pure posterior hemiembryo, because, having seen that the right and left halves of the body can each develop separately, we may assume that the posterior half, which is present only on the left side, likewise develops independently from the blastomere concerned. The neural folds can be clearly seen in this figure. The front half of the right fold is somewhat abnormally shaped externally and a definite *asyntaxia medullaris* can also be seen. In this case this can probably be explained simply by the absence of the front lateral half. Since the lateral lips of the blastopore normally join at the front first and the fusion proceeds from front to rear, that is in cephalocaudal direction, it is easily understandable that an *asyntaxia medullaris* occurs when one of the front lateral halves is missing. The cross-sections through this embryo show that the internal structure of the neural folds is good. Furthermore an indisputable *semichorda dorsalis* is present under the right neural fold. This diagnosis is not subject to doubt, because along a considerable stretch the structure is composed of only three, sometimes four, cells in the cross-section. However, the semichorda is round in cross-section like the questionable semichordas mentioned above. That is to say, half the usual number of cells have joined together and isolated themselves like an epithelium from the environment formed by another germ layer. On the left the chorda is not clearly recognizable. In the rear half the archenteron is present and well formed. In the front the anlage of a half archenteron cavity is present only on the right side, as a narrow inter-space.

The persistence of the blastocoele under a typical roof is of special interest in this embryo. The blastocoele lies toward the middle of the embryo lengthwise, and it thus can be seen clearly that the neural folds are located on the side of the egg opposite to the roof of the blastocoele, so that the roof of the blastocoele, which corresponds to the upper and originally pigmented half of the egg, becomes the ventral side of the embryo, contrary to the assertions of previous authors. One can probably properly assume a causal connection between the asyntaxia of the neural folds and the failure of the blastula cavity to be obliterated.

In my last experiment I attempted in several eggs to destroy only the cells above or below the first horizontal cleavage plane. These produced several clear *semiblastulae superiores* in which only the roof of the segmentation cavity is cellular, while the floor of this well-formed segmentation cavity consists of non-cellular matter. The continuation of these experiments will, we hope, provide us with more exact information on the further development of these latter embryos and thus on the exact part played in the formation of the embryo by the blastomeres located above and below the first horizontal cleavage plane.

INFERENCES FROM THESE FINDINGS

In general we can infer from these results that each of the two first blastomeres is able to develop independently of the other and therefore does develop independently under normal circumstances. Furthermore, in the experimental embryos, this happens in a manner which only rarely deviates from the normal development and only in a few conditions which have a surprisingly simple explanation. The progress of this sort of development was followed to the point of the development of neural folds, the primordia of the cerebral vesicles, the primordium of the chorda dorsalis and the formation of the mesoderm as well as its differentiation into somitic mesoderm and lateral plates, even to the point where the somitic mesoderm becomes segmented. Whether with this degree of development we have reached the upper limit of ability to develop independently I cannot say at this time. At this time, however, nothing would indicate that such an assumption is necessary as long as blood is not necessary for nutrition, since the hemiembryo of Fig. 9 which was the furthest developed at the time of its preservation showed no symptoms of death at all—neither the *framboisia embryonalis minor* nor *major,* which I have described as signs of beginning death. Only direct observation will be able to determine what happens after the blood vessels and heart form. This independent development characterizes also the two front and the two rear blastomeres with all their derivatives.

All this provides a new confirmation of the insight we had already achieved earlier that developmental processes may not be considered a result of the interaction of all parts, or indeed even of all the nuclear parts of the egg. We have, instead of such differentiating interactions, the self-differentiation of the first blastomeres and of the complex of their derivatives into a definite part of the embryo. This is valid both for the case when the first cleavage to appear separates, as normally, the right and left half and for the case when it anachronistically separates the cephalic and caudal halves. Each of these blastomeres contains therefore not only the formative substance for a corresponding part of the embryo but also the differentiating and formative forces. The assumption[21] that I had previously made with respect to the significance of cleavage becomes a certainty for the first cleavages. We can say: cleavage divides qualitatively that part of the embryonic, especially the nuclear material that is responsible for the direct development of the individual by the arrangement of the various separated materials which takes place at that time, and it determines simultaneously the position of the later differentiated organs of the embryo. (This applies also to subsequent typical rearrangements of material.) I would like here expressly to remark that this does not mean a prejudgement as to the distribution of such idioplasm as functions only in regeneration and postgeneration with which we will become more familiar later. A more or less complete idioplasm of this kind is present in every cell, that is to say in each nucleus.[22] Nor is the assertion of the importance of the first cleavages, which our experiments had already established, meant to imply that still other processes do not take place in the cleavage stage, for example, the development of many varied qualities in the embryonic substance or the increase in amount of specifically differentiated embryonic material.

Although according to this assertion the first cleavage separates the material of the right and left halves of the body from one another and even though I have introduced the expression "qualitatively halved" embryonic material, still we must not ignore the fact that this material is not morphologically similar although it is qualitatively alike in its chemical and percentage composition. Its arrangement is, after all, such that a right half of the body is produced on one side and a left half on the other. There are several questions in this connection which must be answered separately and which I mention here merely to prevent incorrect views being imputed to me as a result of excessive brevity in my

[21] Ueber die Bedeutung der Kerntheilungsfiguren. Leipzig 1883. S. 15 und Beiträge zur Entwickelungsmechanik des Embryo. No. 3. Bresl. ärztl. Zeitschr. 1885. No. 6 u.ff. Separ.-Abdr. S. 45.

[22] Thus if the first two blastomeres contain the material for the right and left halves of the body, it is apparent that one of the halves of the body must sooner or later become different, if there is the slightest imperfection of "qualitative halving." If it involves the middle parts, this alteration must extend all the way to the median plane of the individual. We can perhaps thus explain the unilaterality of many variations of development or of maintenance which extend to this plane. For example, premature graying of the hair on one side (particularly when other parts are normal, especially the nerves), *hemiatrophia facialis,* gigantism of one half of the head, etc.

presentation. These concern the arrangements which are the cause of this fundamental dissimilarity, at the time of the first cleavage, on which bilateral symmetry is based. Is it merely in the hemispheric shape of the yolk material and the controlling effect of that shape on the possibly various nuclear components, or is it in their independent arrangement?

It is an obvious further step to extend to the subsequent cleavages the above conclusion regarding qualitative separation of material. I hope to be able to verify by further experiments to what point this extension can be justified. It must similarly be determined whether the derivatives of later blastomeres are capable of self-differentiation or whether the progressive differentiation that forms the embryo is dependent on the coexistence of a whole group, perhaps all the descendants of one of the first four blastomeres. We would then have obtained with each of the first four blastomeres the smallest possible part of the ovum which is capable of self-differentiation. I do not, however, presume this to be the case, in spite of the mechanism of gastrulation which I will describe immediately and which appears to argue for that point.

Let us now proceed to special inferences for developmental mechanics which result from the facts mentioned. First of all it is to be deduced from the normal course of development of the undamaged blastomere that the qualitative division of the cell body and of the nuclear material, which we have just explained and which takes place at the time of cleavage, can proceed properly without any influence from the neighboring cells—and therefore probably does proceed in the normal case without this influence. Secondly, it can be deduced that the nucleus reaches its proper position in the blastomere, so important for the correct arrangement of the separated materials, without being affected by the vital activity of the neighboring cells. The same is true of later cleavages within the region in the neighborhood of the treated cells; therefore this independence can probably correctly be considered general. I further deduce from the dispensability of one vertical half of the egg that the formation of the blastula proceeds without extensive strains in the material, such as far-reaching mechanical interactions of the parts. Because of this I am inclined to attribute the typical formation of the blastula to an active rearrangement of the cells. A contributing factor perhaps is the tendency of many cells to approach the surface as a source of oxygen, which is His' view. The beautiful prismatic form of the epithelia in the roof of the semiblastocoele, which is found in the third (sometimes even the second) cell from the edge and which extends nearly to the rounded and often unattached edge of the cavity, reveals in addition that this shape is also not caused by the crowding together of many cells in a closed surface but by a tendency of the neighboring cells to unite closely and perhaps to extend themselves perpendicularly to the surface at the same time. The stretching may also be just a result of the great intensity of the first tendency.

The anomalous semiblastulas described above, as well as aberrations at later stages of development observed along with normally shaped half-embryos under the same conditions prove that abnormalities can occur more easily in half-embryos than under normal conditions. A task for a later time, which might possibly be very instructive, will be to discover the special causes of these variations and of the predisposition to them created by the incompleteness of the embryo.

The next formative processes cause gastrulation. What I have said earlier, as well as in the last paragraphs, and what I will say further about this process certainly provides sufficient evidence to reveal to the attentive reader the incorrectness of the previous view, most recently presented again by O. Schultze (without giving any real reason), according to which the cavity of the archenteron arises through an upward involution and therefore the originally black upper side of the egg corresponds to the dorsal side of the embryo. However, I will devote a special presentation of my view, along with a refutation of the opposing view, of this process of gastrulation which is of more interest to professional colleagues than my endeavors in the field of developmental mechanics. This is to obviate the necessity of my professional colleagues having to read all my works on developmental mechanics in order to satisfy their curiosity. At this point we will therefore draw only the following conclusions: Gastrulation takes place independently in every antimere and this is the case also in the caudal and cephalic halves. Consequently it is also true for the quarters concerned, and when we take into consideration the further development of these quarters that has been observed we can conclude:

The development of the frog gastrula and of the embryo initially produced from it is, from the second cleavage on, a mosaic of at least four vertical pieces developing independently.

How far this mosaic formation of at least four pieces is now reworked in the course of further development by unilaterally directed rearrangements of material and by differentiating correlations, and how far the independence of its parts is restricted, must still be determined. The well-known rearrangements of the yolk cells during gastrulation are only of secondary importance in so far as these cells represent mere reserve material.

We are further instructed by the *hemiembryones laterales* and the *asyntaxia medullaris* that the lateral half of the notochord also has its primordium in the medial border of the blastopore of the *semigastrula lateralis,* while the neural plate, along with the neural folds, is formed on its adjacent external surface. Furthermore, the primordium of the mesoderm occurs in the dorsal plate. It is of interest that the chorda and the mesoderm are also formed at the places where the intestinal endoderm is missing and even if the intestinal endoderm is missing completely, as is shown by the anentoblasty present in several cases of *asyntaxia medullaris*. It is also illuminating that the lateral part of the ectoderm and the neural plate are separated from one another at the reflected margin, even in our half-embryos, although neither of these two parts of the original ectoderm has the opportunity to unite with its own kind and initially impinges with a free edge against the half treated by operation.

The variant shape of the semichorda of a lateral half-embryo, expressed in a round cross-section instead of a semicircular one, can be easily explained by taking into account the actual process of development. The formation of the chorda of the frog embryo is not accomplished by a constriction from the endoderm cell group concerned, as is usually said, since there are no external parts at the place in question which could produce a constriction. We must rather conclude, in the light of the absence of any device for such a passive transformation, that the separation of the chorda cells from their surroundings occurs through their active rearrangement and transformation. In the lateral half-embryo the surrounding parts are laterally the mesoderm, externally the ectoderm, especially the neural plate, and internally the endoderm, since the chorda epithelium represents here the transition between these two latter layers. After these neighboring parts actively release themselves from one another, the unattached round cells of the chorda, coming from both sides, group themselves together so that their lateral surfaces touch, and thus form a complete strand. This reveals a tendency of the chorda cells to group themselves as closely together as possible and thus to separate themselves from their environment in an epithelium. According to our findings, healing does not take place here by the cells of each half arranging themselves independently in a semicircle but by the closest possible union, and thus isolation from the outside, of cells of the same type. After this the thickening of the semichorda[23] described above takes place very rapidly.

[23] This formation of the semichorda simultaneously throws light on the great diversities of origin of the chorda cells from ecto-, endo- or mesoderm. In closely related classes and even orders and families, we must conclude from the variety of statements by numerous conscientious investigators that this diversity actually exists. Since the chorda dorsalis is formed from the epithelium of the lateral free edge of the lateral blastopore lips and since these lips already unite with one another normally during gastrulation, the ectoderm of the one half usually first merging with that of the other and then simultaneously separating completely from the chorda epithelium, the chorda as a result appears in conjunction with the endoderm and forms a groove which opens into the cavity of the archenteron. Since the primordial mesoderm is in the same transitional area of the layers, it is connected in the beginning with the chorda epithelium which then separates off metamerically, as described previously. Not until this has happened does the chorda epithelium separate from the endoderm by rearrangement

On the other hand we have seen more completely in the neural tube how the cells of each half produce approximately, and in its main features, the typical form of the cross-section; we may conclude from this that these cells possess a special formative power for detailed arrangement. This is nevertheless not quite sufficient for the production of a normal cross-section, since we found the semineurula badly collapsed in a dorsal-ventral direction, probably because of the absence of the other half which also serves as support. This is further confirmation for my view, already presented in the introduction, that the elevation of the neural folds on the material of the neural plate does not occur passively from the pressure of lateral parts, since in such a process the lone lateral half of the neural plate would have to be pushed over simultaneously towards the undeveloped side, which was not observable. The jutting out of the median parts mentioned above was at least not such as could be attributed to this cause.

Now that we have become familiar with the behavior of the undamaged blastomere and discussed its significance for developmental mechanics we will turn to the other half of the egg, to the behavior of the cell treated by operation.

The behavior of this half of the egg showed great variety when observed externally and even more when studied internally in successive cross-sections. The diversity of the structures seen implies a whole series of processes which I shall separate into three groups. First of all, there are processes in the material of the treated half of the egg which make this material more or less unusable and which therefore can be designated as decomposition processes, provided one does not object to the fact that progressive processes are also included, such as numerical increase of nuclei. The products of these nuclei, however, must be seen as equally abnormal in their further behavior. Secondly, processes occur that make usable again the changed material of the egg half treated by operation and that prepare it simultaneously for subsequent development. These

---

of its cells, and it unites from both sides in the manner described above. Nevertheless, slight anachronisms occur in this three-fold separation in the frog and then (according to the view of merely descriptive embryology which does not take into consideration the intrinsic nature of the processes) the chorda sometimes "originates" from the endoderm, sometimes from the ectoderm or mesoderm. Even in classes of animals where the mechanism of gastrulation is no longer of this sort, but where, as I have said, a part of the work of gastrulation is already accomplished by the disposition of material during cleavage, even here, as a result of such originally slight differences, there are relatively slight variations which later become typical which will suffice to force the material of the chorda into the ecto-, endo- or mesoderm, either entirely or partially. I quite realize that these thoughts on developmental mechanics diverge to a high degree from the view of descriptive embryology, especially from the predominant dogma of complete evolutionary homology of the germ layers in the vertebrates. Nevertheless, I believe my view will gradually be accepted.

will be grouped together as reorganization processes. Thirdly, processes then follow which by subsequent development replace the missing body parts completely or almost normally. I will call these processes post-generation for reasons to be explained later and will contrast them fundamentally to the regeneration of lost body parts.

I must preface my more special remarks by mentioning that many of the egg cells punctured by the unheated needle developed normally[24] in spite of rough treatment and large exovations. In contrast in other cases no development took place in spite of a very small loss of material. This leads to the conclusion that substances of varied importance for developmental mechanics are contained in the blastomere. First of all, there must be substances that are not essential for development and, secondly, those whose disruption or loss in very slight quantities from the blastomere destroys its ability to develop. At the present stage of our knowledge we shall consider the latter substances preferably as nuclear components. I attempted when operating with the cold needle to disrupt the arrangement of the nuclear parts by manifold movements within the egg; as mentioned above, I was so rarely successful that I preferred to make use of heat as a destructive agent. This then accomplished the desired effect. The cell which had been operated on and partially emptied by the exovate often filled rapidly from the undamaged neighboring cell. This was observed especially clearly when only one of the four first cells after the second cleavage were punctured. The operated cell normally appeared whitish or at least only darkly speckled on the surface instead of being uniformly brown. As an explanation of this phenomenon we will find the pigment on the inside collected around certain structures.

Even when the hot needle was used the operated cells behaved quite variously. Let us first describe those cases in which the treated blastomeres no longer showed any signs of development, because in these cases the first group of processes mentioned above, the decomposition processes, can be seen most clearly. One should not overlook the fact, however, that I was working at the end of the breeding period when development is often abnormal and disruptive influences are less easily tolerated.

The blastomere material certainly did not remain completely unchanged even in these extreme cases, for the cell body as well as the nucleus experienced changes which were the more extensive the later I preserved the egg after the operation, that is to say, the more the unoperated half was already developed. Still, I would not wish to imply by this last statement that a causal connection exists between the progress of the changes on both sides.

24 With respect to the topographical relationships of the parts of the egg to those of the embryo, it is interesting to note that the stem of the exovate was later on the ventral side of the embryo if it remained attached to the egg and the embryo and if the puncture had been on the black upper hemisphere.

In the cell body proper, that is, the yolk of the operated cell, are located round or oval cavities delineated by a simple but sharp contour. These cavities have a size varying from 10 to 150 μ and may number but a few or several hundred. The content of these "vacuoles" is not stained by borax carmine and is completely unobservable. In this connection I must mention, however, that the sections lie on a finely granulated albumen substrate, so that a similar structure of the unstained vacuole contents would often not be distinguishable in thin sections. Still, I was unable to see the contents even in thick sections placed in Canada balsam. Since these structures answer the definition of a vacuole I will call the process the "vacuolization" of the yolk. This vacuolization is found in the area of the more protoplasmic, formative yolk as well as in the highly granulated nutritive yolk, which are less sharply separated from each other than usually. The vacuolization is often so dense that the individual vacuoles in places are separated from one another in the cross-sections only by a fine protoplasmic thread. Often only the residues of these structures (physically considered, partitioning membranes) are present so that a communication or fusion of the vacuoles is visible. If only a few vacuoles occur, they lie scattered or together in groups. In the latter case the remainder of the yolk then appears normal over large areas.

In addition to this vacuolization there are places in the yolk where the protoplasm forms a coarse or, more frequently, a finely meshed net that lacks yolk granules and is occasionally distinguished by the presence of numerous granules that are brownish black or greenish in transmitted light.

In the operated cell body, further structures are included that I look upon as nuclear. In order to justify this assertion I must first describe the structure of the normal nuclei of the frog embryo as they appear after the treatment mentioned above, that is heating up to 80° C., alcohol, borax carmine, etc. Here, in the various developmental stages of the embryo, the nuclei also show quite a different structure, just as they do in the various highly differentiated cells of the same stage (in accordance with Goette, Ch. van Bambeke and others).

In the blastomeres of the still young morula the nuclei appear as finely granular almost colorless or light-colored masses that are round or oval and from 10 to 30 μ in diameter. These blend into the surrounding protoplasm without a sharp line of demarcation, so that the actual nucleus cannot be separated from an areola of finely granular, unstained material that may possibly enclose it. Because of its size the nucleus extends through several sections and it is therefore easy to overlook several fine dark red granules that represent its extremely sparse chromatin content. Occasionally I have found an equatorial plate consisting of only a few short, clearly granular threads and well-preserved with a regular arrangement of its stained parts. The figures of the other stages of nuclear division appear, as mentioned above, either to have undergone regression during heating or to have been pushed rapidly to a stage of completion, since they are only infrequently observed. (It should be mentioned that granules stained similarly to the chromatin granules of the nucleus are not infrequently found, in greater or lesser number, collected between two of the blastomeres.) Sometimes the environment of the nuclear structure, which is lightly colored and not sharply demarcated, is interspersed with brown granules so that the light-colored structure is ringed with a dark areola. If the nucleus is undergoing division, the brown granules, toward the end of the division, are sometimes found only at the two poles, collected on the distal sides in the protoplasm.

Very infrequently a nucleus of 20 to 30 μ in diameter, consisting of a finely granular substance uniformly stained rose-red, is found in a cell surrounded by cells with the nuclei of the type already described. Its simple and very sharp contour contrasts with the surroundings.

In the blastula stage the nuclei are clearly bordered by a red, double outlined wall and are like round or oval vesicles of 10 to 20 μ in whose interior red granules are dispersed or strung together in a sparse, wide-meshed net of threads. The remaining content is almost colorless and extremely finely granular so that the whole structure appears only a pale pink.

At the gastrula stage substantially the same nuclear appearance is found in the yolk cells as in the blastula, just as pale but a bit smaller, measuring only 8 to 12 μ in diameter. In the epithelial cells of the germ layers, on the other hand, still smaller nuclei, merely 6 to 8 μ in diameter, are quickly noticed due to their more intensive red coloration produced by an abundance of chromatin. They are not, however, substantially changed in their structure; but occasionally only a single boundary line is present instead of the double one and the numerous red granules in the interior frequently do not show the familiar net-shaped arrangement.

After the formation of the neural folds in the embryo, we find their nuclei to resemble those of the epithelia in the gastrula stage. The nuclei of the yolk cells are still paler and larger than those of the epithelial cells, however.

In the undeveloped blastomere treated by operation the following structures are now found, which I would like to consider as nuclear structures:

1. Round or oval structures of 20 to 30 μ, occasionally up to 60 μ in diameter, of a uniformly extremely fine granular substance which is either merely pale or of an intensive red and which is set off from its environment by a simple but sharp outline. Occasionally these structures are further separated from the rest of the protoplasm by a sharply defined

colorless crescent or ring-shaped areola. On the other hand, accumulations of brownish-black granules not infrequently form a pigment areola around the nucleus. These nuclear structures are usually solitary and due to their character are associated with the uniformly pale red and simply outlined nuclei which, as reported, we observed on rare occasions in a semimorula.

Secondly, there are structures related to the vesicular nuclei of the next older stage of development, the blastula. They differ from the latter merely in their unusual size of 40 to 60 μ, their common but not invariable size. They have a double-membraned partition of stained substance and show internally a coarse mesh framework of threads composed of aligned red granules. The main portion of their contents is again extremely finely granular and either only pale red or unstained. In addition to these large structures there are frequently identical ones which are only medium in size (16 to 30 μ) and even some which are as small as those of the gastrula and of the embryo, with a diameter of only 8 μ. These differ from the small normal nuclei of these stages only in their low chromatin content and by the fact that they are agglomerated in dense clusters. Such nuclear nests often combine nuclei of very different sizes and may consist of six to thirty nuclei. Some of these nuclear structures also have again the brownish-black pigment areola which surrounds the whole nuclear net.

Both these types therefore conform to normal nuclear structure and vary only in their unusual size and, in the first case, in their coloration that is deeper than that in the normal embryo.

A third group, in contrast, comprises nuclear types which deviate from normal to a greater extent, namely round or oval structures of 8 to 30 μ of a not very granular substance which appears almost homogeneous and is stained a deep dark red. This contains more or less numerous cavities which are apparently empty and rounded like vacuoles. They are surrounded by a simple but sharp outline. Their sharp rounded boundary and their great capacity to absorb dye are in this case the only characteristics that cause me to attribute these structures to the nucleus and not to the cell body. When the granulation of the red material is clearer and its vacuolization of such a high degree that the red material in the interior represents no more than a thin septum, these structures (Fig. 2K′) acquire an appearance similar to that of the second type just described. The structures belonging to this third group are also often located closely together in groups of three to six and more, thus creating nests like those of the previous forms, which are occasionally enclosed in more or less abundantly accumulated protoplasm with brown pigmentation or none at all (Fig. 2KN). In many nests the structures of both types occur mixed.

Several times I have found large nuclei of 30 to 40 μ with a double red wall. These nuclei showed internally adjacent to this partition first individual red granules and then, further inwards, numerous randomly oriented rods composed of granules strung together to form a second layer that left a still larger colorless space open internally.

The nuclear structures just described are found in the yolk of the operated cell without any position of predilection being evident. In particular, they are not to be found in large numbers in the vicinity of the developed half of the embryo and are nowhere so near this half that one could assume they had migrated from it.

This being so, the only possibility that remains is that these are derived from the segmentation nucleus of the operated blastomere. The known fact that this nucleus shows a great tendency to reproduce argues also for this assumption. I am not able to affirm anything about the cause of the peculiarities of the nuclei formed in these particular cases.

It is of great interest, on the other hand, and testifies likewise for the correctness of our interpretation of the origin of these abnormal nuclei, that quite the same three kinds of nuclear structures—as well as the vacuolization of the yolk described above—are found soon after the fertilization of eggs which, as a result merely of long-delayed spawning, do not develop after fertilization in spite of not having been operated upon. If it were interpreted that here they are derived from the nucleus of the egg or the sperm, in which a tendency to multiply has not yet been found, then one would have to assume a different origin for the same structure than in the case of blastomeres treated by operation where the nuclei of egg and sperm were no longer present. Further, since in whole developing eggs no opportunity exists for transfer from a developed half, only the segmentation nucleus is common to both cases and can be considered the identical source of the same structures.

Of further interest and importance is the behavior of both egg halves with respect to one another.

Frequently an externally visible demarcation is formed when the developed half becomes larger than the operated half and this contracts toward the latter, so that, even at the blastula stage, a groove similar to the blastopore margin is formed.

In section one sees frequently, even at the early stages, a clear line of demarcation as manifestation of a special demarcation layer. This is a layer, 4 to 8 μ thick, of material which is at times colorless and at times stained slightly red, with a partially blackish-brown pigmentation in the vicinity of the upper edge. It is finely granular, that is, free of yolk granules and can be considered as protoplasm separated from one of the two blastomeres. I surmise that it comes from the treated cell since it is continuous with the latter, while the cells of the living half are separated from it at many points by an angular interspace.

This layer of demarcation usually proceeds from the surface of the egg and penetrates it to various degrees, occasionally up to a third of the diameter of the egg. Where the layer of demarcation is missing, a direct contact is possible, as long as the cells of the developed half are not isolated from the treated one by a fissure. No sharp boundary is recognizable at these points because the cells of the living half are not themselves sharply delimited on the side toward the treated half, although this is definitely true on the other side of their periphery.

This brings us to another type of behavior of the operated cell. The changes of the yolk described above and the abnormal, or at least the abnormally accumulated, division products of the segmentation nucleus are present in only about one-third of all the half-embryos sectioned. (In many cases, to be sure when these derivatives of the segmentation nucleus are absent they are found in the exovate.)

RESULTS

After destruction of one of the first two blastomeres the other is able to develop in a normal way into an essentially normal half-embryo. In this manner we obtained *hemiembryones laterales* and *anteriores,* along with the corresponding preliminary stages of the *semiblastula* and *semigastrula.* Three-quarter embryos with one lateral half of the head missing were also obtained by puncturing the egg after the second cleavage. The following principle could therefore be established: the development of the gastrula and of the embryo initially produced from it is, from the four-blastomere stage of the egg on, a mosaic of at least four vertical pieces each developing substantially independently.

We further saw in the malformation of the *anentoblastia* that the external and the middle layers are able to differentiate their specific structures in spite of the absence of intestinal endoderm, even though the shape of the whole embryo is abnormal as a result of its absence. In the same way the *semichorda dorsalis lateralis* is formed on each side.

The blastomere that is deprived of its ability to develop by the operation can be gradually revived.

This reorganization takes place partially by the transfer of a considerable number of cell nuclei (along with protoplasm?) from the normally developed half of the egg. These immigrated nuclei are distributed throughout the whole bulk of the yolk, wherever the latter is not provided with descendants of its own segmentation nucleus. Both these types of nuclei subsequently multiply. This nucleation of the blastomere treated by operation is followed later by cellularization, as division of the yolk into cells proceeds around each nucleus. Parts that are greatly changed resist this sort of reanimation, and yet they also are made usable later in a somewhat modified manner.

A new supplemental development follows the reorganization of the treated egg half; this is postgeneration, which can lead to a complete restoration of the missing lateral or rear half of the embryo.

This postgeneration does not take place in the same manner as the normal development of the primary half. It is not to be considered therefore as normal but merely belated development. This can be seen from the fact that the postgeneration of the germ layers in the supplementary halves does not take place by independent formation of germ layers as in the case of primary development but only proceeds from the germ layers already formed in the developed half. This can occur only in places where the germ layers of the primary developed half of the embryo are already separated from one another in such a fashion that each germ layer makes contact with the undeveloped egg half through a free lateral edge, an "interruption surface," as in the case of an artificial defect. As a result of this restriction no actual gastrulation takes place during the postgeneration of the lateral half-embryos.

Postgenerative formation of the germ layers occurs in the cell material formed by late cellularization, while the process of differentiation proceeds in resting cell substance. The various differentiations necessary for the formation of a germ layer are here propagated at different speeds in the still undifferentiated cell substance.

Since the various yolk materials and the cell nuclei of the treated egg half are not in their typical location but are situated according to chance determination, it could not be assumed that the typical extent and the typical results of postgeneration are determined by a typical arrangement of specifically characterized substances capable of self-differentiation. We therefore felt ourselves obliged to conclude that specific differentiating influences emanate from the already differentiated material to the still undifferentiated cell substance that adjoins it.

While in our findings the primary development of the first blastomeres and of the complex of their derivatives has proved to be self-differentiation, the reorganized egg parts are capable only of dependent differentiation through the influence of already differentiated parts.

In a new form of malformation, *asyntaxia medullaris*, the failure of the two lateral halves of the neural tube primordia to fuse normally, which is usually related to a corresponding lack of endoderm (*anentoblastia*), the external and middle germ layers showed an independent ability to develop when the internal layer was missing.

The Potency of the First Two Cleavage Cells in Echinoderm Development. Experimental Production of Partial and Double Formations

by HANS DRIESCH

Driesch, Hans. 1892. Entwicklungsmechanische Studien. I. Der Werth der beiden ersten Furchungszellen in der Echinodermenentwicklung. Experimentelle Erzeugen von Theil-und Doppelbildung. Zeitschrift für wissenschaftliche Zoologie 53:160-178; 183-184. Tafel VII. Abridged and translated by L. Mezger and M. and V. Hamburger and T. S. Hall for A Source Book in Animal Biology by T. S. Hall (1951).* Reprinted by permission of Harvard University Press.

* The editors have added Driesch's References, Plate VII, and Explanations of the figures.

One of the first investigators to follow in Roux's footsteps as an experimental analyst of development was Hans Driesch (1867-1941). Driesch, like Roux, studied the development of early cleavage blastomeres. However, he used different material for his investigations, echinoderm eggs, and he performed his experiments by different methods. In the article reproduced here, he reports his first attempts. By shaking the eggs of the sea urchin he was able completely to separate the first two blastomeres from one another. The cell separated from its partner exhibited the same pattern of cleavage it would have followed had it remained in the whole egg, but it formed a ciliated blastula, it gastrulated, and it developed into a pluteus dwarf in size but normal in configuration.

Driesch later (1900) modified his techniques and separated the cells by placing them in calcium-free sea water according to the method of his close friend Curt Herbst, and he carried out his experiments also at later stages, isolating blastomeres at the four- and eight-cell and even later stages. The regulation of partial eggs to form whole embryos led him to conceive of the developing egg as a harmonious equipotential system: equipotential because a part has the potency to form the whole, the implication being that all the parts are uniform (isotropic), harmonious because in forming the whole the parts work so wonderfully together. He defined as the prospective significance of an embryonic cell its fate under the normal conditions of development, but he demonstrated experimentally its prospective potency to be much greater than the significance; he stated that the fate of a cell is a function of its position in the whole. He thus emphasized epigenetic aspects of early development that were underestimated by Roux.

Driesch at first attempted to explain development in mechanistic terms. His Analytische Theorie der organischen Entwicklung (1894) is a remarkable treatise, and it is couched in terms and expresses concepts that we all use today. He wrote in it, for instance, of position and induction, of contact induction, even of chemical induction. He explained the polarity of the egg in terms of the arrangement of polarized constituents of the cytoplasm. He expressed the strong belief that the action of the nucleus in heredity and development was mediated through ferments, our enzymes.

As he continued his experimentation and reflection, however, he came to despair of explaining development in such mechanistic terms; he was defeated particularly by its harmonious character. The results of his experiments of separating the blastomeres drove him to vitalism, since he could not conceive of a machine which, when divided, could reconstitute two whole new machines like its original self. He concluded that develop-

ment is regulated by a deus ex machina, *the* entelechy, *a word he borrowed from Aristotle. Subsequently, he completely forsook experimental biology for philosophical vitalism, and became a professor of philosophy. His early discovery, however, and in particular his interpretation of it in epigenetic terms, played a very important role in stimulating interest and progress in analytical embryology.*

THE POTENCY OF THE FIRST TWO CLEAVAGE CELLS IN ECHINODERM
DEVELOPMENT. EXPERIMENTAL PRODUCTION OF PARTIAL
AND DOUBLE FORMATIONS

"Granting that the primordium of a part originates during a certain period, one must, for greater accuracy, describe this by stating that the material for the primordium is already present in the blastoderm while the latter is still flat but the primordium is not as yet morphologically segregated and hence not recognizable as such. By tracing it back we shall be able for every primordium to determine its exact location even in the period of incomplete or deficient morphological organization; indeed, to be consistent, we should extend this determination back to the newly fertilized, even the unfertilized, egg. The principle according to which the blastoderm contains organ primordia preformed in a flat pattern and, vice versa, every point in the blastoderm can be rediscovered in a later organ, I call the principle of organ-forming germ-areas."

In these words, he [His, 1874] formulated the principle so designated by him. Continuing this train of thought, Roux[1] discussed in a perceptive manner the difference between evolution, or the *metamorphosis* of manifoldness, and epigenesis, or the *new formation* of manifoldness; in his well-known experiments on "half-embryos" (of which only the first part concerns us here) he decided the question under consideration, for the frog egg, in favor of evolution.

A not very generally known work by Chabry is the only further investigation of this kind known to me. His specific explanations and figures make it clear that his results are fundamentally contrary to those of Roux. I wish to mention here that I came to know of Chabry's work only after the completion of my own experiments.

As to these, I was interested in repeating Roux's experiments on material which would be resistant, easily obtainable, and readily observable; all three of these conditions are most satisfactorily fulfilled by the Echinoids, which had already served as a basis for so many investiga-

[1] *Beitrage zur Entwicklungsmechanik des Embryo.* I. *Zeitschr. f. Biol.* Bd. XXI. III. *Breslauer ärztl. Zeitschr.* 1885. V. *Virchow's Arch.* Bd. CXIV.

tions. My own experiments were carried out upon Echinus microtuberculatus.

The investigations were made in March and April of 1891. They have
led me to many other problems closely connected with the present one,
problems whose eventual solution will deepen materially our understanding of the part already solved. Nevertheless, I present my results at this
time because they have decided with certainty, for my material, the
cardinal point, that is, the potency of the two first blastomeres.

MATERIALS AND METHODS

The first week of my stay in Trieste was lost, inasmuch as I obtained
almost exclusively useless material. Whereas the following work follows
the above mentioned experiments of Roux in content, the method was
taken from the excellent cellular researches of the Hertwig brothers.
These investigators, by shaking unfertilized eggs, split off pieces and
raised them successfully. It is well known that Boveri used the same
method for the production of his "organisms produced sexually without
maternal characters," although other factors prevented him from carrying
out the procedure exactly.

I therefore went to Trieste with the intention of obtaining one of the
first half-blastomeres of Echinus by shaking at the two-cell stage, in order
to see, provided it lived, what would become of it.

At an average temperature of about 15° C., cleavage of Echinus eggs
occurred 1½ to 2 hours after artificial fertilization. Good material, and
only such was used, displayed in only a very few instances immediate
division into four cells, an inevitable result, according to Fol and Hertwig,
of bispermy.

Shaking was done in small glass containers 4 cm long and about 0.6
cm in diameter. Fifty to one hundred eggs were placed in a small quantity
of water. In order to obtain results, one must shake as vigorously as
possible for five minutes or more; even then one obtains at best only
about ten isolated blastomeres and about as many eggs whose membranes
are still intact but whose cells are more or less separated within these
membranes.

If shaking is done at the moment of completion of first cleavage,
events are, so to speak reversed; the furrow disappears and one obtains
a sausage-shaped body whose two nuclei again show connections. In these
recombined eggs the furrow reappears in a short time and normal development follows. On the other hand if one shakes too late, the second
cleavage occurs prematurely during the shaking. It is therefore necessary
to watch carefully for the right moment.

About one half of the blastomeres are, in addition to being isolated,
dead; nevertheless I obtained about fifty capable of development. This
appears not unfavorable considering the strength of the mechanical

treatment, and considering the fact that the isolated blastomeres are in direct contact with the water on at least one side,—a completely abnormal situation. Isolation is obviously possible only where the membrane bursts.

During cleavage the preparations were observed microscopically as often as possible, and during later development usually once every morning and evening.

One more thing about the treatment of the isolated cells. The contents of the glass used for shaking must be poured into fresh sea water as soon as possible since the water has naturally warmed and evaporated.

It was to be expected that the small quantity of water would not be exactly beneficial, nor the bacteria which were especially numerous toward the end of my experiment and were encouraged by disintegrating pieces which had died.

At any rate my method guarantees that one is observing the same pieces on successive days. Unfortunately, Boveri, in his very important experiments, did not succeed in this respect.

But here I anticipate my results. I turn now to a systematic presentation of findings starting with

CLEAVAGE

First a few words about the normal course of events as revealed in Selenka's excellent investigations.

Following two meridional cleavages there is an equatorial one and the germ now consists of eight cells of equal size. Four of these now give off, toward one pole, four smaller cells, and at the same time the others divide approximately meridionally.

The germ now consists of 16 cells and shows a marked polarity with the four small cells, easily recognized, occupying one pole. Further divisions lead to stages with 28, 32, 60, and 108 cells (Selenka). The four small cells which originated at the 16-cell stage clearly indicate the animal pole for a long time. I was unable to establish certainly any differences between the cells of the blastula. At a later stage of development, but before the epithelial flattening due to close union of cells has led to the blastula proper, the Echinus germ, especially in the half containing the smaller-celled pole, consists of cellular rings.

How, then, do the blastomeres of the first division stages after isolation by shaking accomplish cleavage, assuming they survive?

I shall first describe the behavior observed in a majority of cases. Not once did I observe a completely spherical rounding up of the isolated cell. It is true that the normally flat surface tends toward sphericalness but its radius of curvature always remains greater than that of the original free surface of the hemisphere. The cell now divides into two and then, perpendicularly to this, into four parts. Normal controls fertilized at the same time now have eight similar cells the same size as our four. Simultaneously fertilized normal controls have at this time eight similar cells.

In the Echinoids no "gliding" of cells normally occurs either in the four-cell stage nor the ½ eight-cell stage (i.e., my four-cell stage). This is significant because it facilitates considerably the interpretation of the following fact.

About 5½ hours after fertilization occurs, untreated germs have divided into 16 parts, as described above, and isolated blastomeres into 8 parts.

At this point begins the really interesting part of my experiment in that the last-mentioned division brings into existence a typical single half of the 16-cell stage as described; that is, it behaves in the way expected of it according to absolute self-differentiation; it is actually a half of what Selenka's figure shows.

I will now go on to a description of the normal division of my blastomeres, later speaking about the abnormal cases (about 25%).

I carefully followed the formation of a half-germ of 16 cells, i.e., a typical ½ 32-cell stage. Each of the normal concentric cell rings is present, but each consists of half its normal number of cells. The entire structure now presents the appearance of an open hemisphere with a polarly differentiated opening.

In the majority of cases here referred to as normal, the half-germ presented, on the evening of the day of fertilization, the appearance of a typical, many-celled, open hemisphere, although the opening often seemed somewhat narrowed. As especially characteristic, I will mention here a case upon which I chanced in doing the Roux-Chabry experiment. Instead of one of the blastomeres being isolated, it was killed by the shaking. The living one, which had developed in the above manner into a typical half-formation, was in the afternoon attached to the dead one in the shape of a hemisphere; but by evening its edges were already clearly curled inward.

The cleavage of isolated blastomeres of the two-cell stage of Echinus microtuberculatus is accordingly a half-formation as described by Roux for operated frog's eggs.

As already mentioned, this is by far the most frequent behavior. One will not be surprised to find modifications of it in view of damage caused by the strong mechanical insult due to shaking. A few words about these exceptions:

In some cases, germs consisting of about 32 cells (½ 64-cell stage) presented by late afternoon a spherical appearance; development was here more compact, so to speak, though following the typical scheme. This occurs because of a closer union of the cells and is a phenomenon possibily similar to Chabry's "gliding." Normally, the blastomeres of

Plate VII

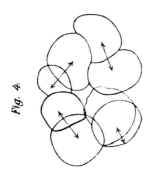

Fig. 4.

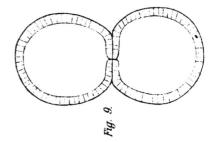

Fig. 9.

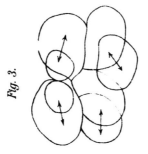

Fig. 3.

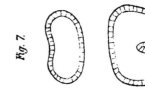

Fig. 7.

Fig. 8.

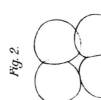

Fig. 2.

Fig. 6.

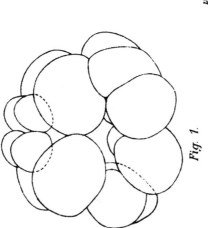

Fig. 1.

Fig. 5.

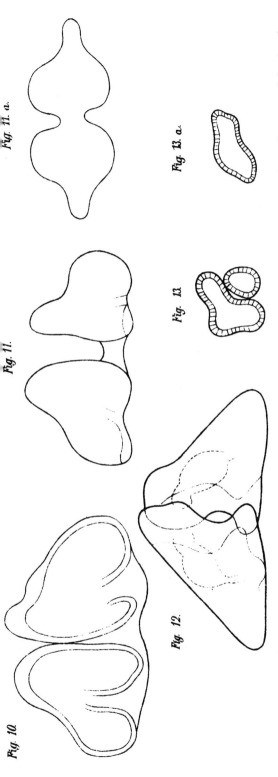

Fig. 11. a.

Fig. 11.

Fig. 10

Fig. 12.

Fig. 13.

Fig. 13. a.

Fig. 1 Sixteen-cell stage, copied from Selenka. Magnification about 400 ×. **Fig. 2** Half-embryo made up of 4 cells (half of an 8-cell stage). Compare with fig. 1. Apochrom. 16 mm. Oc. 8. **Figs. 3 and 4** Half-embryo made up of 8 cells (half of a 16-cell stage). Compare with fig. 1. Apochrom. 16 mm. Oc. 12. **Fig. 5** Half-embryo; cleavage is completed and the half sphere is closing. Apochrom. 16 mm. Oc. 12. **Fig. 6** Half-embryo; one half of the egg is dead. Late cleavage stage. Same magnification as figs. 3 and 4. (The figure attempts merely to give a general impression; only the outlines of the uppermost cells are drawn.) **Fig. 7** Blastula that developed from an extremely distorted 2-cell stage. Although it looks as though it is dividing, it did not form two partial embryos but a single one that was misshapen. **Fig. 8** Blastula in the process of dividing, developed from a very misshapen egg. It formed two partial embryos. **Fig. 9** Blas-

tula in the process of dividing. It formed two conjoined twins. **Fig. 10** The same set of embryos shown as twin gastrulae. Lateral view. **Fig. 11** The same set of embryos shown at the prismatic gastrula stage. Lateral view. **Fig. 11a** Seen from above. **Fig. 12** The same set of embryos as twin plutei. The oral fields face toward each other, and the plutei are somewhat compressed and are therefore seen partially from the side. Apochrom. 16 mm. Oc. 8. (From a Canada balsam preparation, somewhat shrunken. The three divisions of the gut may be seen.) **Fig. 13** Blastula from a greatly misshapen 2-cell stage that at the next division separate into ¾ and ¼ blastomeres. **Fig. 13a** The fragment from the ¼ blastomere has been constricted off. Figures 7 to 13a, with the exception of figure 12, were drawn without a camera lucida, but as accurately as possible. Several of them (Figs. 7, 8, 13 and 13a) were drawn at a low magnification, others at higher magnification.

45

Echinus make contact in only small areas, until shortly before blastula formation.

In other cases—nine were observed in all—there was from the outset (i.e. from the 8 or half 16-cell stage) little to be seen of the usual scheme except as to cell number; specifically, the half germ was spherical from the very beginning, and "gliding" was even more pronounced. I wish to mention especially a case in which the eight cells (half 16) were of almost equal size. Had the role of first cleavage here been different and had I here, to put it briefly, perhaps separated the animal from the vegetal pole instead of the left from the right? By analogy with the experiments of Rauber, Hallez, etc., this seems not unlikely.

The first time I was fortunate enough to make the observations described above, I awaited in excitement the picture which was to present itself in my dishes the next day. I must confess that the idea of a free-swimming hemisphere or a half gastrula with its archenteron open lengthwise seemed rather extraordinary. I thought the formations would probably die. Instead, the next morning I found in their respective dishes typical, actively swimming blastulae of half size.

I have already described how toward the evening of the day of fertilization the, as yet not epithelial, hemisphere had a rather narrowed opening and I have emphasized that tracing of individual cells and hence of the side of the opening corresponding to the animal pole proved impossible. True, I occasionally saw two smaller cells somewhere along the edge but attached no meaning to them. The question as to the actual mode of closing of the blastula must for the time being, therefore, remain unsolved. I may perhaps be briefly permitted to indicate the significance of this.

Now another general question the solution of which I intend soon to undertake: how far does the totipotency of the blastomeres go? That is, up to what stage are blastomeres still able to produce a complete, small organism? In the future I shall call these "part-formations" in contrast to Roux's "half-formations." The polar course of the cleavage, as well as the above hypothesis concerning the closure of the blastula, suggested that perhaps elements of all concentric rings must be present; that would mean, however, that the four-cell stage would be the last from which isolated cells could produce part-formations, since the equatorial cleavage (namely, the third) divides the material into north and south polar rings, so to speak. This is, as stated, for the time being still merely a question; the totipotency of the cells of the four-cell stage seems to me probable in view of the three-quarter + one-quarter blastulae which will be briefly mentioned later. If, on the other hand, the above-mentioned assumption concerning differences in the effect of the first cleavage should prove true, the latter hypothesis, that material from all three rings is necessary for part-formation, would no longer hold.

But let us leave these conjectures and return to the facts. Thirty times I have succeeded in seeing small free-swimming blastulae arise from cleavage as described above of isolated blastomeres; the rest, about 20 cases, died during cleavage or were sacrificed so I could inspect them under higher magnification. Almost all of them at this stage were still transparent and entirely normal structurally though half-sized. I was not, by a method of estimation, able to discover any difference in size between these cells and those of the normal blastula; therefore, the number of cells is probably half the normal number, which is also to be expected from their cleavage behavior.

At the end of the second day, the fate of the experimental cases seemed to be sealed; they showed the effects of strong mechanical insult and of the small amount of water. For germs still transparent at this time, one could count on raising them further; unfortunately, this was the case with 15 specimens only, that is half the total.

The Gastrula and Pluteus

In healthy specimens invagination at the vegetal pole usually begins at the end of the second day; on the morning of the third day little gastrulae swam about actively in the dishes. As stated, I succeeded in observing 15 such specimens.

Three of the formations finally became actual plutei, differing from the normal only in size.

Therefore, these experiments show that, under certain circumstances, each of the first two blastomeres of Echinus microtuberculatus is able to produce a normally developed larva, whole in form and hence a part-, not half-, formation.

This fact is in fundamental contradiction to the theory of organ-forming germ areas, as the following simple consideration specifically demonstrates.

Imagine a normal blastula split along the median plane of the future pluteus; let us now examine one of the hemispheres preserved this way, for instance the left (see Fig. II*). The material at $M_o M_u$ would normally supply material for the median region, that at L material for the left side. But suppose that we imagine the hemisphere closing, as explained above, to form a sphere but still maintaining polarity along BC. Then M_o will come to lie upon M_u, and hence possibly upon the right side of the future part-formation. Or, if in closure the original median areas supplied materials for the median region of the part-formation, then this could be thought of only as the upper or lower median region. If it is thought of as the upper, then the lower would come from a part which would otherwise have formed the left side. However one regards

* Editors' note: This text figure replaces an incorrect one in the translation.

it, one cannot escape the fundamental difference in the role which identical material is called upon to play depending upon whether one whole- or two part-formations arise from it,—something which can be brought about artificially. "I'l n'est pas des lors permis de croire que chaque sphere de segmentation doit occuper une place et jouer un role, qui sont assignés a l'avance" (Hallez); not, at any rate, in Echinus.

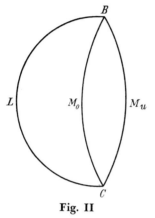

Fig. II

That this is a particularly pleasing result one could scarcely contend; it seems almost a step backward along a path considered already established.

When compared with Roux's, my results reveal a difference in behavior in the sea urchin and frog. Yet perhaps this difference is not so fundamental after all. If the frog blastomeres were really isolated and the other half (which was probably not dead in Roux's case) really removed, would they not perhaps behave like my Echinus cells? The cohesion of the blastomeres, conforming to the law of minimal surface formation, is much greater in the frog than in my object.

I have tried in vain to isolate amphibian blastomeres; let those who are more skillful than I try their luck.

It will not have escaped the reader that the results described might throw light on at least one aspect of the theory of

Double Formation

On this subject, I am in a position to supplement what has already been said. If, from one isolated cell of the two-cell stage, a perfect embryo of half-size is formed (namely a part-formation, in contrast to mere division which yields half-formation as in the case of Roux's frog embryos), it follows unequivocally that both cells of this stage if they are isolated and kept intact will form separate embryos, or twins.

It is highly probable that the separation of blastomeres by shaking was the direct cause of double formation and that without shaking whole-formation would have resulted.

This is certain since part-formations show that an isolated blastomere, provided it lives at all, always develops into a structure which differs from the normal only in size. With other twins, the situation is different, since they are too numerous to be considered accidental formations of this kind, such having never been seen in thousands of larvae observed by the Hertwig brothers and me.

Roux's theory of double formation, must, together with the principle of organ-forming germ-areas previously discussed, be discarded, at least in its general form. I have already remarked that, for our theoretical conceptions, this might be considered a backward rather than a forward step if establishment of facts did not always constitute progress.

Whether or not mechanical isolation or separation of the first two cleavage cells is the only way to obtain twin formation will be left open at this time.

It is an old controversy whether double-formation takes place by fusion or fission; birds and fish would, as mentioned, elsewhere, provide rather unfavorable material for a solution of this problem which in its usual formulation is rather a descriptive than a fundamental one. The observations communicated by other workers as well as my own experiments establish splitting as a cause, to which I may add on the basis of my results, splitting without postgeneration.

Obviously fission- and fusion-double-formation would be two quite different things, hence twinning could be of a dual nature. It is certain that the above mentioned double-fertilization modifies cleavage in such a way that immediate four-cell formation occurs; this is in support of our position, as shown before.

What forces come into play when the blastula closes? Can perhaps part of this process be understood in physical terms? The cell mass takes the form of a sphere, the form, that is, which possesses minimal surface. Further, why is it, after all, that a strong pulling apart of the half blastomeres without destroying them results in two individuals? These and other questions present themselves, but it were futile to indulge in idle speculation without actual facts.

Summary

If one isolates one of the first two blastomeres of Echinus microtuberculatus it cleaves as if for half-formation but forms a whole individual of half-size which is a part-formation.

Therefore the principle of organ-forming germ-areas is refuted for the observed species while the possibility of artificial production of twins is demonstrated.

Addendum: In proof-reading, I will briefly add that I have just succeeded in killing one cell of the two-cell stage of Spherechinus by shaking and in raising from the other half a small pluteus after half-cleavage.

Naples, October, 1891

REFERENCES

1. BORN, Die Furchung des Eies bei Doppelmissbildungen. Breslauer ärztl. Zeitschrift. 1887. Nr. 15.

2. Boveri, Ein geschlechtlich erzeugter Organismus ohne mütterliche Eigenschaften. Sitz.-Ber. d. Ges. f. Morph. u. Physiol. München 1889.

3. Chabry, Contribution à l'embryologie normale et tératologique des ascidies simples. Journ. de l'anat. et de la physiol. 1887.

4. Driesch, Die mathematisch-mechanische Betrachtung morphologischer Probleme der Biologie. Jena, Fischer 1891.

5. Fol, Recherches sur la fécondation et le commencement de l'hénogenie. Memoires de la soc. de phys. et d'hist. nat. de Genève. XXVI.

6. Gegenbaur, Beiträge zur Entwicklungsgeschichte der Landpulmonaten. Diese Zeitschr. Bd. III.

7. Hallez, Recherches sur l'embryologie des Nématodes. Paris 1885.

8. O. u. R. Hertwig, Über den Befruchtungs- und Theilungsvorgang des thierischen Eies etc. Jena 1887.

9. O. Hertwig, Experimentelle Studien am thierischen Ei etc. I. Jena 1890.

10. His, Unsere Körperform. Leipzig 1874.

11. Klaussner, Mehrfachbildungen bei Wirbelthieren. München 1890.

12. Kleinenberg, The development of the Earth-Worm. Quarterly Journal, 1879.

13. Korschelt, Zur Bildung des mittleren Keimblattes der Echinodermen. Zool. Jahrb. Bd. IV.

14. Metschnikoff, Über die Bildung der Wanderzellen bei Asteriden und Echiniden. Diese Zeitschr. Bd. XLII.

15. Plateau, Statique des liquides etc. 1873.

16. Rauber, Formbildung und Formstörung in der Entwicklung von Wirbelthieren. Leipzig 1880. Auch Morph Jahrb. Bd. VI.

17. ———— Neue Grundlagen zur Kenntnis der Zelle. Morph. Jahrb. VIII.

18. 19. 20. Roux, Beiträge zur Entwicklungsmechanik des Embryo. I. Zeitschr. f. Biol. Bd. XXI. III. Breslauer ärztl. Zeitschr. 1855. V. Virchow's Arch. Bd. CXIV.

21. Selenka, Studien über Entwicklungsgeschichte der Thiere. II. Wiesbaden 1883.

See also references on duplicities (Gegenbaur, Dareste, Lacaze-Duthiers etc.) in Rauber, Klaussner, in Ziegler's Lehrbuch der allgemeinen Pathologie etc.

1898

Cell-Lineage and Ancestral Reminiscence

by **EDMUND B. WILSON**

Biological Lectures from the Marine Biological Laboratory, Woods Holl, Mass. 1898, pp. 21-42. Reprinted by permission of the publisher, Ginn and Company.

Around the turn of the century Wilson and his contemporaries (C. O. Whitman, E. G. Conklin, F. R. Lillie and others) at the Marine Biological Laboratory (Woods Hole, Mass.) were actively engaged in a study of cell-lineage in a variety of eggs of marine and fresh-water invertebrates by methods that were descriptive, comparative, and experimental. The period has been aptly referred to as "the epoch of cell-lineage at Woods Hole." Broadly speaking the main question the investigators of cell-lineage sought to answer was in what form the potencies of the cleavage pattern exist in the unsegmented egg and how they become realities during the course of development.

It should be noted here that the study of cell-lineage really began with C. O. Whitman's article on "The Embryology of Clepsine" (1878). In that paper Whitman observed bilateral symmetry of the uncleaved egg and traced the individual blastomeres to the principal organs of the body. His general conclusions were expressed in these words: "In the fecundated egg slumbers potentially the future embryo. While we cannot say that the embryo is predelineated we can say that it is predetermined" (p. 263). Although these observations and conclusions were epoch-making, they failed at that time to excite the imagination of some of the foremost embryologists as did the much later studies of Wilson and others on the organization of the egg and its cell-lineage.

With the broad question raised by Whitman in mind, Wilson traced the development of the egg of the marine annelid Nereis in minute detail, cell by cell, from the fertilized egg to the free-swimming larval stage, commonly known as the trochophore. His classical account of the development of this worm, published in 1892, clearly marked him as one of the most outstanding pioneer students of cell-lineage (the name that Wilson gave to this type of study). Thus, he succeeded in demonstrating that cleavage in Nereis is a well-ordered process in which every individual cell has a definite morphological value in the formation of the body of an annelid that has a determinate type of cleavage.

In tracing the developmental fate of the individual blastomeres in Nereis, Wilson put much emphasis upon the mode of origin and fate of the teloblasts, the original stem cells of the mesoderm. His interest in tracing the developmental pattern of these stem cells was initially aroused in an earlier work on earthworm embryology (1890). In this form he succeeded in showing that the mesoderm is formed by teloblasts or pole cells which are large specific cells set aside in early cleavage. From each of the two teloblasts new smaller cells form in orderly succession at a fixed point so as to form long chain-like cords of cells, the so-called mesodermal bands.

By comparing his findings on the earthworm and Nereis *with those of other investigators, Wilson pointed out that these annelids and other animals (such as polyclad flatworms and mollusks) belonging to the "teloblastic series," although widely divergent groups, have in common far-reaching similarities in cleavage pattern and in the developmental fate of the different blastomeres. These findings on teloblasts and other blastomeres increased the significance of these features of development for the determination of homologies and in bringing out the important facts of animal relationships.*

We are thus brought to the lecture reprinted here, which is characterized by its masterly style of writing and by its cautious analysis of the meaning of the remarkable parallelism in cleavage pattern of widely different forms in terms of which ancestral features have been retained or modified during the course of their evolution.

In his lecture Wilson did not touch upon the far deeper questions of cellular differentiation and of egg organization that were brought into sharp focus by the study of cell-lineage. Nevertheless, he was aware of these problems, for in his 1892 article on cell-lineage he wrote, "It is impossible to reflect upon the complicated yet perfectly ordered events of the cleavage of Nereis *without attempting to discover the nature of the causes by which their course is determined" (p. 443). Indeed, in this same article Wilson noted that the developmental fate of the individual cells during early cleavage had been tested by means of experiment by Roux (1888) and Driesch (1892) whose articles are presented in translation on p. 4 and p. 40. The period of the 1890's marks a turning point in the direction of investigation from the morphological to the experimental analysis of cell-lineage and as a consequence indirectly influenced the whole subsequent theory of cellular transformation and differentiation.*

CELL-LINEAGE AND ANCESTRAL REMINISCENCE.[1]

Every living being, at every period of its existence, presents us with a double problem. First, it is a complicated piece of mechanism, which so operates as to maintain, actively or passively, a moving equilibrium between its own parts and with its environment. It thus exhibits an adaptation of means to ends, to determine the nature of which, as it now exists, is the first task of the biologist. But, in the second place, the particular character of this adaptation cannot be explained by reference to existing conditions alone, since the organism is a product of the past as well as of the present, and its existing characteristics give in some manner a record of its past history. Our second task in the investigation of any problem of morphology or physiology must accordingly be to look into the historical background of the phenomena; and in the course of this inquiry we must make the attempt, by means of comparisons with related phenomena, to sift out adaptations to existing conditions from those which can only be comprehended by reference to former conditions. Phenomena of the latter class may, for the sake of brevity, conveniently be termed "ancestral reminiscences,"—though it may not be superfluous to remark that every characteristic of the organism is in a broad sense reminiscent of the past.

It is in embryological development that ancestral reminiscence is most familiar and most striking. We all know that development rarely takes the shortest and most direct path, but makes various detours and sometimes even moves backward so that the adult may actually be simpler than the embryo. Such vagaries of development are in many cases only intelligible when regarded as reminiscences of bygone conditions, either of the adult or of the embryo. Sometimes these records of the past are so consecutive and complete that the individual develop-

[1] This lecture is based on a paper entitled "Considerations on Cell-Lineage and Ancestral Reminiscence, Based on a Reëxamination of Some Points in the Early Development of Annelids and Polyclades," in *Ann. N. Y. Acad. Sci.,* 1898. In some passages the wording of that paper has been reproduced with only slight change. With the exception of Fig. 4, *the figures are entirely schematic and are designed to show only the broadest and most essential topographical features.* For this purpose the subdivisions of the micromeres have been omitted, and, except in Fig. 4, none of the figures represent the actual condition of the embryo at any given period. While, therefore, very misleading in matters of detail, they are, I think, true to the essential phenomena; and through the simplification thus effected the reader is spared a mass of confusing descriptive detail in no way essential to the broad relation on which it is desired to focus the attention.

ment, or ontogeny, may be said to repeat or recapitulate the ancestral development, or phylogeny. The development of the toad's egg, for example, probably gives in its main outlines a fairly true picture of the ancestral history of the toad race, which arose from fish-like ancestors, developed into aquatic air-breathing tailed forms, and finally in their last estate became tailless terrestrial forms. It was such facts as these that led Haeckel, building on the basis laid by Darwin and Fritz Müller, to the enunciation of the famous so-called "biogenetic" law, that the ontogeny, or history, of the individual tends to repeat in an abbreviated and more or less modified form the phylogeny, or history, of the race. The event has shown that actual recapitulation or repetition of this kind is of relatively rare occurrence. Development more often shows, not a definite record of the ancestral history, but a more or less vague and disconnected series of reminiscences, and these may relate either to the adult or to the embryonic stages of the ancestral type. Thus the embryo mammal shows in its gill-slits and aortic arches what must probably be regarded as reminiscences of a fish-like adult ancestor, while in the primitive streak it gives a reminiscence not of an adult form but of an ancestral mode of development from a heavily yolk-laden egg like that of the reptiles.

If we survey the general field of embryology, we find that ancestral reminiscence in development is most conspicuously shown and has been longest known in the later stages, and many of the most interesting and hotly contested controversies of modern embryology have been waged in the discussion of the possible ancestral significance of larval forms, such as the trochophore, the *Nauplius,* the ascidian tadpole, and many others. It is generally admitted, too, that ancestral reminiscences may occur in earlier embryonic stages. While few naturalists would to-day accept Haeckel's celebrated Gastræa theory in its original form, probably still fewer would deny that the diblastic embryo (gastrula, planula, etc.) of higher forms is in a certain sense reminiscent of the origin of these forms from diblastic ancestors having something in common with existing coelenterates.

It is in respect to still earlier stages, namely, those including the cleavage of the egg, that the greatest doubt now exists; and there is hardly a question in embryology more interesting or more momentous than whether these stages may exhibit ancestral reminiscence, and whether they, like the later stages, exhibit definite homologies, and thus afford in some measure a guide to relationship. None of the earlier embryologists were disposed to answer this question in the affirmative. To them, and it should be added to some of our contemporaries as well, the cleavage of the ovum was "a mere vegetative repetition of parts," the details of which had no ancestral significance, and the ontogeny first acquired a definite phyletic meaning and interest with the differentiation of the embryonic tissues and organs. To these observers the cleavage of the ovum presented merely a series of problems in the mechanics of cell-division, and its accurate study was almost wholly neglected as having no interest for the historical study of descent. And yet it was long ago shown that the blastomeres of the cleaving ovum have in some cases as definite a morphological value as the organs that appear in later stages. Kowalevsky and Rabl traced the mesoblast-bands in annelids and gasteropods back to a single cell, which still later research has shown to have the same origin and fate, and hence to be homologous in the two cases by every criterion at our command. A long series of later researches, beginning with Whitman's epoch-making studies on the cleavage of *Clepsine,* has demonstrated analogous facts in the case of many other cells of the cleaving ovum, and has finally shown that in many groups of animals (though apparently not in all) the origin of the adult organs may be determined cell by cell in the cleavage stages; that the *cell-lineage* thus determined is not the vague and variable process it was once supposed to be, but is in many cases as definitely ordered a process as any other series of events in the ontogeny; and that it may accurately be compared with the cell-lineage of other groups with a view to the determination of relationships.

The study of cell-lineage has thus given us what is practically a new method of embryological research. The value and limitations of this method are, however, still under discussion, and among special workers in this field opinion as to its morphological value is still so widely divided that most of its results should be taken as suggestive rather than demonstrative. Like other embryological methods, it has already encountered contradictions and difficulties so serious as to show that it is no *open sesame.* In some cases closely related forms (*e.g.,* gasteropods and cephalopods) have been shown to differ very widely, apparently irreconcilably, in cell-lineage. In other cases (echinoderms, annelids) the normal form of cleavage has been artificially changed without altering the outcome of the development. In still other cases (*e.g.,* in teleost fishes) the form of cleavage has been shown to be variable in many of its most conspicuous features, so that apparently no definite cell-lineage exists. These and many other facts, less striking but no less puzzling, can be built into a strong case against the cell-lineage program, and I wish to acknowledge its full force. Admitting all the difficulties, I am nevertheless on the side of those who as morphologists believe that the study of cell-lineage has demonstrated its value, and that it promises to yield more valuable results in the future. In this lecture I propose to illustrate some of the more interesting results already attained, and some of the suggestions that they give for future work, by a broad consideration of the cell-lineage of three related groups of animals which on the one hand have been very carefully examined as regards their anatomical and general embryological relationships, while on the other hand their cell-lineage has been more exhaustively studied than that of any other forms. These groups are the platodes (more especially the *Turbellaria*), the mollusks, and the annelids.

That these three groups belong in the same morphological series will probably be admitted by all zoölogists, and most will no doubt further agree with the view of Lang, that in the essential features of their organization the platodes are not very far removed from the ancestral type from which the two higher groups have sprung, the former having remained non-metameric like the platodes, while the latter have acquired metamerism. Accepting this view we should expect, if there be any evidence of race-lineage in cell-lineage, to find in the annelids and mollusks a common type of cleavage, and one which in its main features may be derived from that of the platode. Recent studies in cell-lineage have, on the whole, justified this expectation, and have brought to light some cases of vestigial processes in cleavage which are, I believe, to be reckoned among the most striking and beautiful examples of reminiscence in development. It is especially to these cases that I wish to direct attention.

The cleavage of a number of *Turbellaria* and nemerteans, and of many annelids, gasteropods, and lamellibranchs, has now been shown to conform to a common type which, though complex in detail, is exceedingly simple in its essential plan. A few exceptions there certainly are; but some of these are apparent only (for example, in the accœlous *Turbellaria*), and are readily reducible to the type, while others are undoubtedly correlated with bygone changes in the mode of nutrition of the ovum (as in some of the earthworms and leeches). The most conspicuous exception is afforded by the cephalopods, which have a mode of cleavage entirely unrelated to that of the other mollusks; but the entire development of this group is of a highly modified character. Fully recognizing the real exceptions, we nevertheless cannot fail to wonder at the marvellous constancy with which the cleavage of the polyclades, nemertines, annelids, gasteropods, and lamellibranchs conforms to the typical mode of development. In all these forms the egg first divides into four quadrants. From these at least three and sometimes four or five quartets of cells—usually smaller, and hence designated as *micromeres*—are successively produced by more or less unequal cleavages towards the upper pole. The arrangement of these micromeres (Fig. 1) is constant and highly characteristic, the first quartet being more or less displaced, or, as it were, rotated in a direction corresponding with the hands of a watch (clockwise), the second in the opposite direction (anti-clockwise), the third clockwise again, and so on, the spindles of each division being at right angles to those of the preceding and following. In the later subdivisions of the micromeres, also, a most remarkable agreement has been observed; but I shall pass this over entirely in order to focus attention on the broader features of the development.

A large part of the work in cell-lineage during the past ten years has been devoted to a comparison of the morphological value of these quartets of cells in the annelids, mollusks, and platodes; and the remarkable and interesting fact is now becoming apparent that while they do not have exactly the same value in all the forms, they nevertheless show so close a correspondence both in origin and in fate that it seems impossible to explain the likeness save as a result of community of descent. The very differences, as we shall see, give some of the most interesting and convincing evidence of genetic affinity; for processes which in the lower forms play a leading *rôle* in the development are in the higher forms so reduced as to be no more than vestiges or reminiscences of what they once were, and in some cases seem to have disappeared as completely as the teeth of birds or the limbs of snakes. The processes in question relate to the formation of the mesoblast in its relation to the micromere-quartets, and on them the whole discussion may be made to turn.

The higher types—*i.e.*, the annelids, gasteropods, and lamellibranchs —have for some time been known to agree closely in the general value of the quartets. Rabl first demonstrated that in *Planorbis* the entire ectoblast is formed from the first three quartets, while the mesoblast-bands arise from the posterior cell of the fourth quartet, the other three, with the remains of the primary quadrants, giving rise to the entoblast (Fig. 1). The same general result has been reached by subsequent investigators of molluscan cell-lineage, though there are one or two apparent exceptions (*e.g., Teredo,* according to Hatschek) that demand reinvestigation. The same remarkable fact holds true throughout the annelids,[2] the well-determined exceptions being some of the earthworms and leeches referred to above, in which the typical relations seem to have been disturbed through changes in the nutrition of the embryo. Wherever the typical quartet formation takes place—and this is the case in nearly all the forms that have been adequately examined—the general value of the quartets is the same, the first three giving rise to the entire ectoblast, the fourth giving rise, one cell to the mesoblast-bands and the other three to entoblast, while the remnants of the primary quadrants, including the fifth quartet if one is formed, give rise to the entoblast. This result seems almost too simple and produces an impression of artificiality which may probably account for the reluctance with which it has been accepted in some quarters; but I think it is not too much to say that few facts in embryology have been more patiently studied or more accurately determined. The above statement does not,

[2] See footnote at p. 67 for reference to Eisig's widely divergent account of the development of *Capitella.*

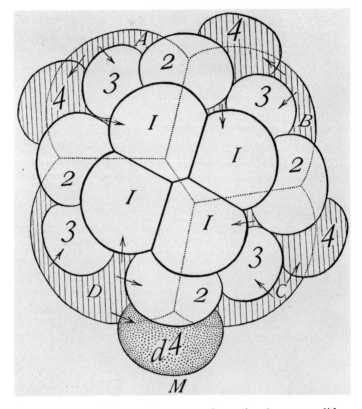

Fig. 1 Diagram of the typical quartet-formation in an annelid or
gasteropod; the quartets numbered in the order of their formation;
A, B, C, D, the basal quadrants. Ectoblast unshaded, mesoblast
dotted, entoblast ruled in parallel lines. In many forms (*e.g.,
Aricia*) a fifth quartet (entoblastic) is formed; in others (*e.g.,
Nereis*) only three complete quartets and the posterior member of
the fourth quartet (d^4 or *M*).

however, contain the whole truth; but before completing it we may
advantageously turn to the development of the *Turbellaria*.

It was long since shown by researches, beginning with Hallez and
Götte and culminating in those of Lang, that the cleavage of polyclades
shows an extraordinary precise resemblance to that of the annelids and
mollusks. Taking Lang's work on *Discocœlis* as a type, we find four
quartets of cells successively produced from the primary or basal quadrants following exactly the same law of displacement as in the higher
types, assuming the same arrangement, and in their subsequent subdivision up to a relatively late stage following so exactly the plan of the
annelid egg that even a skilled observer might easily mistake one for

the other (Fig. 4, *A*). Despite this accurate agreement in the form of cleavage, Lang's observations seemed to show that the cell-quartets had a totally different value from those of the higher forms; for he believed the first quartet to produce the entire ectoblast, the second and third to give rise to the mesoblast, while the fourth quartet, with the basal cells, formed the entoblast (Fig. 2, B). Such a result was more than a stumbling-block in the way of the comparison. It was subversive of the whole cell-lineage program; for it seemed to show that the cell-lineage of derivative animals (*i.e.*, annelids and gasteropods), while exactly conforming to the ancestral *form* of cleavage (*i.e.*, that of the *Turbellaria*), differed *toto cœlo* from it in morphological significance. When, some years ago, I first called attention to this difficulty, I felt constrained to the admission that, in the face of such a contradiction, the study of cell-lineage could only be regarded as of very restricted value in morphological investigation; indeed, in a lecture delivered here four years

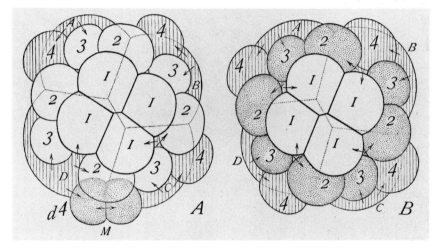

Fig. 2 Diagram contrasting the value of the quartets in an annelid or gasteropod (*A*) with those of a polyclade according to Lang's original account (*B*). Lettering and shading as in Fig. 1. (The true proportions of the basal quadrants and the fourth quartet, which are here misrepresented, are shown in Fig. 4. It is characteristic of the polyclades that the fourth quartet-cells are greatly enlarged at the expense of the basal quadrants.)

ago on the inadequacy of the embryological criterion of homology,[3] I cited this very case as representing a climax in the contradictions of comparative embryology.

[3] "The Embryological Criterion of Homology." Wood's Holl Biological Lectures, 1894, p. 113.

It is not rare in the history of science to find that fuller knowledge may so change the point of view as to transform a seeming difficulty into a pillar of support; and it seems not unlikely that such may be the case with the present one, though some new difficulties have arisen which still await solution. The new evidence relates, on the one hand, to the annelids and mollusks, on the other hand to the polyclades; and since on both sides it tends to bridge a gap which once seemed hopelessly wide, I shall consider it in some detail. In approaching this evidence the two principal difficulties should be clearly borne in mind. The first lies in the fact that the mesoblast-bands of the annelids and mollusks arise from one cell of the *fourth* quartet, while in the polyclade the mesoblast was stated to arise from all of the eight cells of the *second* and *third* quartets. The second difficulty relates to the ectoblast, which in the annelid and mollusk arises from the twelve cells of the first, second, and third quartets; while in the polyclade it was believed to arise solely from the first quartet (Fig. 2). We may consider these two difficulties in order.

As regards the first point, a series of researches during the past three years have shown that in some of the mollusks and annelids the mesoblast has a double origin, a part—and usually the major part—arising from the posterior cell of the fourth quartet, as stated above, while a part arises from cells of the second or third quartet, as in the polyclade (Fig. 3). The major part—which, for reasons that will appear beyond, I propose to call the *entomesoblast*—gives rise to the so-called mesoblast-bands. The minor part, or *ectomesoblast* ("secondary meso-blast," "larval mesoblast," of various authors), apparently does not contribute to the formation of the mesoblast-bands, and in at least one case—namely, that of *Unio*, as described by Lillie—it gives rise to cells of a purely larval character and designated as "larval mesenchyme." The first step in this direction was that of Lillie, just referred to, who in 1895 announced the discovery that in a lamellibranch, *Unio*, one cell of the *second* quartet (a^2 on the left side) gives rise not only to ectoblast, but also to a single mesoblast-cell which passes into the interior, divides, and gives rise to some of the larval muscles ("larval mesenchyme," Fig. 3, *C*). Lillie's discovery was quickly followed by the no less interesting one of Conklin that in another mollusk, the gasteropod *Crepidula, three* cells of the second quartet, median anterior, right and left (b^2, c^2, d^2), likewise give rise to mesoblastic as well as to ectoblastic elements (Fig. 3, *B*),—a process still more forcibly recalling the origin of the mesoblast in the polyclade.

Two years later mesoblastic cells were found, both in the mollusks and in the annelids, to arise from members of the *third* quartet. The first of these cases was observed by Wierzejski (1897) in the case of *Physa,* where the two anterior cells of this quartet (c^3, b^3) give rise to

mesoblastic as well as to ectoblastic cells, and exactly similar facts were
soon afterwards observed by Holmes in *Planorbis*. Simultaneously with
these researches I independently discovered in the annelid *Aricia* two
mesoblast cells arising from the two posterior cells of either the second or

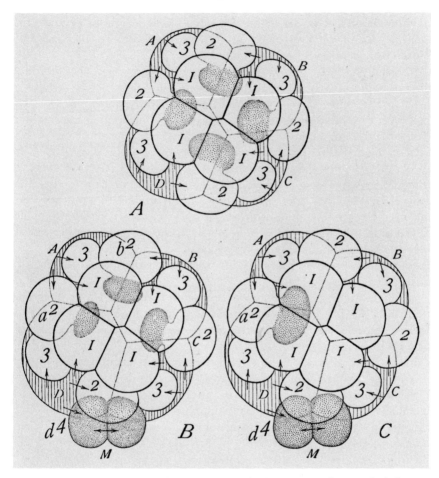

Fig. 3 Diagrams illustrating the value of the quartets in a polyclade
(*Leptoplana*), a lamellibranch (*Unio*), and a gasteropod (*Crepidula*).
Lettering and shading as in Fig. 1. (For comment on these figures see
footnote at first page.) *A, Leptoplana,* showing mesoblast-formation in
the second quartet. (Cf. Fig. 4.) *B, Crepidula,* showing source of ectomesoblast (from a^2, b^2, c^2) and entomesoblast (from quadrant *D*). *C,
Unio,* ectomesoblast formed only from a^2.

the third quartet (*i.e.,* from c^3 and d^3 or from d^2 and c^2), though I
could not positively determine which. This was immediately followed by
Treadwell's discovery that in the annelid *Podarke* mesoblast cells are

formed from three cells of the third quartet, namely, the anterior median and the two lateral cells (a^3, c^3, d^3). It was thus shown that in at least four genera of mollusks and two of annelids a part of the mesoblast has an origin which recalls that of the polyclades, and the view is irresistibly suggested that the formation of this *ectomesoblast* in one, two, or three quadrants in the higher types is a vestigial process or ancestral reminiscence of what occurred in all four quadrants in the ancestral prototype and still persists in the polyclade.

The second difficulty—*i.e.,* the origin of the ectoblast—has entirely disappeared upon a reëxamination of the cell-lineage of a polyclade (*Leptoplana*) which I was enabled to make in the summer of 1897. In this form careful study shows in the clearest manner that the formation of ectoblast is not confined to the first quartet, but that all of the twelve cells of the first three quartets contribute to the ectoblast, precisely as is the case in the annelids and mollusks (Fig. 3, *A;* Fig. 4, for details). A comparison with Lang's figures gives every reason to believe that the same is true in *Discocœlis* and the other forms studied by him, and that on this point he fell into an error which was certainly very pardonable at the time. The quartet-cells from which in the polyclade the mesoblast arises are, therefore, not pure mesoblasts, as Lang supposed, but are *mesectoblasts,* precisely like the cells from which the "larval mesoblast" arises in *Crepidula* or *Unio*.[4]

The researches reviewed up to this point have cleared up the contradiction relating to the second quartet. Passing now to the third and fourth quartets, we find that the newer researches have introduced a new difficulty with respect to each of these quartets; but the new difficulties differ from the old in that they suggest a number of highly interesting problems for future research. As regards the third quartet I was unable to find in *Leptoplana* any evidence that it gives rise to mesoblastic elements such as we should expect to find in the *Turbellaria* in view of the formation of ectomesoblast from this quartet in *Physa, Planorbis, Podarke,* and probably in *Aricia.* As far as I could find, the third quartet gives rise only to ectoblast cells at the lip of the blastopore (Fig. 4), and Lang's results seem to me inconclusive on this point. Only renewed researches can determine whether this difficulty be real or only apparent. In the mean time it would be well not to lose sight of the fact that the polyclades cannot, of course, be the actual ancestors of the annelids and mollusks, and that the cleavage in the former may differ

---

4 In *Leptoplana* each cell of the second quartet divides off in succession three ectoblast cells before the delamination of mesoblast into the interior occurs at the fourth division (Fig. 4). In *Unio,* according to Lillie, the larval mesoblast is definitely separated at the third division of the micromere (a^2). Professor Conklin informs me that in *Crepidula* the ectomesoblast is formed at about the fourth or fifth division of the micromeres (a^2, b^2, c^2).

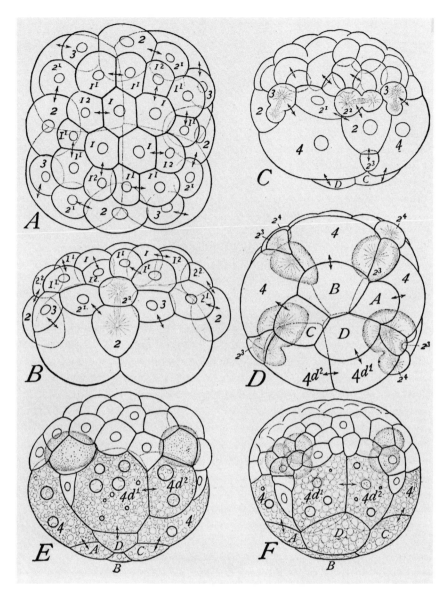

Fig. 4 *Leptoplana.*—(Camera drawings from the transparent living embryos. In these figures the subdivisions of the micromeres are accurately shown.) *A*, 32-cell stage, from the upper pole; *B*, 36-cell stage, from the side, showing second division of 2; *C*, side view approximately 60 cells, showing the third ectoblast cell (2^3) derived from 2, the fourth quartet (4), and the basal entoblasts (*D*, *C*). *D*, delamination of mesoblast in the fourth division of 2 (shaded), from the lower pole, showing the basal quartet of entomeres (*A-D*), and the two somewhat unequal cells ($4d^1$, $4d^2$) formed by the vertical division of the posterior cell of the fourth quartet. *E*, posterior view of the ensuing stage, showing the two posterior mesoblast cells (shaded) lying in the interior, and a marked inequality between ($4d^1$ and $4d^2$). *F*, later stage; multiplication of the mesoblast cells (shaded), equality of $4d^1$ and $4d^2$, as in *Discocoelis*.

very considerably from the common ancestral type. A natural hypothesis is that in the ancestral mode of development all of the first three quartets gave rise both to ectoblast and to mesoblast, and that in all the existing forms the mesoblast formation has been lost in the first quartet and variously reduced or entirely suppressed in one or both of the two succeeding quartets. I think, therefore, that we need not hereafter be surprised to find the formation of ectomesoblast from more than one of the first three quartets, whether in the *Turbellaria* or in the higher forms.

It is when we attempt to bring the foregoing considerations into relation with the history of the fourth quartet in annelids and mollusks that we arrive at a far more serious difficulty; but we can hardly regret a difficulty that is so suggestive of further research. In the polyclade the fourth quartet is relatively very large, the basal quadrants being correspondingly reduced (Fig. 4). All of the eight cells formed give rise, as far as known, to entoblast only. In the annelids and mollusks, on the other hand, only three cells of this quartet—anterior, right, and left—are purely entoblastic, while the fourth, or posterior, cell ("d⁴") divides into symmetrical halves to form the "primary mesoblasts," or pole-cells, from which arise the two mesoblast-bands characteristic of these groups (Fig. 2, *A*). Now, in comparing this mode of development with that of the polyclade, we must choose between the following alternatives. *Either* the mesoblast of the annelid or mollusk, as a whole, corresponds with that of the polyclade—in which case we must assume that in the course of the phylogeny the posterior cell of the fourth quartet has gradually taken upon itself more or less completely the mesoblast formation formerly occurring in the second or third quartet; *or* the mesoblast of the polyclade has dwindled away, perhaps has even disappeared, in the higher forms, where it is represented only by the ectomesoblast, its place having been taken, through a process of substitution, by the mesoblast-bands derived from the fourth quartet. To vary the statement we must assume that a substitution has taken place either in the cell-mechanism by which the mesoblast is formed or in the mesoblast itself, and upon our choice between these alternatives depends the entire point of view from which we regard cell-lineage.

Now, it must be admitted, forthwith, that we have not at command sufficient data to give any certain answer to this question, and we should be careful not to draw premature conclusions in a matter which involves further consequences of such importance. But there are a number of well-ascertained facts drawn from widely diverse sources that point towards the second of the above alternatives; *i.e.,* the view that the mesoblast-bands of the annelid or gasteropod are not as such represented at all in the polyclade, but, phyletically considered, are neomorphs which have more or less completely replaced the ancestral mesoblast. This evidence may be arranged in three lines:—

1. As a result of exact and thorough studies upon the histology and larval development of the annelids, Eduard Meyer was several years ago led to the conclusion that the mesoblast-bands, both in origin and in fate, differed widely from the scattered larval mescenchyme-cells, though the lineage of the latter was then unknown. Developing this idea, Meyer was led to the remarkable conclusion that the mesoblast-bands of the higher types represent the paired *gonads* of the ancestral form—a view nearly related with the earlier one of Hatschek, that the primary mesoblasts were originally eggs, which, in the course of the phylogeny, became in part transformed into peritoneal and other somatic cells, and in part remained as germ-cells. Thus the original mesoblast— *which Meyer definitely compared with that of the Turbellaria*—was gradually replaced, though still persisting in a reduced form as the larval mesenchyme.

I would not at present urge the acceptance of this daring hypothesis; but in the light of later research it has become highly significant, and whether true or false is of great interest as giving a clear picture of how such a process of substitution may have been possible.

2. In the second line of evidence lies Lillie's discovery that the ectomesoblast of *Unio* (derived from a^2) gives rise to purely larval transitory structures; namely, to the adductor muscle and the scattered contractile myocytes of the *Glochidium* larva. In the annelids, too, the same conclusion seems probable, and my friend Professor Treadwell informs me that in *Podarke* there is every reason to believe that the ectomesoblast (derived from a^3, c^3, d^3) is entirely devoted to the formation of the ring-muscle and myocytes of the trochophore, which apparently take but an insignificant part, if any, in the building of the adult body. This result tallies with the view that the ectomesoblast formation in the higher types is a reminiscence of the ancestral process still existing in the polyclade, but in the higher forms relegated to the early stages, and even in them is more or less reduced.[5]

[5] Eisig has very recently (*Mitth. Zool. Station,* Neapel, xiii, 1, 2, 1898) published the results of a study of the cell-lineage and later development of *Capitella,* which are totally at variance with the view here suggested, and the facts on which it is based. Broadly speaking, his results exactly reverse those of all the authors cited above, the mesoblast-bands ("Cœlomesoblast") being derived from the third quartet ($c^{3.1}$ and $d^{3.1}$), while the larval mesoblast ("Pædomesoblast") arises from a portion of M (d^4), the remaining portion giving rise to ectoblast. If well founded, this result is not only fatal to the view I suggest, but is, I believe, nothing less than a *reductio ad absurdum* of the whole cell-lineage program, regarded as a method of morphological research. No one will lightly call in question the results of so conscientious and eminent an observer; and they must be regarded as by far the most serious obstacle that the morphological study of cell-lineage has thus far encountered. I will not attempt to explain away this adverse

3. In the third line lies the evidence, recently obtained, that the pole-cells or teloblasts of the mesoblast-bands of the annelids and mollusks are to be regarded as derivatives of the archenteron, and hence differ wholly from the ectomesoblast in their relation to the primary germ-layers. Kowalevsky, the discoverer of these teloblasts, expressed the

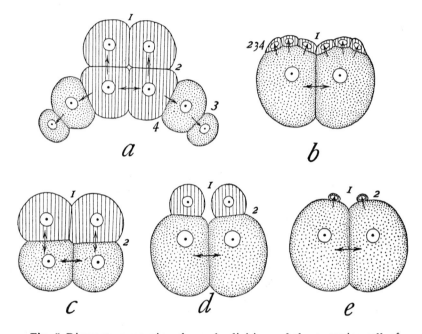

Fig. 5 Diagrams comparing the early divisions of the posterior cell of the fourth quartet (d^4 or M) in *Crepidula(a)*, *Nereis(b)*, *Clymenella(c)*, *Unio(d)*, and *Aricia(e)*. The numerals show the order of the division. Cells destined to form entoblast (their fate as actually observed in *Crepidula* and *Nereis,* but only inferred in other cases) ruled in parallel lines, mesoblast dotted. After the divisions here shown, the symmetrical mesoblast-bands are formed from the dotted cells.

opinion, more than twenty-five years ago (1871), that they were to be regarded as derivatives of the archenteron; and a large number of later workers from the time of Rabl (1876) have accepted his view, though

evidence, based on so prolonged and thorough a research. It should not be forgotten, however, that, as Professor Eisig is himself careful to point out, the nature of the material has forced him to contend with great difficulties, since the eggs are normally distorted by pressure (a factor which, as I have experimentally shown in *Nereis,* may greatly alter the form of cleavage) between the membranes of the tube; and, further, the development cannot be continuously followed in life. A result, based on this material, which stands in such flat contradiction to what is known in other and more favorable forms, must await the test of further research.

only very recently has the full strength of the evidence been developed. In the first place, it was shown through the studies of Rabl, Blochmann, and later workers, that while the posterior cell of the fourth quartet gives rise to the mesoblastic pole-cells the other cells are purely entoblastic. In the second place, the recent studies of Conklin and myself have shown that even the posterior cell of the fourth quartet (d^4) may contain entoblastic as well as mesoblastic material. I showed several years ago that in *Nereis* each of the cells into which d^4 divides buds forth several small cells (Fig. 5, *b*), which do not enter into the mesoblast-bands, though I did not correctly determine their fate. More recently Conklin was able to show that a similar process occurs in *Crepidula* (Fig. 5, *a*), and that the cells thus formed are *entoblast-cells* which enter into the formation of the archenteron. On reëxamining the matter in *Nereis* I found the clearest evidence that the same was true here. In both these cases, therefore, the posterior cell of the fourth quartet is of mixed character, and divides into two mesentoblasts, each of which first gives rise to a number of entoblast cells (two in *Crepidula*, four or five in *Nereis*), the residue constituting the mesoblast. In both these forms, therefore, the ectoblast (and in *Crepidula* the ectomesoblast) are the first completely segregated, and the archenteron which remains gives rise to the mesoblastic pole-cells. The latter are, therefore, of entoblastic rather than ectoblastic origin, and may be designated as the *entomesoblast*.

Further examination of these phenomena brings out some highly interesting facts which seem to constitute a striking case of ancestral reminiscence in cleavage. Several years ago I found in two genera of annelids, *Aricia* and *Spio,* that the small entoblast-cells of *Nereis* and *Crepidula* (*i.e.,* those budded forth from the two mesoblasts derived from the division of d^4 or M) are represented by a single pair of quite rudimentary cells, scarcely larger than polar bodies (Fig. 5, *e*), which apparently take no part in the building of the archenteron, and can only be explained as vestiges or reminiscences of such a process as occurs in *Crepidula* or *Nereis*. Later researches have revealed the presence of these vestigial entoblasts in several other forms, and have shown further that they are connected by several intermediate steps with the larger functional cells found in *Crepidula*. Thus in *Amphitrite* (Mead) and *Planorbis* (Holmes) they are quite vestigial, agreeing essentially in size and origin with those of *Aricia*. In *Unio* (Lillie) they are considerably larger (Fig. 5, *d*), in *Clymenella* (Fig. 5, *c*) they are as large as the mesoblastic moiety (Mead); while in *Crepidula* (Fig. 5, *a*) their bulk surpasses that of the mesoblastic part.[6] Such a series creates a strong probability that we have before us a vanishing series like those so well known in adult organs, such as the limbs, the tail, or the teeth. Further, just as the lateral

---

[6] I am here placing my own interpretation on Mead's and Lillie's observations.

toes of the horse seem to have wholly vanished, even from the ontogeny,
so the vestigial entoblasts would seem to have disappeared in some annelids and mollusks, leaving the posterior cell of the fourth quartet
purely mesoblastic.

These considerations invest with a special interest the corresponding
cell in the *Turbellaria* (*i.e.*, the posterior member of the fourth quartet,
4d); and this interest is heightened by Lang's discovery that in *Discocœlis* this cell divides earlier than the other cells of the quartet,
and into equal halves which lie symmetrically at the posterior end of
the embryo. These two cells thus correspond exactly in origin and position with the paired mesentoblasts of the annelids and gasteropods, and
the facts naturally led to the suggestion, made by Mead, that they would
perhaps be found to give rise to paired mesoblast-bands, as in the higher
types. In *Leptoplana* (Fig. 4, *D, E, F*) a similar division occurs, but as
far as their fate is concerned my own observations do not sustain Mead's
suggestion, on the one hand giving no evidence that these cells give rise
to anything other than the posterior cells of the archenteron, on the
other showing that they are often unequal or asymmetrically placed (Fig.
4, *D, E*) and only rarely conform to Lang's scheme (Fig. 4, *F*). If, therefore, the polyclades represent the ancestral type in this respect, we must
conclude that the entomesoblast was a later development. The remarkable fact is that, if such has been the case, the new mesoblast-formation
has been fitted, as it were, upon an old form of cleavage occurring regularly in *Discocœlis* and ocassionally in *Leptoplana*. The two symmetrical
posterior entoblast-cells of the polyclade might thus be conceived as the
prototypes of the primary mesoblasts or mesentoblasts of the higher
forms, which in the course of the phylogeny undertook the formation of
mesoblastic as well as of entoblastic elements.[7] The old building pattern
was still retained but adapted to a new use, precisely as has been the
case with the evolution of larval or adult organs, such as the branchial
or aortic arches and the limbs. As the change progressed the posterior cell
of the fourth quartet became more and more strictly given over to the
formation of mesoblast, its entoblastic elements becoming correspondingly
reduced to truly rudimentary or vestigial cells (*Aricia*, etc.), or finally,
perhaps, disappearing wholly.

I have endeavored to place these special conclusions in strong re-
lief, not because they can yet be accepted as demonstrated,—and it is
quite possible that some other interpretation may yet be placed upon
some of the facts,—but because they seem to me highly suggestive of
further research in the field of cell-lineage. There are among them
two general considerations on which I would lay emphasis.

First, the study of cleavage or cell-lineage in the case of these groups

[7] Lang has pointed out a motive for this form of cleavage in the polyclade, correlat-
ing the early and symmetrical division of d^4 with the posterior bifurcation of the gut.

raises a number of highly interesting and suggestive questions in pure morphology. If the mesoblast-bands are a new formation, what is the motive, so to speak, for their origin? Did they perhaps arise through the developments of a new body-region, or a new growth-zone, or budding-region from the posterior part of the ancestral body, as has been assumed by Leuckart, Haeckel, Hatschek, and Whitman in explanation of metamerism? Is the body of the turbellarian homologous to the entire body of an annelid or mollusk, or does it represent only the head or the larval body, to which a trunk-region is afterwards added? What is the relation of the entomesoblast to the archenteric pouches of the enterocœlous types? How do the above results harmonize with the general doctrine of development by substitution? These are examples of some of the morphological questions suggested by the general inquiry. They are admittedly of a highly speculative character, and I, for one, am not prepared to give a positive answer to any of them. But the mere fact that morphological questions of such character and scope are inevitably suggested by studies in pure cell-lineage shows that such studies must not be passed over by the morphologist as having no interest or value for his own researches.

Second, the phenomena we have considered seem to leave no escape from the acceptance of ancestral reminiscence in cleavage, with all that that implies. That the rudimentary entoblasts of *Aricia* or *Spio* are such reminiscences of former conditions seems almost as clear as that the mammalian yolk-sac or the avian primitive streak are such. The formation of the ectomesoblast in annelids and mollusks is nearly if not quite as strong a case. Both these are processes that appear to be vestigial, or, at any rate, approach that character. But the evidence of genetic affinity is no less clearly shown in processes that are not vestigial, such as the formation of the ectoblast in *Turbellaria,* annelids, and gasteropods or lamellibranchs, from neither more nor less than three quartets of micromeres, or in the origin of the archenteron from the fourth quartet with the remains of the basal quadrants. Between the annelids, gasteropods, and lamellibranchs a far more precise and extended series of resemblances exists. The question has been much discussed of late whether such resemblances can be called homologies. Probably no one will deny that the ectoblast-cap, arising from twelve cells, is as a whole homologous in the annelid and the gasteropod embryo. Are the individual micromeres respectively homologous? In the present state of our knowledge this is a question of name rather than of fact; for homologies only gradually emerge during development from their unknown background in the egg. It is for this reason that, as I have urged in a preceding lecture, *the ultimate court of appeal in this question lies in the fate of the cells.* If the structures to which they give rise are homologous, I can find no logical ground for refusing the claim to the cells from which they arise. Furthermore, this homology must be irrespective of the origin of the cells, just as the ganglion of a bud-embryo of *Botryllus* is homologous with that of an egg-embryo in the same form, despite the total difference of origin in the two cases. When, however, we find that the homologous protoblasts or parent-cells have the same origin as well as the same fate, the homology becomes the more striking; and it is in the determination of common origin as well as common fate, as has been done in so many cases, that the principal significance of recent work in cell-lineage seems to me to lie. Some of the objections urged against the reality of cell-homology have, I think, arisen through a failure to recognize among cell-homologies the same distinction between complete and incomplete homology that was long ago urged by Gegenbaur in the case of organ-homologies. The posterior member of the fourth quartet in annelids, for example, is in a broad sense homologous throughout the group; but the homology is probably not an absolute or complete one, since this cell may contain functional entoblast (*Nereis*), rudimentary or vestigial entoblast (*Aricia*), or apparently in some cases no entoblast, as I have described in *Polymnia*. Again, the acceptance of cell-homology does not, I think, carry with it the necessity of finding a homologue for every individual cell throughout the ontogeny; for in the case of later structures no one demands or expects that, in the comparison of related forms, an exact equivalent shall be found for every subdivision of homologous nerves or bloodvessels or sense organs. Finally, the fact that cleavage *may* show no constant or definite relation to the adult parts— as is the case in the teleost fishes—does not alter the equally indubitable fact that cleavage often *does* show such a constant relation. The probability that the *Nauplius* larva is not a true ancestral form does not come into collision with the probability that the ascidian tadpole is such a form. How far in the course of phylogeny the ontogeny has adhered to its original type and retained the same relation to the adult parts is a question which stands, as far as I can see, both *a priori* and *a posteriori* on essentially the same basis, whether it be applied to the cleavage or to the later stages. Let us not forget the difficulties that still beset us in the application of the biogenetic law to the larval stages and to general organogeny, and let us not make a greater demand in this regard upon cell-lineage than on other lines of embryological research. The time has not yet come for a last word on this subject, and we shall probably have to await the result of much more extended research before a satisfactory point of view can be attained.

PART FOUR

1902

On Multipolar Mitosis as a Means of Analysis of the Cell Nucleus

by THEODOR BOVERI

Boveri, Th. 1902. Über mehrpolige Mitosen als Mittel zur Analyse des Zellkerns. Verhandlungen der physikalisch-medizinischen Gesellschaft zu Würzburg. Neue Folge 35:67-90. Translated by Salome Gluecksohn-Waelsch and printed by permission of Prof. Dr. Hans L. duMont, Schriftführer der Physikalisch-Medizinischen Gesellschaft Würzburg.

Embryologists of the mid-twentieth century take so much for granted that an embryo is constructed of cells whose nuclei have become what they are by appropriate processes of meiosis or mitosis that they tend to forget that at the beginning of this century the role of cell inclusions, including the nucleus, in development and heredity was not yet known. Although the role of the egg and sperm in fertilization, and something of the behavior of chromosomes, had been elucidated by Fol (1877, 1879), Van Beneden (1883), O. Hertwig (1875, 1878), and others, it was left to Theodor Boveri (1862-1915) to make important contributions to our understanding of the nature and functions of the centrosomes, spindles, and asters, and of the polarity of the egg, and of the influences exerted by the cytoplasm on the nucleus. His most important contributions, however, were those concerning the nucleus itself.

He worked almost exclusively on the eggs of nematodes and echinoderms. He confirmed van Beneden's observation that in Ascaris *equivalent groups of chromosomes are furnished by the two parents. He discovered the process of diminution of the chromatin in the germ-cell line in* Ascaris *and performed an experimental analysis demonstrating that the influence of a particular part of the cytoplasm determines in which cells the diminution occurs. This remains even today the most clear-cut demonstration of cytoplasmic influence on the nucleus that has yet been achieved. He attempted to assess the relative roles of nucleus and cytoplasm in development by fertilizing enucleated egg fragments of one species of sea urchin with the spermatazoon of another species. But his most important contribution of all was his demonstration, on solely embryological and cytological grounds, of the individuality of the chromosomes—a premise independently established by the geneticists and one at the basis of the development of the gene theory as we know it.*

Fol and O. Hertwig had shown that echinoderm eggs fertilized by two spermatazoa divide simultaneously, by multipolar mitosis, to form three or four cells, then continue their development, often abnormally. In the paper reproduced here, Boveri related the abnormalities of development to the abnormal distribution of chromosomes. In an analysis that is a masterpiece of induction, he showed that it is not the number of the chromosomes but their abnormal combination that is responsible for the aberrations in development, and by the most ingenious considerations he proved that the various chromosomes differ qualitatively from one another.

This work was the subject not only of the article presented here, but also of an expanded publication, Zellenstudien VI (1907). *The illustrations reproduced here are taken from* Zellenstudien VI; *the 1903 publication contained none. E. B. Wilson, Boveri's peer as a pioneer in the cytological investigation of development, wrote of the 1902 article, in a commemorative essay on Boveri, that "it may be doubted whether a finer example of experimental, analytical and constructive work, compressed within such narrow limits—the paper on multipolar mitosis comprises but twenty pages and is without figures—can be found in the literature of modern biology." Earlier in the same essay he prophesied that Boveri's writings would "long endure as classical models of conception, execution and exposition." History has amply confirmed his judgment. (See Erinnerungen an Theodor Boveri. Ed. by W. C. Röntgen Verlag von J.C.B. Mohr. Tübingen 1918.)*

ON MULTIPOLAR MITOSIS AS A MEANS OF ANALYSIS OF THE CELL NUCLEUS

It has been known since the investigations of Fol and O. Hertwig that the penetration of two spermatozoa into the sea urchin egg results in the formation of a tetrapolar spindle and consequently in the simultaneous division of the egg into four blastomeres.[1] Driesch (13) isolated 82 such quadripolar eggs and found that they were unable to develop beyond the stage of an abnormal blastula (the so-called stereoblastula); at the very most, the first beginning of invagination could be observed. "Even an approximately typical gastrula was never formed." I had this same experience three years ago in unpublished investigations in which approximately ten dispermic eggs of *Echinus* were cultured separately. Later I was able to achieve an analogous effect in normally fertilized eggs as a result of suppression of the first cleavage division, a procedure which, as in dispermy, results in the formation of four centrosomes instead of two in the cell. Eggs of this sort cultured in isolation did not develop beyond stereoblastulae.

Several possibilities could conceivably account for this result, and it was possible to subject at least a few of these to experimental tests. I therefore decided to try to ascertain if it were possible to solve the question by means of a most careful analysis of doubly fertilized eggs.

1. Since O. and R. Hertwig (21) had found that damage to the eggs facilitated the penetration of several spermatozoa, it was necessary first of all to consider the possibility that the pathological development of dispermic eggs was caused not by the penetration of two spermatozoa, but by a pre-existing pathological condition of the eggs. The following experiment designed to test this possibility is based on an observation of mine, reported previously (7, p. 439), which indicated that the percentage of doubly fertilized eggs depends largely on the amount of sperm present.

[1] Cf. Boveri (8) concerning exceptions to this rule.

Undamaged eggs of a female were divided into two groups, one of which was exposed to very little, the other to very much sperm; examination of these eggs after the appearance of the first cleavage furrow showed that the first group had very few and the second group very many dispermic eggs. The percentage of abnormal larvae in both groups corresponded to that in dispermy.[2] It was demonstrated therefore that the pathological development of the eggs is a result of the dispermy.

2. Since, as one of the certain consequences of dispermy with resulting quadripolar eggs, each of the four blastomeres contains as a rule a different number as well as a different combination of chromosomes, the next question to be asked was whether this differential distribution of the chromatin might have an effect on the properties of the four cells. The discovery of Herbst (20), who showed that calcium-free sea water separated the individual blastomeres of the sea urchin egg from each other, makes it possible to isolate each single blastomere and to follow its fate. In this way Driesch (17) discovered that quarter blastomeres of normally fertilized eggs are able to develop into normally formed though dwarfed plutei. Whether each one of the four blastomeres is capable of such development was not determined by Driesch. I therefore repeated the experiment in such a way that I separated isolated eggs after the appearance of the second cleavage furrow into their four blastomeres, culturing separately each of these four cells of common origin. As was to be expected, each cell gave rise to a pluteus.

The result is completely different if the four blastomeres of a dispermic quadripolar egg are separated from each other. First of all, such blastomeres will not—except for rare cases—develop into plutei. Secondly, however, many of them develop into at least more or less normal gastrulae in such a high percentage that on the average almost one quarter gastrula is found for every two dispermic eggs; therefore, if we take into account the fate, previously mentioned, of whole dispermic eggs, certain quarters achieve more separately than do all four quarters together. Thirdly and finally—and this is the most significant result of the experiment—as a rule, each of the four blastomeres develops differently. Since development in most of them does not proceed very far, these differences do not ordinarily amount to very much; however, there are also striking cases in which beside one quarter that broke up into separate cells at the blastula stage, or that became a permanent stereoblastula, a more or less normal gastrula is found, or even a young pluteus with segmentation of the gut and skeletal primordia. Whereas, therefore, the four blastomeres of a normally divided egg are equivalent, the properties of the blastomeres of a dispermic egg differ from each other in many respects and to varying degrees.

[2] Numerical evidence for this and other statements will be given elsewhere.

3. After this result it was to be expected that different potencies of the four quarters should frequently be demonstrable in the development of whole dispermic eggs also. This indeed turned out to be the case. When the eggs have developed into swollen blastulae with polar differentiation, a stage at which, as a rule, they still appear perfectly normal, one or two of the quadrants of the blastula located between two meridians now begin in many cases to slough cells into the interior. Conse-

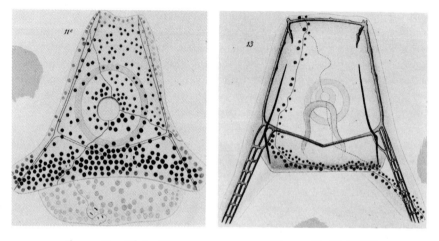

Figure 11c, Plate II   **Figure 13, Plate III**

Two figures from Plates II and III of Boveri's definitive 1907 publication on the development of dispermic sea-urchin eggs. Figure at left, Fig. 11c, Plate II. Pluteus from a *Strongylocentrotus* egg that divided into 3 cells at the first cleavage, viewed from behind. Magnification about 650×. Figure at the right, Fig. 13, Plate III. Pluteus from a *Sphaerechinus* egg that divided into three cells at the first cleavage, viewed from in front. The border of the third containing small nuclei is shown by a line (red in the original figure). A few nuclei on either side of this border, along its course on the front surface, are shown to illustrate the difference in their sizes.

quently, this entire marginal portion appears opaque, or the whole quarter dissolves, shedding its cells to the outside. Finally the remaining part, which is at first still open, closes up again into a vesicle. But there are further events, and here my results differ from the experiences of Driesch mentioned above and from my own earlier ones. Some of the quadrants of the embryo develop into gastrulae and form a skeleton, but now usually in a way that expresses the different potencies of the individual regions, e.g., with an archenteron asymmetrical in degree of differentiation or in location, or with the skeleton present on one side only and even there more or less abnormal.

4. However, even plutei varying from grossly abnormal to completely

normal in structure may develop from dispermic eggs, and here an experimentally obtained variety of dispermic development is particularly
illuminating. In the experiments described above in which the development of isolated blastomeres of dispermic eggs was studied, it was necessary to remove the fertilization membrane, which can be accomplished,
according to Driesch, by shaking the eggs a few minutes after fertilization.
With this procedure, I observed almost regularly the phenomenon which
Morgan (24) already described but whose origin has not been explained,
namely, that some eggs divided simultaneously into three blastomeres.
There are two ways to demonstrate[3] that the three blastomeres are
derived from dispermic eggs in which, as a result of shaking, one of the
sperm centrosomes did not divide; this one gave rise to one pole, whereas
the two other poles were the result of the normal division of the second
sperm centrosome. Morgan studied the development of ten such tripolar
eggs and three of these reached the stage of fully formed gastrulae. I
myself have cultured more than 900 isolated specimens some of which
were whole, some of which were separated into their three blastomeres;
in principle I made the same observations as on quadripolar eggs, noting,
in particular, the same lack of equivalence of the regions originating from
multipolar cleavage. However, the tendency for normal development is
much stronger in the tripolar than in the quadripolar eggs and consequently a quite considerable percentage of plutei, some of them completely normal, are obtained from them. Even the quadripolar dispermic
eggs give rise to plutei in a very small percentage of cases; however, I
never found a completely normal one among these.

5. To explain the facts just reported, we had best start with the
question of the possible origin of the differences in developmental
potencies of the cells resulting from multipolar cleavage. The differential
cannot lie in the cytoplasm. The reason for this is that the tetraster of a
dispermic egg—only these were used for the blastomere separation experiments—and similarly the triaster, are located in a plane (karyokinetic
plane[4]) perpendicular to the axis of the egg. This can be directly observed
in *Strongylocentrotus* by the relation to the pigment ring and can be indirectly concluded from a consideration of the two abnormal cleavage
types studied by Driesch (13) and Morgan (24) in connection with the
axial relations demonstrated by myself. The four blastomeres of the
quadripolar egg are just as equipotential in their protoplasm as those of
the normal four blastomere stage. Similarly, a differential in the centrosomes cannot be assumed. The reason for this is that each two of the
four centrosomes of dispermic eggs correspond to one of the two of the
normally fertilized egg which have identical properties as can be concluded from the study of normal development and all pertinent experi-

[3] In respect to this and other evidence I refer for the time being to the more detailed
description elsewhere.
[4] Cf. my evidence in 9 and 10.

ments. At most in the tripolar eggs the possibility might be considered that the one undivided centrosome differed qualitatively from the two others. However, quite aside from the completely identical behavior of the three cells in the subsequent stages of division, it is specifically the tripolar eggs that may give rise to completely normal larvae. But even different potencies of the centrosomes could not cause what is demonstrated to us by the development of the dispermic eggs, namely, an almost unlimited variability from complete normality to abnormalities of the highest degree, and specifically the so extremely variable and in each particular case so differently combined potencies of the blastomeres derived from simultaneous multiple division. These phenomena could only be explained on the basis of a process which itself is subject to corresponding variability and such a process is presented only in the manner of *distribution of the chromosomes.*

After I realized in 1887 (1) that the karyokinetic figure results from a secondary connecting together of two cell organelles previously independent of each other, on the one hand the centrosomes with their spheres, on the other hand the chromosomes, I was able to demonstrate in 1888 (3, pp. 180 ff), as a result of the first detailed analysis of multipolar division figures, that the distribution of the chromosomes between more than two poles is determined by chance. "Karyokinesis, which in the presence of two poles is a mechanism of almost ideal perfection for the purpose of dividing a nucleus into two daughter nuclei identical in quantity and quality, turns these advantages practically into the reverse as soon as a larger number of centrosomes begins to take effect. . . . Number, size, and—if we have to assign different qualities to the individual chromatic elements—also the quality of the resulting daughter nuclei are determined by chance" (3, p. 185). If we consider our particular case, the number of chromosomes of the mature *Strongylocentrotus* egg is approximately 18, and the identical number is found in the spermatozoon. The first cleavage spindle therefore contains 36 elements each of which divides into half, so that each daughter cell similarly contains 36. The number of chromosomes in the doubly fertilized eggs amounts to $3 \times 18 = 54$. As a result of division of each chromosome into two halves, 108 daughter chromosomes are produced, which are distributed (in the typical case) into four cells. In the case of equal distribution, each of these four cells would contain 27 elements, that is nine less than normal. Actually, such an equal distribution occurs probably only in extremely rare exceptions; the four cells therefore, obtain on the average not only fewer, but also different numbers of chromosomes, and particularly quite different combinations of them. If we designate the individual chromosomes of the dispermic first cleavage nucleus A, B, C, D, etc., then we see that in the case of multipolar cleavage of the egg into four blastomeres only two blastomeres can have a representative of A, or of B, etc., whereas no representative of this particular chromosome gets into the other two blastomeres.

6. Now the question arises: Is the different potency of each individual blastomere of the quadripolar egg based on unequal quantitative distribution or do we have to ascribe different qualities to the individual chromosomes in order to explain this heterogeneity? That a particular number of chromosomes in itself is not required for normal development was demonstrated by myself in experiments, confirmed by Delage (11) and Winkler (32), in which the development of enucleated egg fragments fertilized by one sperm was studied and in which normal plutei developed although they had only half of the normal amount of chromatin and number of elements, that is, only the chromosomes of one sperm nucleus. What was demonstrated here for the sperm nucleus has since been shown to be true also for the egg nucleus as a result of the investigations on artificial parthenogenesis by J. Loeb (23) and E. B. Wilson (30).[5]

We could now also put up the following argument: The number of chromosomes, above a certain minimal limit, does not matter as long as the same number is present in each cell. If the individual regions of the same embryo contain nuclei with different numbers of chromosomes, then abnormalities occur. However, this assumption can also be refuted in two ways. First of all, on the basis of the experiments of blastomere dissociation. Each isolated blastomere of the quadripolar egg has on the average more than the necessary minimal number of chromosomes, and even in the most unfavorable distribution, at least two of the four blastomeres have to obtain more than the minimal number. According to our assumption therefore, each quadripolar egg dissociated into its four blastomeres should yield at least two plutei, which is however not the case.

However, the untenability of this hypothesis may be demonstrated

---

[5] It is irrelevant for this argument whether the normal number of chromosomes is restored in later embryonic stages, a fact which, incidentally, I still doubt on the basis of my investigations. Delage, however, recently extended (12) to artificial parthenogenesis his contention, proposed originally for merogony, that the normal number of chromosomes could be found in later embryonic stages. He was able to count with certainty and in numerous cases, 16 to 19, on the average 18, chromosomes in the cells of parthenogenetic embryos of *Strongylocentrotus*, and thus he considers his earlier statements completely proven. However, it escaped him here that the normal chromosome number of *Strongylocentrotus* is not as he assumes 18 on the average, but 36, as I have found without exception in three different years (1888, 1896 and 1902); the chromosome number of the individual pronucleus is therefore on the average 18, a figure which R. Hertwig (22) actually determined thus (16 to 18) for the egg nucleus in preparation for independent division. According to the hypothesis of the individuality of the chromosomes, therefore we would expect the average number of 18 as found by Delage in the parthenogenetic as well as in the merogonic egg of *Strongylocentrotus;* thus Delage's new counts prove exactly what he believes to disprove, namely, the *failure of regulation of chromosome number.*

in the whole dispermic egg. Also, I had determined previously in my
experiments on merogony (5, 7) that larvae from enucleated egg fragments had considerably smaller nuclei than those from nucleated fragments or from whole eggs. This observation I have found to be confirmed
in the clearest possible way in a repetition of these experiments just
completed, as I shall report in detail in a separate paper. I only would
like to mention here the following observation: If one selects from the
fragmented eggs of a female on the one hand nucleated, and on the other
hand enucleated fragments, and fertilizes these with identical sperm, the
larvae developing from the latter fragments contain considerably smaller,
and, as I now must add, considerably more nuclei than larvae of the
same size[6] and age developing from the former fragments. Thus, the size
and number of the nuclei and accordingly also the size and number of cells of a sea urchin larva are respectively—other things being equal—directly and inversely proportional to the number of
chromosomes in the mother cell. I was able to determine without doubt,
by raising larvae in which I knew with certainty the chromosome number
of the individual blastomeres, that this rule holds not only for different
larvae but also for different regions of one and the same larva, provided
that these regions are derived from blastomeres with different numbers
of chromosomes. I cite here merely the not infrequent case of dispermy
where only one sperm nucleus unites with the egg nucleus and a normal
first cleavage spindle is formed by the chromosomes of these two, whereas
the other sperm nucleus comes to lie in a separate spindle which therefore contains only half as many chromosomes. Such eggs almost always
divide, as I have described previously (8), into two cells, each with one
large and one small nucleus. However, it occurs, sometimes in the beginning, more frequently in one of the later cleavage divisions,[7] that
regions with small nuclei separate cleanly from those with large nuclei
and consequently, larvae develop whose properties and significance I shall
discuss below. Here it may suffice to state that these larvae consist of one
part with large nuclei and another part with small nuclei and correspondingly more numerous cells, quite in the same relation that we have estab-

---

[6] This sentence holds true also, even if not quite as strictly, for larvae developing
from fragments of different sizes. It is true furthermore, not only for cases with decreased but also for those with an abnormally increased number of chromosomes. I
have succeeded in obtaining cleavage of the egg with twice the normal number, that is,
in *Strongylocentrotus*, with approximately 72 instead of 36 chromosomes. The larvae
contain accordingly much bigger nuclei than those developing from normal control
eggs, and, in connection with this, much bigger and many fewer cells. They show only
about half the normal number of mesenchymal cells, and never produce, obviously because of this small number of cells, completely normal plutei.

[7] Dr. E. Teichmann will report more details from his own investigations about the
variations which occur here.

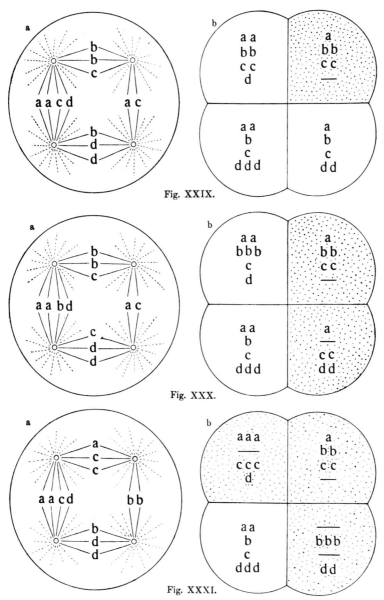

Fig. XXIX.

Fig. XXX.

Fig. XXXI.

Text figures (XXIX, XXX and XXXI) from Boveri's definitive 1907 publication on the development of dispermic sea-urchin eggs, indicating possible random combinations of chromosomes on the spindles of tetrapolar eggs. These figures bore no legends in the original; they were explained in the text. The blastomeres that are unstippled contain chromosomes a, b, c, and d, and presumably develop normally; those lacking a, b, c, or d, or several of these, are stippled and would develop abnormally.

lished between larvae developed from nucleated and those from enucleated egg fragments.

Once this is established, the conclusion is unavoidable: since larvae from normally cleaved eggs possess nuclei of equal size in corresponding regions of the organism, those larvae in which regions with different nuclear sizes are found must be derived from eggs in which each of these regions starts out from a blastomere with a different chromosome number. Now, I have found, among the almost normal plutei of the tripolar eggs described above, four in which one-third of the larvae contain very small and correspondingly more numerous nuclei, and the remaining two-thirds contain large nuclei.[8] In the living pluteus, the border at which two such regions meet usually cannot be recognized. Thus it is proven that the different number of chromosomes as it happens to be distributed to the various regions of the egg as a result of multipolar division is not to blame for the pathological development of dispermic eggs.

It should be noted as an important supplement to this statement that I have obtained numerous highly pathological products from tripolar eggs in which size differences between the nuclei could not be demonstrated; in these, therefore, an equal or practically equal distribution of the chromosomes into the three primary blastomeres must have occurred. In this way, the irrelevance of a definitive amount of chromatin has been proven from the opposite direction.

One other idea might perhaps come to mind, namely, that different numbers of chromosomes could occur in the individual cells, but only certain quite definite numbers, namely, those typical for the individual pronucleus and their multiples, but no intermediate numbers. If we consider that it is possible to obtain hybrids between species with different numbers of chromosomes, then such a possibility already becomes highly improbable. However, it also can be disproved more strictly. Namely, if we assume for the plutei described above with a third containing small nuclei, that these small nuclei contain the chromosome number of the individual pronucleus, then it is a necessary consequence that the two other thirds with their nuclei of almost identical size present *intermediate numbers,* thus refuting the hypothesis.

7. Thus, only one possibility remains, namely that not a definite number, but a *definite combination of chromosomes* is essential for normal development, and this means nothing else than that *the individual chromosomes must possess different qualities.* At the moment, we are unable to give a more definite setting to this irrefutable conclusion;

---

[8] It should be noted that this third with small nuclei may belong to different regions of the pluteus. It always, however, represents a region which comprises all zones from the animal to the vegetative pole so that therefore a third of the gut also has correspondingly small nuclei.

only one more exact statement can be made, namely, that all qualities, at least those essential to reach the pluteus stage that can be raised in our aquaria, have to be represented in the dispermic egg at least three times. For according to the experiments on merogony and parthenogenesis the egg nucleus as well as each sperm nucleus contain all qualities.

If we now consider all chromosomes of a dispermic egg to be unselectively mixed in a uniform first cleavage nucleus, and if we suppose that each quality exists in three chromosomes only—in one element from each pronucleus—then the probability that a certain quality is transmitted into each blastomere amounts to 70% in tripolar and 40% in quadripolar eggs. If the individual qualities of each pronucleus are distributed between nine chromosomes (the actual number in *Echinus microtuberculatus*), then the probability that each blastomere of the tripolar eggs obtains all qualities, that is, at least nine chromosomes, representing the whole set, is calculated at 4%, and in the quadripolar egg at 0.0026%.[9]

A strictly absolute value cannot be assigned to these figures. There exist in these distributions conditions which evade all calculations. In addition, it is doubtful what still can be considered a normal pluteus, and particularly it is conceivable that an occasional larva is excluded whose abnormality may be explained in another fashion than by a defect of chromatin qualities. Finally, the number of cases available to me (695 tripolar and 1170 quadripolar eggs) is not very considerable; also, these are derived from three different species. If we take all this into consideration, then we shall find the agreement of the expected with the actual result nevertheless significant. I have found, among the 695 tripolar eggs cultured as wholes, 58 almost normal plutei, that is 8.3% compared with the expected 4%. Among the ten larvae considered to be plutei obtained from the 1170 quadripolar eggs, there was not a single one as normal as the 58 obtained from the tripolar eggs and just mentioned. According to our calculation of course, their occurrence here can hardly be expected.

8. However, not only are the chances for a favorable distribution of the chromosomes greater in the tripolar eggs in general, but there is the additional possibility of a particularly regular distribution which is lacking in the quadripolar eggs. In the case of three poles, it is possible for a complete pronucleus to get into each of the three spindles and from this constellation there could be derived a chromatin complement of the three blastomeres which corresponds almost completely to that of the normal; each cell would possess the normal number of chromosomes and a double set of all qualities, one, that of the egg nucleus and of one of the sperm nuclei, the second, that of the egg nucleus and of the second sperm nucleus, the third that of both sperm nuclei. From this condition,

---

[9] This calculation is based on the assumption that all three or four poles are connected by spindles into a triangle or quadrangle.

I would like to derive, in addition to the very interesting asymmetrical forms, the few absolutely normal plutei that I obtained from tripolar eggs and whose nuclei of consistently equal size demand the assumption of an equal distribution of chromatin.

9. If we now examine the abnormal and pathological larvae from the point of view we have reached, they may be usefully divided into three groups:

a) Highly pathological. Here I include all those larvae that had not attained the morphological properties of a normal pluteus in any respect. This group contains, by the way, great variations that will not be considered in detail here.

b) Larvae in which certain pluteus characteristics are missing or appear to have developed abnormally whereas the others are normal. A few examples of this group may be cited: A case where a vesicle-shaped, completely anenteric larva has a perfectly developed skeleton on the left side, whereas the right one is missing completely; furthermore, cases where an otherwise normal pluteus from a tripolar egg lacks completely one or two thirds of the skeleton as though they had been cut away; finally, cases also from tripolar eggs where one third of the pluteus, otherwise practically normal, has no pigment cells. In some of these cases, it was possible to conclude from the nuclear size that the border-line of the defect coincides with the borderline between two regions derived from two different primary blastomeres.

c) Larvae derived from tripolar eggs which though normal within each separate part show the same trait in a different "individual" type on each side, so that they appear more or less asymmetrical. These cases relate closely to my earlier experiments of hybridization of enucleated egg fragments, and if on the one hand they do not operate with differences as great as species differences, on the other hand they are also not open to the objections that could be raised against the hybridization experiments. It is undoubtedly true in the cases just mentioned that different nuclear substance in identical cytoplasm produces a different larval type. These larvae could be explained by the kind of particularly regular chromatin distribution mentioned under 8 where it may happen, for example, that one larval third which contains the right part of mouth and anus contains in addition to the derivatives of all the maternal chromosomes those of one sperm nucleus, whereas the corresponding parts of the other side have obtained in addition to the maternal elements those of the other sperm nucleus. In this case, the individual differences inherent in the two sperm nuclei, differences which otherwise would appear in two different larvae, develop next to each other in the symmetrical organs of one and the same larva. As a matter of fact, I was able to make drawings from the different types of normal control larvae where I combined the right half of one type of larvae with the left half of another one; such pictures corresponded almost exactly to the plutei of tripolar eggs in question.

The experiments just reported appear to me to explain the symptoms of pathological dispermy. We are able to say: double fertilization and pathological development are not related to each other only indirectly in such a way that a pathological condition of the egg leads to pathological development on the one hand, and on the other hand makes dispermy possible, but pathological development is a consequence of dispermy, since the penetration of two spermatozoa ruins the previously perfectly normal egg. However, dispermy does not under all circumstances lead to pathological development, but only under certain conditions which however are almost always present. These conditions are not necessarily inherent in the increase of the number of centrosomes to three or four; for we have found that plutei may develop also from tripolar and quadripolar eggs. And since the *cytoplasm* behaves alike in all cases of multipolar division, it follows from the development of these plutei also, in agreement with the results of E. B. Wilson (31), that simultaneous division into more than two cells is not injurious to the cytoplasm.[10] Rather, the harmful effect of multiple poles is due to the fact that as a rule they cause an abnormal chromatin complement in the daughter cells.

The number of cells is irrelevant in this abnormal distribution. To be sure, the chromosomes as carriers of different qualities have to be present in each cell in a certain minimal number comprising all qualities; but beyond this, their number is irrelevant up to an upper limit harmful for other reasons; and in the reverse sense, a normal chromosome number in all cells, which is possible in tripolar eggs, does not guarantee normal development.

That in spite of the distribution of the dividing chromosomes into more than two cells, all these cells still may obtain all qualities is due to the fact that each quality is represented at least in three different chromosomes in the dispermic eggs. In the case of simultaneous multiple division of a normal first cleavage nucleus each cell could also obtain all qualities; however, the occurrence of such a case would be almost infinitely improbable.

These results on dispermy are in complete agreement with those obtained in studies of cells which for other reasons contain several centrosomes. As mentioned in the beginning, the suppression of the first cleavage furrow has the effect that the two spindles that should belong to

---

[10] Already in 1888 (3, p. 185) the analysis of multipolar mitoses led me to the conclusion "that indeed the cell substance is prepared for a simultaneous multiple division, not, however, the nucleus." However, just now I have reason to assume that this statement does not apply to all egg cells.

the two half-blastomeres come to lie next to each other in the undivided egg. E. B. Wilson (31) recently described cases of this kind, in which this condition led to a direct quadripolar division of the egg, and he obtained normal plutei from such eggs. In my own earlier experiments (8), such eggs divided first of all into two binucleate cells, in which again two spindles appeared and this condition was perpetuated until, sooner or later, the two spindles united into a four-polar figure; then, due to quadripolar division, uninucleate cells resulted which in turn continued to divide regularly. As mentioned above, these eggs did not develop beyond the stage of pathological blastulae. The experiences with dispermy provided the simple explanation for this different development. In Wilson's cases, each of the four simultaneously arising blastomeres obtains the very same chromosomes as in normal cleavage; in the cases observed by myself, the nuclei are also normal as long as they remain separate; however, as soon as a four-polar figure replaces the two separate spindles, the daughter nuclei must, as a rule, just as in dispermy, obtain faulty combinations of chromosomes and thus become pathological.

Closely related to these cases is that type of dispermy where one sperm nucleus remains separate, leading to the formation of two separate, usually parallel, spindles. We reported briefly above (6) about the early development of such eggs. Since the separate sperm nucleus possesses all the qualities necessary for pluteus development, the potentialities of this type of doubly fertilized eggs must be essentially identical to those of the cases just described where the first cleavage furrow is suppressed. If, as in Wilson's experiments, simultaneous division into four blastomeres were to occur, normal, even though not completely normal, development would be expected. In the dispermic eggs isolated by myself with two parallel spindles, such an immediate division into four blastomeres never occurred. However, several underwent a tripolar division into one binucleate and two uninucleate cells. I do not want to elaborate here the rather variable details; we may formulate the result on the basis of the various cases by stating that such eggs maintain the ability of normal development as long as, and to the extent that, the four centers present in the egg or the succeeding cell generations are not combined into one multipolar figure. If, before this happens, a division into uninucleate cells takes place, then the region of the embryo originating from this part has been definitely salvaged for further normal development. Thus, it can be explained that the percentage of larvae reaching a stage beyond that of the blastula is considerably greater in this constellation than where both sperm nuclei have united with the egg nucleus; and it is a beautiful confirmation of all our conclusions that the best developed larva that I obtained from a *tetrapolar* dispermic egg was derived from such a case with a separate sperm spindle.

In general, we may say this for the *Echinus* egg: multiple centrosomes in a cell are harmless for the cell complex that will eventually develop as long as only two poles each unite into one karyokinetic figure and as long as the original nucleus or nuclei were normal. If eventually a cell is formed around each of the centrosomes and around the nuclei resulting from the successive mitotic processes, then all of these will be normal as Wilson actually showed recently in his experiments on the suppression of cell division, and as we have known for some time from a similar process in some cleavage types. Multiple centrosomes have a pathological effect only if groups or more than two divide the available nuclear substance among themselves. In this case, there is no guarantee, or even the possibility, that all cells will be supplied with a portion of all the different qualities represented by the individual chromosomes.

With this we proceed from a consideration of our special case to the general significance of the results just described. A differential value of the chromosomes,[11] as concluded frequently before from studies of the morphology of mitosis, has now been proven and thus a first step has been made towards the analysis of the physiological constitution of the cell nucleus. The difference of our experiments on the nucleus from the previous ones[12] lies in the fact that until now, nothing else could be done but remove the entire nucleus and examine the results of its absence. We supply the cell with a nucleus which lacks certain portions and we follow the consequence of this defect. We have found that such a nucleus is sufficient for certain processes of ontogenetic events but not for others, so that it transmits, for example, the ability of invagination to the derivatives destined to form the gut, but it does not transfer the necessary qualities to the cells destined to form skeleton, or vice versa. We have to conclude from this that only a certain combination of chromosomes, probably no less than the total of all those present in each pronucleus, represent the entire essence of the organism's structure insofar as this is determined by the nucleus.

This recognition leads to the conclusion that the most important aspects of the physiological constitution of the nucleus are completely

[11] I myself have maintained until now (4, p. 56), primarily on the basis of my experiences with *Ascaris meg.*, that the chromosomes are essentially equal but individually different formations, and the same opinion I find maintained by Weismann in the recently published "Lectures on the Theory of Descent." This assumption has been refuted for the sea urchin egg by my experiments; and it is clear that therefore the simple considerations which Weismann developed for the reduction division also require at least considerable modification since random distribution of the chromosomes into two groups should in general be equally harmful as a multipolar mitosis. These and related problems, as well as the relevance of this to the results of botanists in studies of hybrids and their descendants, will be discussed separately.

[12] My own experiments on fertilization and particularly on hybridization of enucleated egg fragments constitute a certain exception here.

inaccessible to an analysis with the present methods of physiological chemistry. In this respect, Biology has at its disposal means of analysis of much superior resolving power. Even if the biologist is not capable of removing individual chromosomes as would be the ideal case, he possesses, nevertheless, in multipolar mitosis a tool for the production of the most diverse combinations, and embryogeny during which the qualities of the original nucleus unfold themselves provides the analysis of those qualities which are made possible by the various combinations ("Embryonalanalyse" of the cell nucleus).

What could be demonstrated here for the nucleus of the sea urchin egg is valid, with certain modifications, for all nuclei that divide mitotically. For mitotic division itself, however, we may consider as proved what has been assumed for a long time; namely that its goal lies in the transfer of the qualities present in *one* nucleus into many nuclei, and that it is specifically the function of the *bipolar* mitotic figure to multiply successively the nucleus in its totality. These statements, I believe, will from now on be counted among the firm basic principles of general physiology.

If we now consider some details more closely, the experiments offer us the first exact indications about the role of the nucleus in ontogenesis by the certainty with which they permit us to ascribe the disturbances of development exclusively to the chromosomes. It appears that the initial steps up to the blastula stage are independent of the quality of nuclear substance, even though it is essential that the nuclear substance be of a kind capable of existing in the egg.[13] The necessity for particular chromosomes becomes apparent first with the formation of the primary mesenchyme and from then on shows up in all processes as far as development can be observed. But not only do certain chromosomes prove to be essential in this connection; in addition, it appears that with respect to those characters in which we are able to recognize individual variations, the nuclear substance and not the cytoplasmic cell substance imposes its specific character on the developing trait.

Since the dependence of the developmental processes subsequent to the blastula stage on certain definite chromosomes has been determined, and since, on the other hand, it has been demonstrated that the chromosomes of the sperm nucleus, even in the absence of those of the egg nucleus, possess the qualities necessary for the development of all these characters, it may be supposed that the spermatozoon in the normally fertilized egg has an effect on all the processes beginning with the formation of the primary mesenchyme. If this were not the case, then it would have to be concluded in connection with the results of merogony that the sperm chromosomes serve to make possible the development of the

---

13 Cf. in this connection, my discussion in 6 (p. 469) and 8 (pp. 14 ff). Incidentally, the statements hold of course for the time being only for Echinids.

traits under discussion, but that the character of these traits is determined not by them but by the egg protoplasm. Actually, Driesch (15) did conclude from his experiments on hybridization of various sea urchin species that all larval characters with the exception of the skeleton were *purely maternal* and not affected by the sperm chromosomes. My own experiments however, demonstrated to me that these statements were erroneous. Not only, as I have shown previously (5, 7), the form and skeleton of the pluteus, but also the shape of the larvae before the formation of the skeleton, the amount and the pattern of the pigments and the number of primary mesenchyme cells may be influenced by the spermatozoon. This means, therefore, that precisely from the time when certain definite chromosomes, known to be present both in the egg and in the sperm nucleus, prove essential for further development, precisely from this point on, developmental processes show themselves influenced in their specificity by both parents equally; whereas earlier stages, for which, according to our results, specific chromosomes are not necessary, demonstrate a purely maternal character (Boveri, 6, p. 469; Driesch, 15). From all these facts, it will have to be concluded that the role of the chromosomes in ontogenesis corresponds rather exactly to the views which have found a brief though not very fitting expression in the designation of these structures as "carriers of heredity."

I would like to ascribe to the cytoplasm of the sea urchin egg only the initial and simplest of properties responsible for differentiation. Polarity and bilateral symmetry depend on the cytoplasmic pattern, and all malformations connected with these axial relations, such as duplications of larvae or the perpetual blastulae originating from fragments of the animal half only and incapable of undergoing polar differentiation, are based on disturbances of defects of the cytoplasm.[14] The structure of the egg cytoplasm takes care, if I may say so, of the purely "promorphological" tasks, that is, it provides the most general basic form, the framework within which all specific details are filled in by the nucleus. Or, the relationship may perhaps also be expressed by stating that simple cytoplasmic differentiation serves to start the machine whose essential and probably most complicated mechanism is located in the nuclei.

I am able to clarify this interpretation still further if I compare it briefly with the opinions that Driesch (18, 19) recently expressed about all attempts to explain ontogenetic events. He says: only a complicated

---

[14] Cf. here my experiments (9). Since that time I have repeated and extended the experiments on the development of purely animal (completely free of pigment) fragments of the *Strongylocentrotus* egg; not one of such cultured fragments from three different females developed beyond the stage of the blastula, whereas all pigmented fragments cultured as controls, and among them considerably smaller ones, developed into plutei.

machine could achieve what we are facing in ontogenesis; however, we are not dealing with a machine here, since a machine would not remain the same if random parts were removed or if parts were transposed in a random fashion, as can be done without harmful effects both in the cytoplasm and nuclei of the *Echinus* egg. The contradiction construed here by Driesch which, in addition to other considerations, leads him to postulate an "autonomy of living processes," appears to me not to exist in reality. I want to disregard completely the fact that the statement that *any part of the cytoplasm* could be removed without harming the potencies of the remaining parts has now had to be restricted very considerably. However, what is more important, also, the assumption that the *cytoplasm could be transposed at random* in the young egg without harmful effects is based on insufficient experience. I have demonstrated earlier (9), and since have been able to determine even more exactly, that minute translocations of the cytoplasm at the vegetative pole lead to the formation of duplications; in the meantime, I have obtained larvae with a duplicated or even triplicated archenteron and others with severe deformations and malformations of the skeleton[15] from clusters of translocated blastomeres provided that the translocations were not corrected, as is often the case. The *Echinus* egg therefore, is nothing less than a harmonic equipotential system. Finally, however, and this is the decisive point, any portion of "nuclei" but not any portion of "a nucleus" may be removed from the young *Echinus* egg. Taking something away from the nucleus has not even been tried in the experiments of Driesch; my own experiments, which did accomplish this, teach us that the nucleus, whose structure may have any degree of complexity, behaves just as Driesch demands from a "machine" in the discussion quoted above.

The conflict that Driesch feels is in my opinion resolved by these facts in a simple manner. It is certainly true that the hypothesis maintained by Roux and Weismann (25, 26, 29) of a differential distribution of that complex structure, postulated now also by Driesch, by way of differential nuclear division, has been disproven, at least for the early development of Echinids, by the experiments of Driesch.[16] However, it appears to me that the quite peculiar interaction of the cytoplasm with its simple structure and differential division and the nucleus with its complex structure and manifold total multiplication may still achieve

---

15 My colleague Driesch kindly informed me that he also repeated his earlier experiments on the translocation of blastomeres (14, 16) and that he obtained now essentially the same results as I did.

16 Cf., also, my speculations in 3 (pp. 182 ff), and in 8 (pp. 7 ff) about the difficulties which the development and constitution of multipolar mitoses present for the assumption of a differential nuclear division. The objections raised against these speculations on the basis of the pathological effect of multipolar mitoses are based on a logical mistake.

what Weismann and Roux attempted to explain with the help of differential nuclear division. When the primitive differences of the cytoplasm, as expressed in the existence of layers, are transferred to the cleaved egg without any change in the relationships of the layers, they affect the originally equal nuclei unequally by unfolding (activating) or suppressing certain nuclear qualities, as may be visualized directly in the cleavage of *Ascaris*. The inequalities of the nuclei, in some cases perhaps of temporary nature only, lend different potencies to the cytoplasm, that to begin with was differentiated only by degrees. Thus new cytoplasmic conditions are created which again release in certain nuclei the activation or suppression of certain qualities thus imprinting on these cells in turn a specific character and so on, and so on. In short: a continually increasing specification of the originally totipotent complex nuclear structure, and consequently, indirectly, of the cytoplasm of the individual cells, appears conceivable on the basis of physico-chemical events once the machine has been set in motion by the simple cytoplasmic differentiation of the egg. To explain the origin of normal larvae from isolated blastomeres, as well as from fragments of the egg and the blastula, it is, according to this view, necessary only to propose the assumption—well supported, incidentally—that these fragments obtain from the egg differences such that they release the first nuclear differentiations in the identical manner as does the cytoplasm of the entire egg. The sea urchin egg, apparently one of the eggs with the simplest cytoplasmic structure, teaches us that not every region is able to do this; and we know of other eggs (Ctenophores) in which the releasing egg structure is differentiated so highly that no isolated part of the cytoplasm is able to take the place of the whole.

Whoever has followed the literature on these questions that are under so much discussion knows that various authors have opinions that agree more or less closely in one or the other point with those just expressed. O. Hertwig, Weismann, de Vries, should be cited here. Furthermore, Driesch earlier developed possibilities, which he later rejected again, corresponding in many respects to my own point of view. Also with respect to Roux's doctrine, the common points, such as the interpretation of the nucleus as the real determinant, and that of the differentiation of the cytoplasm as a releasing factor, appear to outweigh by far the difference which lies in his assumption of qualitatively unequal nuclear division. The progress which, as I believe, has been attained by my experiments consists in just this: that now, even though in a field that is still narrow, speculations have been replaced by facts.

Of the manifold relations to other problems inherent in our results, only two points should be considered here briefly; first of all, whether any phenomena are known which appear in a new light as a result of the new insight. In this respect, it appears to me that certain asymmetries, that appear as abnormalities in bilateral animals, particularly in insects, may find a simple explanation on the basis of my results. If a bee has the structure of a drone on its right side and of a worker on its left side, then the right side has developed like a parthenogenetic and the left side like a fertilized egg, i.e., the right side like an egg which has maternal chromosomes only, the left side like one with chromosomes of both parents. On the basis of this consideration, and since it could be demonstrated that in the sea urchin egg asymmetries of a definite kind may be created by an unequal chromosomal composition of different egg regions, the conclusion is almost unavoidable that the reason for asymmetries of insects consisting in a mosaic configuration of male and female areas will also have to be looked for in nuclear differences. In the case just mentioned of purely symmetrical hermaphroditism, it cannot be a question of dispermy. We have to consider a different abnormal chromatin distribution such as I have found earlier in sea urchin eggs (2).[17] Here one half-blastomere contains maternal chromosomes only and the other mixed maternal and paternal chromosomes, i.e., precisely what had to be assumed for the hermaphroditic bees if the reason for this abnormality lies in the chromatin. Due to the peculiar conditions of bee development, the occurrence of such an abnormality is apparently much favored since it appears possible that the egg nucleus is already divided before union with the sperm nucleus as a result of its parthenogenetic potencies, and that the sperm nucleus unites only with one of the cleavage nuclei. This union could even be postponed until later cleavage stages and polyspermy, which is known to occur in bees, could have the effect that sperm nuclei unite with certain derivatives of the egg nucleus and not with others. In this way, the most diverse mixtures of male and female characters could result, as has been actually observed.[18]

Finally, a second question which should be touched upon briefly is that of the consequences of multipolar mitoses in later embryonic stages and in mature tissues. A beginning in this direction may be reported already. In the *Echinus* egg I succeeded in certain individual blastomeres, e.g., in one of the half or quarter blastomeres, to produce multipolar division figures in the macromeres or mesomeres and thus to render

17 Cf. here also the more detailed demonstration which E. Teichmann (28) gave in this connection based on material preserved by me.

18 Compare C. Th. von Siebold (27). It could perhaps be objected, against the explanation mentioned above, that a cleavage nucleus capable of division by itself and a sperm nucleus together would cause a quadripolar figure and thus pathological development of the corresponding egg region, similarly to two blastomere nuclei with their two centrosomes in the *Echinus* egg. However, just as the sperm nucleus in the bee egg forms a regular division figure with the egg nucleus capable of independent division, so this will also be possible with a later cleavage nucleus. We are dealing here no doubt with conditions of the cytocenters which deviate from those of the sea urchin egg and probably of most other eggs.

pathological the particular egg region arising from these. The details, interesting in other connections, shall not be discussed here;[19] it is of importance for our considerations that in those experiments which cause pathological conditions exclusively in the derivatives of the macromeres or of the mesomeres, the formation of the pluteus is usually not hindered. The pathological cells frequently enter the cleavage cavity (primary coelom) sooner or later in large numbers, but the normal parts group themselves into a smaller whole, just as in the case of complete removal of portions of the egg.

The fate of the pathological cell clusters that enter the interior cannot be determined in view of the limited life span of sea urchin larvae raised artificially. If, however, we want to classify these formations according to the points of view of pathological anatomy, then we have to designate them as "tumors" and thus arrive at the statement that multipolar mitosis might under certain conditions lead to the development of tumor-like formations. Could not this conclusion throw some light on the riddle of tumors? We are confronted here with quite a peculiar phenomenon, namely that a cell complex loses to some extent the normal qualities of its tissue, and by the maintenance or even occasionally an increase of the ability of the cells to multiply, a departure from the parent tissue and an abnormal proliferation contrary to the plan of the whole occur. It is not disease in the sense of a decrease of vitality, but in the sense of an aim in the wrong direction, that is probably the essential property of the tumor cell. Since it could be shown on the one hand that multipolar mitoses lead to the origin of such cells which have lost their balance, and since on the other hand it is known that simultaneous multipolar divisions are found in tumors, the hypothesis of a connection between these two phenomena seems worthy of an examination. However, it would have to be supposed, in addition, that not only in the developing, but even in the originating tumor, multipolar mitoses occur. What may cause these is a second question and I note that my hypothesis is not irreconcilable with the assumption that the first cause of tumors is of parasitic nature. If I survey reports about the etiology of carcinoma and the many suggestions of physical and chemical insults, and if I consider on the other hand that pressure, shaking, narcotics, abnormal temperatures are precisely the agents with whose help we may produce multipolar mitoses in young eggs, then it appears possible to me that we have before us, in the elements just considered, the entire causal sequence of certain tumors.

[19] It may however be mentioned that the pathological development of one half blastomere always leads to an exclusive defect in the right or left body half, from which one may conclude that the first cleavage furrow determines the median plane, unless stronger influences, such as I have demonstrated in the deformation of the egg (9), inhibit this.

REFERENCES

1. Boveri, Th., Über die Befruchtung des Eies von Ascaris megalocephala. Sitz.-Ber. d. Ges. f. Morph. u. Phys. München, Bd. 3. 1887.

2. Boveri, Th., Über partielle Befruchtung. Sitz.-Ber. d. Ges. f. Morph. u. Phys. München, Bd. 4. 1888.

3. Boveri, Th., Zellen-Studien, Heft 2, Jena 1888.

4. Boveri, Th., Zellen-Studien, Heft 3, Jena 1890.

5. Boveri, Th., Ein geschlechtlich erzeugter Organismus ohne mütterliche Eigenschaften. Sitz.-Ber. d. Ges. f. Morph. u. Phys. München, Bd. 5. 1889.

6. Boveri, Th., Befruchtung. Ergebn. d. Anat. u. Entw.-Gesch. Bd. 1. 1892.

7. Boveri, Th., Über die Befruchtungs- und Entwickelungsfähigkeit kernloser Seeigeleier und die Möglichkeit ihrer Bastardierung. Arch. f. Entw.-Mech. Bd. 2. 1885.

8. Boveri, Th., Zur Physiologie der Kern- und Zellteilung. Sitz.-Ber. d. phys.-med. Ges. Würzburg 1897.

9. Boveri, Th., Über die Polarität des Seeigel-Eies. Verh. d. phys.-med. Ges. Würzburg, N. F., Bd. 34. 1901.

10. Boveri, Th., Die Polarität von Ovocyte, Ei und Larve des Strongylocentrotus lividus. Zoolog. Jahrbücher Bd. 14. 1901.

11. Delage, Y., Études sur la Mérogonie. Arch. de Zool, exp. et gén., 3. sér., T. 7. 1899.

12. Delage, Y., Études expérimentales sur la Maturation cytoplasmique chez les Echinodermes. Arch. de Zool. exp. 3. sér., T. 9. 1901.

13. Driesch, H., Entwicklungsmechanische Studien V. Von der Furchung doppeltbefruchteter Eier. Zeitschr. f. wiss. Zool. Bd. 55. 1892.

14. Driesch, H., Betrachtungen über die Organisation des Eies und ihre Genese. Arch. f. Entw.-Mech. Bd. 4. 1896.

15. Driesch, H., Über rein-mütterliche Charaktere an Bastardlarven von Echiniden. Arch. f. Entw.-Mech. Bd. 7. 1898.

16. Driesch, H., Die Lokalisation morphogenetischer Vorgänge. Ein Beweis vitalistischen Geschehens. Arch. f. Entw.-Mech. Bd. 8. 1899.

17. Driesch, H., Die isolierten Blastomeren des Echinidenkeimes. Arch. f. Entw.-Mech. Bd. 10. 1900.

18. Driesch, H., Die organischen Regulationen. Leipzig 1901.

19. Driesch, H., Kritisches und Polemisches. Biolog. Centralblatt Bd. 22. 1902.

20. Herbst, C., Über das Auseinandergehen von Furchungs- und Gewebezellen in kalkfreiem Medium. Arch. f. Entw.-Mech. Bd. 9. 1900.

21. Hertwig, O., und R., Über den Befruchtungs- und Teilungsvorgang des tierischen Eies unter dem Einfluss äusserer Agentien. Jena 1887.

22. Hertwig, R., Über die Entwicklung des unbefruchteten Seeigeleies. Abh. d. k. b. Ak. d. Wiss., II. Kl., Bd. 29. 1898.

23. Loeb, J., On the Nature of the Process of Fertilization and the Artificial Production of Normal Larvae (Plutei) from the Unfertilized Eggs of the Sea Urchin. Americ. Journ. of Physiol. Vol. 3. 1899.

24. Morgan, T. H., A Study of Variation in Cleavage. Arch. f. Entw.- Mech. Bd. 2. 1895.

25. Roux, W., Über die Bedeutung der Kernteilungsfiguren. Leipzig 1883.

26. Roux, W., Beiträge zur Entwicklungsmechanik des Embryo. III. Breslauer ärztliche Zeitschr. 1885.

27. v. Siebold, C. Th., Über Zwitterbienen. Zeitschr. f. wiss. Zool. Bd. 14. 1864.

28. Teichmann, E., Über Furchung befruchteter Seeigeleier ohne Beteiligung des Spermakerns. Jenaische Zeitschr. Bd. 37. 1902.

29. Weismann, A., Das Keimplasma. Eine Theorie der Vererbung. Jena 1892.

30. Wilson, E. B., Experimental Studies in Cytology. I. A Cytological Study of Artificial Parthenogenesis in Sea-urchin Eggs. Arch. f. Entw.-Mech. Bd. 12. 1901.

31. Wilson, E. B., Experimental Studies in Cytology. III. The Effect on Cleavage of Artificial Obliteration of the First Cleavage-Furrow. Arch. f. Entw.-Mech. Bd. 13. 1901.

32. Winkler, H., Über Merogonie und Befruchtung. Jahrb. f. wissenschaftl. Bot. Bd. 36. 1901.

PART FIVE

1907

The Living Developing Nerve Fiber

by **ROSS G. HARRISON**

Harrison, Ross G. 1907. Observations on the living developing nerve fiber. Anatomical Record, 1:116-118 (Also Proc. Soc. Exp. Biol. and Med., 4:140-143). Reprinted by permission of the Wistar Institute.

Although the cell theory was proposed before the middle of the nineteenth century, it was not yet clear by the beginning of the twentieth century which particular cells in the animal embryo are responsible for forming the axon, the long conducting fiber of the nerve cell. There were then three theories as to the possible origin of the fiber: the cell-chain *theory, first enunciated by Schwann (1839), postulating that the fiber is formed by the chain of cells that form the sheath of Schwann; the* plasmodesm *theory, proposed by Hensen (1864), suggesting the fiber to be formed* in situ *along preformed protoplasmic bridges as a result of functional activity; and the* outgrowth *theory, first postulated by Bidder and Kupffer (1857) and strongly supported by W. His (1886-1890) and S. Ramon y Cajal (1890). This theory maintained that the nerve fiber is an outgrowth of a single cell, the neuroblast, which becomes the nerve cell of the adult.*

In the experiment described in the article reproduced here, Ross G. Harrison (1870-1959) demonstrated the validity of the outgrowth theory by following Roux's precept that independent differentiation may be demonstrated by isolation experiments. Harrison's experiment was crucial. He isolated under aseptic precautions a group of neuroblasts, before the fibers had differentiated, in a hanging drop of frog lymph in which no plasmodesms nor sheath cells were present, and he observed directly that protoplasmic fibers with branched ameboid endings extended from the neuroblasts into the frog lymph. This investigation established the fact that the neurone as a single cell is the developmental, structural, and functional unit of the nervous system and has thus provided the foundation for all subsequent investigation of the nervous system. It was also of great importance in demonstrating the usefulness of tissue culture as an invaluable embryological and biological technique. In 1917 a majority of the Nobel Prize Committee recommended Harrison for an award in physiology and medicine "for his discovery of the development of the nerve fibers by independent growth from cells outside the organism," but the actual award was not made. In 1933 the Committee again considered Harrison's work but decided against an award "in view of the rather limited value of the tissue culture method and the age of the discovery" (Nobel. The Man and His Prizes, by H. Schück, et al., 1951, p. 245). A Nobel Prize was awarded jointly to Enders, Robins and Weller in 1954 for their studies on the growth of human viral infections of embryonic tissues in tissue culture, and the wide application of the technique is now recognized not only by embryologists but by geneticists, virologists, microbiologists, physiologists, and by investigators in many other active fields of biology.

Harrison was also the first embryologist to adopt the grafting method of Born (1897) in the analysis of morphogenetic problems, and he made important contributions to our understanding of the development of embryonic symmetry and asymmetry. His directness of thought, simplicity of approach, depth of perception, and cautiousness of judgment have led to his recognition as an outstandingly great embryologist.

THE LIVING DEVELOPING NERVE FIBER[1]

The immediate object of the following experiments was to obtain a method by which the end of a growing nerve could be brought under direct observation while alive, in order that a correct conception might be had regarding what takes place as the fiber extends during embryonic development from the nerve center out to the periphery.

The method employed was to isolate pieces of embryonic tissue, known to give rise to nerve fibers, as for example, the whole or fragments of the medullary tube, or ectoderm from the branchial region, and to observe their further development. The pieces were taken from frog embryos about 3 mm. long at which stage, *i.e.*, shortly after the closure of the medullary folds, there is no visible differentiation of the nerve elements. After carefully dissecting it out, the piece of tissue is removed by a fine pipette to a cover slip upon which is a drop of lymph freshly drawn from one of the lymph-sacs of an adult frog. The lymph clots very quickly, holding the tissue in a fixed position. The cover slip is then inverted over a hollow slide and the rim sealed with paraffine. When reasonable aseptic precautions are taken, tissues will live under these conditions for a week and in some cases specimens have been kept alive for nearly four weeks. Such specimens may be readily observed from day to day under highly magnifying powers.

While the cell aggregates, which make up the different organs and organ complexes of the embryo, do not undergo normal transformation in form, owing, no doubt, in part, to the abnormal conditions of mechanical tension to which they are subjected; nevertheless, the individual tissue elements do differentiate characteristically. Groups of epidermis cells round themselves off into little spheres or stretch out into long bands, their cilia remain active for a week or more and a typical cuticular border develops. Masses of cells taken from the myotomes differentiate into muscle fibers showing fibrillæ with typical striations. When portions of myotomes are left attached to a piece of the medullary cord the muscle

1 Read before the Society for Experimental Biology and Medicine at the 23d meeting, New York, May 22, 1907.

fibers which develop will, after two or three days, exhibit frequent contractions. In pieces of nervous tissue numerous fibers are formed, though, owing to the fact that they are developed largely within the mass of transplanted tissue itself, their mode of development cannot always be followed. However, in a large number of cases fibers were observed which left the mass of nerve tissue and extended out into the surrounding lymph-clot. It is these structures which concern us at the present time.

In the majority of cases the fibers were not observed until they had almost completed their development, having been found usually two, occasionally three, and once or twice four days after isolation of the tissue. They consist of an almost hyaline protoplasm, entirely devoid of the yolk granules, with which the cell-bodies are gorged. Within this protoplasm there is no definiteness of structure; though a faint fibrillation may sometimes be observed and faintly-defined granules are discernable. The fibers are about 1.5-3 μ thick and their contours show here and there irregular varicosities. The most remarkable feature of the fiber is its enlarged end, from which extend numerous fine simple or branched filaments. The end swelling bears a resemblance to certain rhizopods and close observation reveals a continual change in form, especially as regards the origin and branching of the filaments. In fact, the changes are so rapid that it is difficult to draw the details accurately. It is clear we have before us a mass of protoplasm undergoing amœboid movements. If we examine sections of young normal embryos shortly after the first nerves have developed, we find exactly similar structures at the end of the developing nerve fibers. This is especially so in the case of the fibers which are connected with the giant cells described by Rohon and Beard.

Still more instructive are the cases in which the fiber is brought under observation before it has completed its growth. Then it is found that the end is very active and that its movement results in the drawing out and lengthening of the fiber to which it is attached. One fiber was observed to lengthen about 20 μ in 25 minutes, another over 25 μ in 50 minutes. The longest fibers observed were 0.2 mm. in length.

When the placodal thickenings of the branchial region are isolated, similar fibers are formed and in several of these cases they have been seen to arise from individual cells. On the other hand, other tissues of the embryo, such as myotomes, yolk endoderm, notochord, and indifferent ectoderm from the abdominal region do not give rise to structures of this kind. There can, therefore, be no doubt that we are dealing with a specific characteristic of nervous tissue.

It has not as yet been found possible to make permanent specimens which show the isolated nerve fibers completely intact. The structures are so delicate that the mere immersion in the preserving fluid is sufficient to cause violent tearing and this very frequently results in the tearing away of the tissue in its entirety from the clot. Nevertheless, sections have

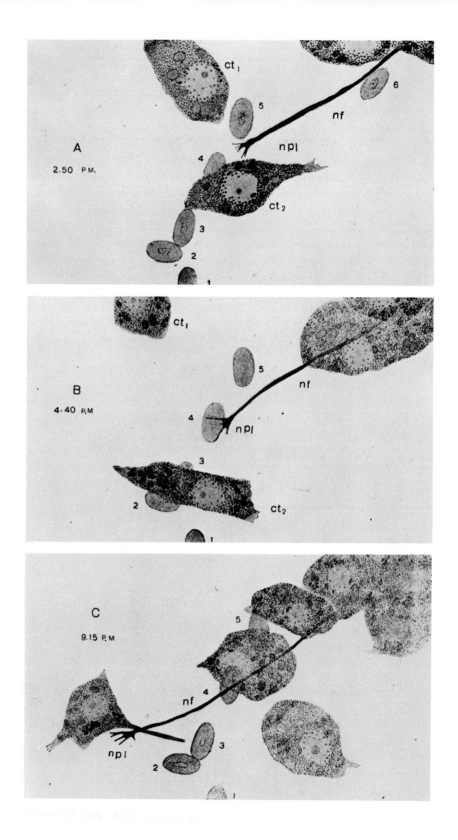

been cut of some of the specimens and nerves have been traced from the walls of the medullary tube but they were in all cases broken off short.

In view of this difficulty an effort, which resulted successfully, was made to obtain permanent specimens in a somewhat different way. A piece of medullary cord about four or five segments long was excised from an embryo and this was replaced by a cylindrical clot of proper length and caliber which was obtained by allowing blood or lymph of an adult frog to clot in a capillary tube. No difficulty was experienced in healing the clot into the embryo in proper position. After two, three, or four days the specimens were preserved and examined in serial sections. It was found that the funicular fibers from the brain and anterior part of the cord, consisting of naked axones without sheath cells, had grown for a considerable distance into the clot.

These observations show beyond question that the nerve fiber develops by the outflowing of protoplasm from the central cells. This protoplasm retains its amœboid activity at its distal end, the result being that it is drawn out into a long thread which becomes the axis cylinder. No other cells or living structures take part in this process.

The development of the nerve fiber is thus brought about by means of one of the very primitive properties of living protoplasm, amœboid movement, which, though probably common to some extent to all the cells of the embryo, is especially accentuated in the nerve cells at this period of development.

The possibility becomes apparent of applying the above method to the study of the influences which act upon a growing nerve. While at present it seems certain that the mere outgrowth of the fibers is largely independent of external stimuli, it is, of course, probable that in the body of the embryo there are many influences which guide the moving end and bring about contact with the proper end structure. The method here employed may be of value in analyzing these factors.

The paper chosen for reproduction in this volume was not illustrated. The figures shown on the facing page are taken from Ross G. Harrison, 1910. The outgrowth of the nerve fiber as a mode of protoplasmic movement. *Jour. Exp. Zool.*, 9:787–846, Figure 2. They represent "Three views of a growing nerve fiber, observed alive in a clotted lymph preparation. 1, 2, 3, 4, 5, red blood corpuscles in fixed position; ct_1, and ct_2, single cells which were seen to wander across the field; *nf,* nerve fiber; *npl,* growing end of motile protoplasm. ×420. *A,* As seen at 2:50 p.m., two days after isolation of the embryonic tissue. *B,* As seen at 4:40 p.m., the same day. Note change in form and position of the loose cells. *C,* As seen at 9:15 p.m., the same day. Movement of cells has covered over the proximal part of the fiber."

PART SIX

1908

Observations on Oxidative Processes in the Sea Urchin Egg

by OTTO WARBURG

*from the Chemical-Physiological Division
of the Zoological Station, Naples
(Received 16 July 1908)*

Warburg, Otto. 1908. Beobachtungen über die Oxydationsprozesse im Seeigelei. Hoppe-Seyler's Zeitschrift für physiologische Chemie. 57:1-16. Translated by H. Ursprung and printed by permission of the author and Walter de Gruyter and Co.

Early in the twentieth century, at a time when relatively little was known about the role of oxygen in metabolic processes, J. Loeb (1905, 1906), Warburg (1908, 1910), Child (1911) and others were engaged in investigating by physiological methods respiratory metabolism of cells or organisms. It was Otto Warburg (1883-   ) who, applying the relatively simple techniques then available, first determined oxygen consumption by Winkler's method and estimated nitrogen by Kjeldahl's method in studying the respiratory behavior of cells. In order to have large quantities of cells relatively free of yolk he judiciously selected the sea urchin egg as favorable experimental material. In the 1908 article reprinted in translation below he showed for the first time that fertilization causes a sharp and immediate increase in the respiration of sea urchin eggs. This paper was followed in rapid succession by a series of other important contributions in attempting to analyze the underlying conditions of change in oxygen utilization after fertilization of the sea urchin egg. During the course of these studies on respiration Warburg, on the basis of a chance observation, showed that traces of iron are present in the sea urchin egg. With iron as the cue he then showed in an experimental test that substances from crushed sea urchin eggs to which traces of iron are added form an effective catalyst that accelerates the rate of oxygen consumption. Through an extensive study of oxidation by means of the hemin charcoal model (respiration model) and by crucial experiments he was led to the discovery of the iron-containing Atmungsferment *or respiratory enzyme that is known today as cytochrome oxidase.* "For his discovery of the nature and mode of action of the respiratory enzyme" Warburg was awarded the Nobel prize in physiology and medicine for 1931.*

The pioneer studies of Warburg on respiratory metabolism of the sea urchin egg provoked much interest and research on the nature of the chemical mechanisms involved in cell metabolism. Of particular influence embryologically were his discoveries that the respiratory rate of the sea urchin egg increases after fertilization, continuing to increase up to the time of gastrulation. Although it was found later that these results on the sea urchin egg could not be generalized to cover certain other species, it seems safe to say that Warburg's studies were contributing factors in stimulating the more precise analytical studies that have led to better understanding of biochemical mechanisms in development.

* For Warburg's own account of this discovery see M. L. Gabriel and S. Fogel (eds.). 1955. The enzyme problem and biological oxidations. Great experiments in biology. Englewood Cliffs, N.J.: Prentice-Hall, Inc.

OBSERVATIONS ON OXIDATIVE PROCESSES IN THE SEA URCHIN EGG

Very little is known about the chemical processes that accompany cleavage. The numerous investigations on developmental processes in eggs deal with more advanced stages of ontogenesis; most of them have been carried out on meroblastic eggs, in which the abundance of yolk makes the precise measurement of changes at early stages impossible.

In the sea urchin egg, the amount of living substance is large as compared to the amount of yolk, and the changes after fertilization proceed in rapid sequence, so that within a short time much takes place within little substance. Therefore, I have undertaken some studies on this egg, first on oxidative processes.

Two papers deal with gas exchange in cleaving eggs. Godlewski, Jr.[1] obtained 3.5 cc. CO_2 in 79 hours from 700 frog eggs (760 mm., 0°); the duration of the experiment is so long, and the amount of CO_2 so small that bacteria as well as gases dissolved in the jelly coat and other sources of error could not be excluded. Lyon[2] reports on "rhythmic" excretion of carbon dioxide during the division of *Arbacia* eggs without, however, giving any numerical data.

In chicken eggs cleavage is already in progress in the oviduct. For this reason the paper by Hasselbalch on the liberation of oxygen during the first hours of incubation is not pertinent to our subject.

METHOD

All experiments were carried out on eggs of *Arbacia pustulosa*. In order to measure the intensity of the oxidative processes, I determined the amount of oxygen that disappeared from the surrounding sea water in a given time. For this purpose I collected the eggs according to the method of Lyon[3] and transferred them to a spacious dish in which they sank to the bottom within a few minutes. The supernatant fluid was siphoned off and replaced by water that had been filtered through paper; this procedure was repeated about five times. By this means ovarial fluid, immature eggs, small parasites, bacteria, etc. are removed. Then water is poured on, which was brought to the experimental temperature in the thermostat. The oxygen content of the water had been determined just previously. It is desirable that the water should be saturated with oxygen corresponding to the temperature and pressure of the experiment. After

---

[1] Archiv für Entwicklungsmechanik, Bd. XI. 1901.

[2] Americ. Journ. of Physiol., Vol. XI. 1904. Science N.S., Vol. XIX. 1904.

[3] Americ. Journ. of Physiol., Vol. IX, p. 308, 1903.

the eggs have sunk to the bottom, the water is siphoned off as completely as possible and they are transferred to the experimental flask, which is filled with water of known oxygen content. In order continuously to renew the water on the surface of the eggs, I fastened the flask on a disc that rotated in an incubator about once every 15 seconds. The temperature was maintained between 20.2 and 20.5° in all experiments. After a certain time the flask—its glass stopper loosened—was immersed in ice water about 2 cm. deep. The eggs soon settled to the bottom, and after exactly one-half hour the water was siphoned off as completely as possible into the determination flask until it was full; necessary precautions were taken to avoid admitting oxygen from the air. The experimental flasks used held 253 or 257 cc., the determination flask 175 or 180 cc. Depending on the purpose of the experiment, water of known oxygen content was again poured on the eggs, or they were immediately incinerated. Oxygen was determined according to the method of Winkler.[4] The solution of thiosulfate used was approximately 1/100 normal. One cc. corresponded to 1.35 mg. iodine or 0.085 mg. oxygen. If organic substances are in solution, the method yields values that are too low. I am convinced that this source of error was not important in my experimental setup. For if oxygen is determined once in the sea water and a second time in the same quantity of sea water in which eggs have cleaved, identical values are found, providing the oxygen content has been made equal. To accomplish this the fluids need only be brought to the same temperature, and shaken vigorously with air for several minutes (while the pressure is kept constant by repeatedly opening the stoppers).

In order to be able to compare the intensity of respiration under different conditions, I did not count the eggs, but rather found it more accurate to incinerate them according to the method of Kjeldahl and to relate the oxygen values to equal amounts of nitrogen. The "respiration" of a known amount of nitrogen, according to expectation, is not constant. For unfertilized eggs the deviations are within the limits of error; for fertilized eggs the largest difference observed is about 20%. If such differences are important, the amounts of nitrogen may be considered equivalent only if obtained from the same batch of eggs. The assumption of the method that in the course of the experiment a measurable amount of nitrogen does not go into solution turns out to be true.

The weight of the eggs, as opposed to their nitrogen content, is probably less meaningful. Since weight varies greatly with the drying temperature, I did not carry out a determination of the water content. Incidentally, data on this question for *Strongylocentrotus lividus* are to be found in the work of Wetzel.[5]

[4] E.g., Treadwell, Quant. Analysis, p. 505, 1902.
[5] Engelmann's Archiv., 1907, S. 519.

SOURCES OF ERROR

A. Bacteria. The oxygen consumption of the unfertilized eggs is the only concern and not the observed difference after fertilization or other manipulations.

1. 180 cc. sea water from the tap, filtered through paper, did not use any measurable amount of oxygen in 12 hours.
2. If at the end of the experiments the eggs are allowed to sink to the bottom, the bacteria remain in the supernatant water. This supernatant did not use any measurable amount of oxygen in 2 hours.
3. The oxygen consumption per hour is independent of the duration of the experiment.

B. Sperm. Assuming that five of the supernumerary spermatozoa would remain attached to each egg, this would represent an error of 1% (see below). Yet with careful washing only rarely does a single spermatozoon remain adhering to an egg.

C. Oxygen pressure. The experiments were so designed that the oxygen concentration usually did not fall below ¾ of the original value. I have convinced myself, however, that absorption takes place regularly even at a concentration as low as ¼ of the original value.

D. Development. Cleavage proceeds normally in the rotating flasks. The yield of larvae is as high as in resting dishes. As it is well known, the yield of swimming larvae never reaches 100%, but about 95%. The causes of this developmental arrest are possibly already present in the seemingly normal first stages of cleavage, and oxidation, for instance, may also proceed differently in such eggs. If it is assumed, however, that 5% of the eggs either do not respire at all, or respire twice as much, this irregularity would still fall within the limits of error of the oxygen determination.

The latest developmental stage that I used for the determination of respiration is the 32-cell stage. Experiments in which for one reason or another cleavage was not normal up to that stage are not reported.

Precision: The errors are essentially those in reading the burettes.

EXPERIMENTS

I. UNFERTILIZED EGGS

(Oxygen in cc. thiosulfate; nitrogen in cc. n/10 NH_3)

N	Duration of experiment	Oxygen in 180 cc. water		Calculated total decrease of oxygen	28 mg. N consume per hr.
		Before the experiment	After the experiment		
14.6	180 minutes	16.0	14.9	1.6	0.7
22.1	90 minutes	15.5	14.7	1.1	0.7
42.0	90 minutes	15.9	14.6	1.9	0.6
29.5	90 minutes	15.6	14.7	1.3	0.6

Thus 28 mg. N consume from 0.05 to 0.06 mg. oxygen per hour.

These figures are perhaps of some interest in connection with an observation of J. Loeb[6] that unfertilized sea urchin eggs can be kept alive for a week or longer in sterilized water. In seven days, 168 × 0.06 mg. = ca. 10 mg. oxygen are consumed per 28 mg. nitrogen; without knowing anything about what becomes of the absorbed oxygen we may conclude that the egg is capable of developing even after considerable qualitative or quantitative chemical changes.

II. THE FERTILIZED EGGS

(Oxygen in cc. thiosulfate; nitrogen in cc. n/10 NH_3)

N	Duration	Oxygen in 180 cc. water		Calculated total decrease of oxygen	28 mg. N consume per hr.
		Before the experiment	After the experiment		
34.9	1) 60 min.	15.9	11.0	7	4
	2) 60 min.	15.6	10.4	7.4	4.2
16.4	1) 60 min.	15.8	13.3	3.6	4.4
	2) 60 min.	15.6	12.8	4.0	4.9
	3) 60 min.	15.6	12.5	4.4	5.3
31.4	1) 60 min.	15.9	11.5	6.3	4.0
	2) 60 min.	15.9	10.6	7.6	4.8
	3) 60 min.	15.9	10.2	8.1	5.2
20.2	1) 60 min.	15.8	12.9	4.1	4.1
	2) 60 min.	15.8	12.8	4.3	4.3
	3) 60 min.	15.8	12.2	5.0	5.0
23.8	1) 60 min.	15.8	11.8	5.7	4.8
	2) 60 min.	15.8	11.4	6.3	5.3

At the beginning of the experiments, depending upon whether washing was carried out in cooled water or in water at room temperature for one hour, the eggs either had not yet cleaved or had divided into 2 blastomeres.

It becomes evident from the figures that oxygen consumption increases six- to seven-fold after fertilization.

The question arises as to what significance the small increases have although they are definitely beyond the limits of error.

A difference of 0.2 cc. thiosulfate between the first and second hour is due to the method, since the water of the first hour cannot be completely siphoned off, but only to ca. 20 cc.

Furthermore, the respiration that continues until 0° is reached may not be entirely negligible. If the increase arose only from these two sources of error, the oxygen consumption should not show any further increase during the third hour; however this is not the case.

Also it had to be considered whether the treatment of the eggs (cooling with ice, turntable) might cause the acceleration of the oxidations.

---

6 Vorlesungen über die Dynamik der Lebenserscheinungen, S. 251. 1906.

In order to exclude this possibility and to increase the differences, I divided the eggs from one female into two portions. In one of them the oxygen consumption was determined at the 8-cell stage. The other portion was allowed to stand for several hours in large dishes at room temperature and when the eggs had reached the 32-cell stage they were transferred to the determination flask.

8-CELL STAGE

(Oxygen in cc. thiosulfate; nitrogen in cc. n/10 NH_3)

N	Duration	Oxygen in 180 cc. water		Calculated total decrease of oxygen	28 mg. N consume per hr.
		Before the experiment	After the experiment		
24.1	60 min.	15.9	12.4	5	4.2

32-CELL STAGE

(Oxygen in cc. thiosulfate; nitrogen in cc. n/10 NH_3)

N	Duration	Oxygen in 180 cc. water		Calculated total decrease of oxygen	28 mg. N consume per hr.
		Before the experiment	After the experiment		
17.6	60 min.	15.8	11.6	6	6.8

Since the difference amounts to 2.6 cc. thiosulfate, the increase in oxygen consumption is established.

In this experiment the nuclei of the 8-cell and 32-cell stages have been formed at the same velocity. The size of each newly formed nucleus is equal to that of the first cleavage nucleus.[7] If the major quantity of oxygen were consumed in the process of nuclear growth, then the "respiration" at the 32-cell stage would have to exceed that of the 8-cell stage by about three-fold. As can be seen, this assumption, which is often mentioned in the literature, is not at all true.

The differences rather appear to increase with the morphological changes. Yet, I think they are too small to overlook the quantitative relationship that exists here.[8]

[7] As a matter of fact, this is already very probable from morphological findings (O. Hertwig, Morphol. Jahrbuch I, 406; Boveri, Zellenstudien, Heft 5). It was firmly established by developmental-physiological investigations of Boveri and Driesch (see especially: The cell number of "amphikaryotic" half eggs after cleavage and of separated blastomeres of the 2-cell stage).

[8] For this kind of problem it would be necessary to determine at first whether respiration is in fact discontinuous as Lyon supposes. I have not obtained any evidence for this myself, yet it would only concern the small fraction of respiration that is a consequence of morphological changes. With the methods described it will be easy to test

III. FERTILIZED EGGS IN WHICH CLEAVAGE HAS BEEN INHIBITED

J. Leob[9] has found that the division of fertilized eggs can be prevented by putting them into sea water in which the osmotic pressure is raised by a specific amount. If this increase in osmotic pressure is appropriately selected, the nucleus continues to divide though more slowly than in normal sea water. Thus, by this experimental method the morphological changes can either be inhibited (cell division) or retarded (nuclear division). In accordance with the above-mentioned results the oxygen consumption should not change materially under these conditions.

At Naples in order just to inhibit cleavage 1 g. NaCl must be added to 100 cc. of sea water. I divided a batch of eggs into 2 approximately equal portions. One portion was transferred into normal sea water, the other into the hypertonic solution and then the oxygen consumption was simultaneously determined in the two.

IN NORMAL SEA WATER

(Oxygen in cc. thiosulfate; nitrogen in cc. n/10 NH₃)

No.	N	Duration	Oxygen Content		Calculated total decrease	28 mg. N consume per hr.
			Before the experiment	After the experiment		
1	17.6	120 min.	175 cc. = 15.4	175 cc. = 10.7	6.8	3.9
2	23.8	60 min.	180 cc. = 15.8	180 cc. = 11.8	5.7	4.8

SIMULTANEOUSLY IN HYPERTONIC SEA WATER

No.	N	Duration	Oxygen Content		Calculated total decrease	28 mg. N consume per hr.
			Before the experiment	After the experiment		
1	14.7	120 min.	180 cc. = 15.2	180 cc. = 11.6	5.1	3.5
2	25.2	60 min.	175 cc. = 14.5	175 cc. = 10.4	5.9	4.7

Comment: The significance of these figures becomes limited by an irregularity which is still unexplained. In the first experiment on May 28, when I transferred the eggs from the hypertonic solution into normal sea water, I found an oxygen consumption of 6.5 cc. thiosulfate per hour and 28 mg. N. I was unable to repeat this experiment until one month later. This time, the eggs (28 mg. N) absorbed an amount of oxygen that corresponds to 5.6 cc. thiosulfate when transferred to normal sea water, as contrasted with 4.7 in the hypertonic solution (experiment 2). However, while in the first experiment almost all the eggs developed into larvae, in the second one the number of larvae formed was very small.

---

these relations; however, since we are dealing with short periods of time, the eggs would have to be carefully centrifuged and not merely be allowed to sink.

9 Untersuchungen über die künstliche Parthenogenese, Leipzig 1906, S. 1.

IV. EGG AND SPERM CELLS

According to well-founded views[10] egg and sperm cells have the same amount of nuclear substance; yet it is under quite different physiological conditions and, in particular, it "governs" completely different amounts of protoplasm. It seems to me not without interest to compare the respiration of these two cells. I counted the spermatozoa in an Abbe chamber (fixation was with osmic acid, which was most successfully carried out by exposing the slides to osmic vapor for several minutes). The eggs were vigorously shaken at an appropriate dilution; then ½ cc. was quickly taken up into a pipette and allowed to flow out onto a filter paper kept in motion. After a short time the eggs dried onto the paper and then were separated by means of pencil lines so that they could be easily counted with a low power magnifying glass.

Sperm

Experiment 1. The liquid contained 20 million sperm cells per cc. (400 counted) or 3600 million per 180 cc.

An immediate[11] analysis of 180 cc. of this solution by Winkler's method yielded 12.1 cc. thiosulfate; after 70 minutes (20°), the yield was 10.4 cc. thiosulfate.

Decrease per hour: 1.5 cc. thiosulfate.

4000 million sperm cells per hour: 1.7 cc. thiosulfate.

Experiment 2. 33 million sperm cells per cubic centimeter. 5940 million per 180 cc. (400 counted).

180 cc. at zero time: 14.9 cc. thiosulfate.

After 55 minutes at 20°: 12.6 cc. thiosulfate.

Decrease per hour: 2.5 cc. thiosulfate.

4000 million sperm cells per hour: 1.7 cc. thiosulfate.

The error in counting the spermatozoa is ca. 4%; in oxygen determination it is ca. 10%.

Eggs

Experiment 1. Total volume 1000 cc. 850 eggs per 0.5 cc.; 1,700,000 eggs per liter.

N after siphoning off the water: $= 9.8$ cc. $n/10\ NH_3$.

One million eggs $= 5.8$ cc. $n/10\ NH_3$.

Experiment 2. Total volume 1000 cc. containing 980,000 eggs. N $=$ 6.1 $n/10\ NH_3$.

One million eggs $= 6.2$ cc. $n/10\ NH_3$.

Error in counting: ca. 10%.

---

[10] O. Hertwig. Handbuch der Entwicklungsgeschichte.

[11] This eliminates the possible error caused by organic substance.

28 mg. N consume 0.6-0.7 mg. thiosulfate per hour (error of 20%). Consequently, one million eggs consume per hour 0.2 cc. thiosulfate or 0.017 mg. oxygen.

Under the same conditions, one million spermatozoa consume 0.0004 cc. of thiosulfate or 0.000034 mg. of oxygen. In other words, the respiration of an egg cell is 500 ($\pm$ 100) times as high as that of a sperm cell.

V. INFLUENCE ON OXIDATIONS IN THE UNFERTILIZED EGG

1. Hypertonic solutions. In the course of his investigations on artificial parthenogenesis J. Loeb became convinced that weakly alkaline hypertonic solutions have an accelerating action on the oxidative processes of the unfertilized sea urchin egg. He arrived at this conclusion mainly from the fact that hypertonic solutions are no longer active if the oxygen has been expelled.[12]

As a matter of fact, the oxygen consumption of unfertilized eggs can be enhanced up to ten-fold in such hypertonic solutions.

When sea water is used that varies considerably in one way or another from normal composition, the eggs are often damaged; in the case of the pigmented eggs of *Arbacia* this can be easily seen from the color of the supernatant fluid. I never continued such experiments.

I determined the oxygen consumption in three solutions of different hypertonicity:

Solution I: 1 g. NaCl per 100 cc. sea water.

Solution II: 2.3 g. NaCl per 100 cc. sea water.
                Per 100 cc., 1.6 cc. n/10 NaOH

Solution III: 4.3 g. NaCl per 100 cc. sea water, plus 3 cc. n/10 NaOH per 100 cc.

The most favorable concentration for obtaining cleavage, after the eggs were returned to normal sea water, was approximately between II and III. However, in these experiments the morphological changes were of less importance to me.

The addition of alkali was carried out according to Loeb's direction. It was not feasible to separate the effects of alkali and salt concentration since each reagent when used alone destroyed the eggs. Yet Loeb was never able to induce parthenogenesis by alkali alone;[13] other observations also support the view that what is effective is the increase in osmotic pressure, and that in this case the alkali plays merely a protective role.

---

12 Biochem. Zeitschrift, Bd. I, S. 183; Bd. II, S. 34. Pflüger's Archiv, Bd. CXVIII, S. 30. Untersuchungen über der künstliche Parthenogenese, Leipzig 1906, S. 491.

13 Pflüger's Archiv., Bd. CXVIII, S. 30.

(Oxygen in cc. thiosulfate; nitrogen in cc. n/10 NH_3)

SOLUTION I

N	Duration	Oxygen Content		Calculated total decrease of oxygen	28 mg. N consume per hr.
		Before the experiment	After the experiment		
51.5	60 min.	175 cc. $=$ 14.8	175 cc. $=$ 13.1	2.5	1.0

SOLUTION II

N	Duration	Oxygen Content		Calculated total decrease of oxygen	28 mg. N consume per hr.
		Before the experiment	After the experiment		
11.4	80 min.	180 cc. $=$ 14.4	180 cc. $=$ 12.8	2.3	3.0

SOLUTION III:

(2 experiments)

Date	N	Duration	Oxygen Content		Calculated total decrease of oxygen	28 mg. N consume per hr.
			Before the experiment	After the experiment		
June 7	26.3	80 min.	180 cc. $=$ 14.1	180 cc. $=$ 5.8	11.7	6.7
June 8	10.4	80 min.	175 cc. $=$ 13.1	176 cc. $=$ 10.3	4.1	5.9

The oxygen consumption of the unfertilized eggs amounts to 0.6-0.7 thiosulfate per 28 mg. N per hour. Thus the increase in solution I is only slightly above the limit of error; in solution II the oxygen consumption is raised by four- to five-fold, in solution III by nine- to ten-fold. The increase of oxygen consumption is not proportional to the increase of the osmotic pressure.

Approximate increase of osmotic pressure[14]	In solution	Increase of oxygen consumption
25%	I	0.2 cc. thiosulfate
50%	II	2.3 cc. thiosulfate
100%	III	5.7 cc. thiosulfate

Apparently the increase can be clearly measured only above a certain concentration. This is in good agreement with the observation just reported by Loeb[15] that the osmotic pressure of the hypertonic solution must exceed a threshold value if it is to exert an effect on the eggs.

2. *Hypotonic solutions.* If unfertilized eggs are put in hypotonic sea water for some time and then returned to normal sea water, an increase in oxygen consumption is observed.

[14] Without taking into consideration the degree of dissociation.
[15] Biochem. Zeitschrift, Bd. XI, S. 148.

Experiment I: The eggs were washed first with normal sea water in the usual way, then three times within a half hour in a mixture of ⅗ sea water and ⅖ distilled water (at 24°). They were then returned to normal sea water.

(Oxygen in cc. thiosulfate; nitrogen in cc. n/10 NH₃)

N	Duration	Oxygen Content		Calculated total decrease of oxygen	28 mg. N consume per hr.
		Before the experiment	After the experiment		
20.2	72 min.	180 cc. = 15.6	180 cc. = 14.6	1.4	1.2

A control experiment carried out simultaneously without pretreatment on eggs of the same batch resulted in 0.7 cc. (28 mg. N per hour).

Experiment II. The same as I, except that the hypotonic water consisted of equal parts of sea water and distilled water. The eggs remained in it for 45 minutes.

N	Duration	Oxygen Content		Calculated total decrease of oxygen	28 mg. N consume per hr.
		Before the experiment	After the experiment		
60.8	55 min.	180 cc. = 15.5	180 cc. = 12.6	4.1	1.5

3. Temperature. For the velocity of development of frog eggs[16] and eggs of the ring snake[17] the temperature coefficient is that characteristic of chemical reactions. As was to be expected, this is also true for the oxidations in the sea urchin egg.

(Oxygen in cc. thiosulfate; nitrogen in cc. n/10 NH₃ Temperature 28°)

N	Duration	Oxygen Content		Total decrease of oxygen	28 mg. N consume per hr.
		Before the experiment	After the experiment		
59.2	60 min.	180 cc. = 13.8	180 cc. = 11.0	4	1.4

28 mg. consume per hour at 20°: 0.7 cc. thiosulfate
28 mg. consume per hour at 28°: 1.4 cc. thiosulfate
Increase per 10°: 0.9 cc. thiosulfate

When at the end of the experiment sperm was added all eggs formed membranes.

A rather remarkable feature is the sensitivity to elevated temperature. If eggs are kept at 35° for 20 minutes, they no longer form membranes upon addition of sperm nor do they cleave. Eggs kept for 2 minutes at 40° are already unable to develop; keeping them at 40° for 3 minutes prevents the formation of membranes.

[16] O. Hertwig, Archiv f. mikroskopische Anatomie u. Entwicklungsgeschichte, Bd. LI, S. 319.
[17] Bohr, Skand, Arch. für Physiologie, Bd. XV, S. 29.

4. Negative experiments. I considered the possibility that any movement within the egg might accelerate the oxidative processes. In order to test this supposition, I changed the volume of the eggs 8 times in the course of 80 minutes by putting them alternately in normal and hypotonic sea water. No increase in oxygen consumption was observed than where they had been in the hypotonic solution for 40 minutes.

Besides, I put the eggs upon a machine that shook vigorously up and down. As is known, such treatment may induce the eggs of the starfish to develop. Yet the oxidations in the egg of *Arbacia* were not accelerated.

I am greatly indebted to the staff of the Zoological Station for their constant helpfulness, especially to Dr. M. Henze, the director of the division, and to Professor Herbst who was kind enough to show me how to handle the material.

Heidelberg, July 15.

PART SEVEN

1913

The Mechanism of Fertilization

by FRANK R. LILLIE

Lillie, Frank R. 1913. The Mechanism of Fertilization. Science 38:524-528. Reprinted by permission of Science.

Lillie's interest in the process of fertilization can probably be attributed in part to the philosophical climate that invested the problem of cell lineage at the turn of the century at the Marine Biological Laboratory (see comments on E. B. Wilson, p. 53) and still more importantly to his own detailed and exact observations on the changing disposition of visibly different particles (yolk spherules and other microscopically visible inclusions) in the cytoplasm of the egg of Chaetopterus *(a marine annelid) during the course of maturation and fertilization and their differential spatial distribution during cleavage and subsequent stages. To Lillie such natural phenomena as these give the basis for analyzing the nature of the underlying mechanisms in accord with physiological principles (see comments on Free-martin, p. 137). In his words, ". . . the aim of 'physiology of development' is to discover mechanisms of control of developmental processes" (1932).*

On the basis of this approach, a two-fold experimental analysis of the meaning of the observed cytological phenomena had its origin. First, by the simple method of centrifuging the egg Lillie found that although the visible inclusions were abnormally distributed, typically normal cleavage and development occurred. Out of this analysis came the stimulating concept that the ground substance of the cytoplasm is organized, i.e., it has a definite architecture or ultramicroscopic structure and is the molecular basis of the localization pattern in normal development.

Still more important was the role of the studies on Chaetopterus *in leading immediately to an analysis of the act of fertilization. The changes in the distribution of the particles in the egg cytoplasm, especially upon sperm contact and penetration, were so striking and dramatic that the hunch came to Lillie that the underlying mechanisms involved in the union of the egg and spermatozoon can be analyzed.*

Before the second important paper on Chaetopterus *was published in 1909, he began to study the mechanism of fertilization, a subject that was to engage Lillie and his students for a period of over ten years (1910-1921). The methods used were beautiful in their simplicity, for he had at hand only a microscope, glass slides and covers, finger bowls, test tubes and pipettes. With these tools he soon discovered that the eggs of the sea urchin,* Arbacia *(also* Nereis *eggs) secrete a substance into sea water which causes agglutination of the sperm of the same species.*

The article reprinted here is the seventh of a series of papers published within four years, each one of which was a necessary link in a chain of detailed analyses, the ultimate goal of which, as in all of Lillie's major investigations, was to discover new principles. Indeed, he succeeded in laying down the fundamental truth that fertilization involves the inter-action of specific substances borne by the egg and sperm. Moreover, in this paper he applied for the first time the then current immunological con-cept and terminology of Ehrlich to these interacting substances. They were conceived as linked and reacting with one another in the manner of lock and key combinations. The theory here proposed later became a notable feature of the "Fertilizin Theory," a theory that formulated all of the then known main aspects of the processes of fertilization. A full account of the studies of Lillie was published in 1919 in a small lucidly written book entitled Problems of Fertilization.

In 1912 Lillie summed up with foresight his view of the fundamental problem of fertilization in these words: "The union of ovum and sper-matozoon is not a process in which the sperm penetrates by virtue of its mechanical properties, but one in which a peculiarly intimate and specific biochemical reaction plays the chief role."

In keeping with Lillie's expressed hope, his systematic study of egg-sperm interacting substances and his theories of the mechanism of egg activation, and of the specific adherence of the spermatozoon to the egg and its penetration into the egg, pointed the way for further investigation. During the succeeding four decades intensive investigations by Max Hartmann, Albert Tyler, Lord Rothschild, John Runnström and many others have contributed many new discoveries of significance in the areas of the structural and metabolic changes occuring in the fertilization process, and the immunological nature of the reactions between substances isolated from eggs and sperm. These findings in turn have led to new problems and theories, not to definitive solutions. Much more investiga-tion will be required before the immunological and biochemical aspects of fertilization and initiation of development will be satisfactorily ex-plained.

THE MECHANISM OF FERTILIZATION

In previous papers[1] I have described the secretion of a substance by the ova of the sea-urchin, *Arbacia,* in sea water, which causes ag-glutination of the sperm of the same species. The eggs of *Nereis* also secrete a substance having a similar effect upon its sperm. I therefore named these substances sperm-isoagglutinins. During the present sum-mer I have ascertained that in the case of *Arbacia,* and presumably also of *Nereis,* the agglutinating substance is a necessary link in the fertiliza-tion process and that it acts in the manner of an amboceptor, having one side-chain for certain receptors in the sperm and another for certain

[1] SCIENCE, N. S., Vol. 36, pp. 527-530, October, 1912, and *Journ. Exp. Zool.,* Vol. 14, No. 4, pp. 515-574, May, 1913.

receptors in the egg. As this substance represents, presumably, a new class of substances, analogous in some respects to cytolysins, and as the term agglutinin defines only its action on sperm suspensions, I have decided to name it fertilizin.

My main purpose this summer was to study the rôle of the *Arbacia* fertilizin in the fertilization of the ovum.

1. *The Spermophile Side-chain.*—The first need in such a study was to develop a quantitative method of investigation, and this was done for *Arbacia* as follows: The agglutinative reaction of the sperm in the presence of this substance is, as noted in previous studies, reversible, and the intensity and duration of the reaction is a factor of concentration of the substance. The entire reaction is so characteristic that it was possible to arrive at a unit by noting the dilution at which the least unmistakable reaction was given. This was fixed at about a five- or six-second reaction, which is counted from the time that agglutination becomes visible under a magnification of about 40 diameters until its complete reversal. The unit is so chosen that a half dilution gives no agglutination of a fresh 1 per cent. sperm suspension. It was then found that the filtrate from a suspension of 1 part eggs left for ten minutes in 2 or 3 parts sea water would stand a dilution of from 800 to 6,400 times, depending on the proportion of ripe eggs and their condition, and still give the unit reaction. Such solutions may then be rated as 800 to 6,400 agglutinating power, and it is possible, therefore, to determine the strength of any given solution. This gives us a means of determining the rate at which eggs are producing fertilizin in sea water.

Determinations with this end in view showed that the production of fertilizin by unfertilized eggs of *Arbacia* in sea water goes on for about three days and that the quantity produced as measured by dilution tests diminishes very slowly. Such tests are made by suspending a given quantity of eggs in a measured amount of sea water in a graduated tube; the eggs are then allowed to settle and the supernatant fluid poured off and kept for testing. The same amount of fresh sea water is then added and the eggs stirred up in it, allowed to settle, the supernatant fluid poured off for testing, and so on. In one series running three days in which the quantity of eggs was originally 2 c.c. and the total volume of sea water and eggs in the tube 10 c.c., 6 to 8 c.c. being poured off at each settling, thirty-four changes were made and the agglutinating strength of the supernatant fluid diminished from 100 at first to 20 at the end. Simultaneously, with this loss of agglutinating strength, two things happen: (1) the jelly surrounding the eggs undergoes a gradual solution; (2) the power of being fertilized is gradually lost.

It is obvious that the presence of fertilizin in such considerable quantities in so long a series of washings shows either (1) that solution of the jelly liberates fertilizin, or else (2) that the eggs secrete more fertilizin each time they are washed. Both factors enter into the case inasmuch as (1) eggs killed by heat (60° C.) will stand 14 or 15 such washings, but with more rapid decline of agglutinating power than the living eggs. The jelly is gradually dissolved away in this case also, and is presumably the only possible source of the agglutinating substance. (2) Eggs deprived of jelly by shaking continue to produce the fertilizin as long as eggs with jelly, though in smaller quantities at first, and they are equally capable of fertilization.

The fertilizin is therefore present in large quantities in the jelly, which is indeed saturated with the substance, but the eggs continue to produce it as long as they remain alive and unfertilized. When the eggs are fertilized the production of this substance suddenly ceases absolutely.

The total disappearance of fertilizin from fertilized eggs can not be demonstrated unless the fertilizin-saturated jelly with which the eggs are surrounded be first removed. This is very easily done after membrane formation by six vigorous shakes of the eggs in a half-filled test tube. Three or four washings then are sufficient to remove the remains of the jelly, and the naked eggs no longer produce the substance.

Such disappearance may be due either to complete discharge from the egg, or to fixation of all that remains by union with some substance contained in the egg itself. That such a substance—anti-fertilizin—exists in the egg can be shown by a simple test-tube experiment: If eggs deprived of jelly are washed 34 times in sea water during three days, they are so exhausted that they produce but little fertilizin; the supernatant fluid may be charged only to the extent of 2 to 10 units. The eggs are now on the point of breaking up. If they are then vigorously shaken and broken up so that the fluid becomes colored with the red pigment of the eggs, it will be found that agglutinating power has entirely disappeared from the solution. The fertilizin present has been neutralized. The same phenomenon may be demonstrated also by treating eggs, deprived of jelly in order to get rid of excess of fertilizin, with distilled water which lakes the eggs and extracts the anti-fertilizin.

It is probable, therefore, that any excess of fertilizin remaining in the egg not bound to the sperm is neutralized by this combination, and polyspermy is thereby prevented.

We have noted (1) the secretion by unfertilized eggs in sea water of a sperm agglutinating substance, fertilizin; (2) the extreme avidity of the sperm for it as shown by dilution tests; (3) in my previous papers the fixation of this substance in sperm-suspensions of the same species (quantitative measurements will be given in the complete paper); (4) the sudden cessation of fertilizin production by fertilized eggs; (5) the existence of an antifertilizin in the egg; (6) in eggs submitted to a series of washings decrease of the fertilization capacity with reduction of the fertilizin. The fact that fertilized eggs can not be refertilized is associated with the absence of free fertilizin in them; (7) I may add that, similarly, eggs in which membrane formation has been induced by butyric acid can not be fertilized by sperm and they contain no free fertilizin.

It is therefore very probable that the substance in question is essential for fertilization.

It may be maintained that these facts do not constitute demonstrative evidence of the necessity of this substance for fertilization, for the presence or absence or diminution of this material associated with presence or absence or decrease of fertilizing power could always be regarded as a secondary phenomenon. However, the second part of this paper dealing with the other, or ovophile side-chain of the fertilizin, strongly reinforces the argument.

Before passing on to this, I may be allowed to note some other properties of the fertilizin: In my previous papers I noted the extreme heat-resistance of the fertilizin, being only slowly destroyed at 95° C. I also noted that strongly agglutinating solutions of *Arbacia* may contain a substance which agglutinates *Nereis* sperm and stated that this was probably different from the iso-agglutinating substance. This turns out to be the case and the two can be readily separated. The substance must possess great molecular size, as it is incapable of passing through a Berkefeld filter. It is also non-dialyzable; it does not give the usual protein reactions; a fact for the determination of which I am indebted to Dr. Otto Glaser.

2. *The Ovophile Side-chain.*—Assuming, then, that the union of this substance with the spermatozoon enters in some significant way into the process of fertilization, the problem was to ascertain in what way. The simplest idea, viz., that the union is in itself the fertilization process, was soon shown to be untenable, for the reason that the perivisceral fluid (blood) of the sea-urchin, especially of ripe males and females, often contains a substance which absolutely inhibits fertilization in the presence of any quantity of sperm, but that this substance has no inhibiting effect at all upon the sperm-agglutination reaction. It does not enter into combination with the spermophile side-chain. In other words, the binding of the agglutinin by the sperm may be complete, but in the presence of an inhibitor contained in the blood none of the usual effects of insemination, no matter how heavy, follow.

The details of the experiments upon which the above statement depends are too complex for consideration here. But they showed that the effect is neither upon the egg alone nor upon the sperm alone, for both may stand for some time in the presence of this agent and after washing be capable of normal behavior in fertilization, though there may be some decrease in the percentages. No poisonous effect is involved on either sexual element.

The next suggestion was fairly obvious, viz., that the substance which we had been calling agglutinin, on account of its effect upon the spermatozoa, is in reality an amboceptor with spermophile and ovophile side-chains, and that the binding of the sperm activates the ovophile side-chains which then seize upon egg receptors and fertilize the egg. If this were so, it is obvious that the spermatozoon is only secondarily a fertilizing agent, in the sense of initiating development, and that the egg is in reality self-fertilizing, an idea which agrees very well with the facts of parthenogenesis and the amazing multiplicity of means by which parthenogenesis may be effected. For the agents need only remove obstacles to the union of the amboceptor and egg receptor.

The inhibiting action of the blood from this point of view is a deviation effect due to occupancy of the ovophile side-chain of the amboceptor, either because the inhibitor in the blood is an anti-body to the amboceptor or because it possesses the same combining group as the egg receptor. In such a case, the ovophile group of the amboceptor, being already occupied by the inhibitor, fertilization could not take place.

Fortunately, this idea is susceptible of a ready test; for, if the blood acts in this way in inhibiting fertilization, all that is necessary to neutralize the inhibiting action would be to occupy the inhibitor by the amboceptor (fertilizin) for which *ex. hyp.* it has strong affinity. This experiment was repeated many times in different ways with various dilutions, and the result was always to lessen or completely remove the inhibiting action of the blood.

The plan of such an experiment is this: to divide the filtered blood (plasma) in two parts, one of which is used for control while the other is saturated with fertilizin by addition of eggs. In ten minutes the latter are precipitated by the centrifuge and the supernatant fluid filtered. Fertilizations are then made in graded dilutions of this and the control blood. In some cases the inhibiting action of the blood was completely neutralized, and in all largely neutralized.

The results so far are in agreement with the theory. But if it be true that the egg contains its own fertilizing substance, it might also be possible to induce parthenogenesis by increasing the concentration of this substance to a certain point; though it is conceivable that no increase in concentration would break down the resistance that normally exists to union of the amboceptor and egg receptors. As a matter of fact, Dr. Otto Glaser[2] has shown this summer that a certain amount of parthenogenetic action may be induced in *Arbacia* in this way. I have been in consultation with Dr. Glaser during part of his work and can confirm his statements.

In connection with the assumption that the sperm activates an already existing side-chain of a substance contained in the egg itself, I may be allowed to cite the following statement of Ehrlich:

[2] SCIENCE, N. S., Vol. XXXVIII., No. 978, September 26, 1913, p. 446.

The significance of the variations in affinity will be discussed connectedly at a subsequent time. We shall content ourselves here by pointing out that an understanding of the phenomena of immunity is impossible without the assumption that certain haptophore groups become increased or decreased in their chemical energy, owing to changes in the total molecule. Chemically, such an assumption is a matter of course.[3]

This principle might explain the activation of the fertilizing amboceptor by the sperm.

The question will of course be raised whether there is not another and simpler interpretation of the facts. There are three general classes of these facts: (1) the sperm agglutination phenomena, and the apparent necessity of the agglutinating substance for fertilization; (2) the presence of an inhibiting agent in the blood, especially of ripe males and females; (3) the neutralization of this inhibiting agent by the agglutinating agent (amboceptor). It may be questioned whether these facts have the particular causal nexus that I have given them. But I think it would be difficult to construct a theory taking account of all the facts which would differ essentially from that presented here.

The theory is really extremely simple in its character, and the facts on which it rests are readily tested. It has proven a most valuable working hypothesis; indeed, many of the facts referred to were discovered only after the theory was formed. It has the advantage of offering one theory for initiation of development whether by fertilization or by parthenogenesis. It is capable of explaining the whole range of specificities in fertilization by assuming a specific fertilizin for each species. It furnishes the foundation for the chemical conceptions necessary to any theory of fertilization, and it is susceptible of experimental test.

It will be seen that inhibition of fertilization may occur by block in any part of the mechanism.

1. Through loss of fertilizin by the egg.

2. Through occupancy of the sperm receptors.

3. Through occupancy of the egg receptors.

4. Through occupancy of the ovophile side-chain of the amboceptor (fertilizin).

5. Through occupancy of the spermophile side-chain group.

Of these I have shown the occurrence of the first, fourth and fifth in *Arbacia*. The first in the case of long-washed eggs; the fourth in the case of the inhibitor contained in the blood; the fifth is, I believe, the mechanism for prevention of polyspermy.

The mechanism of fertilization appears to be the same in *Nereis*, though I have not a complete set of data. However, the data that I have are in accord with the theory, and will be described in the complete paper.

[3] "Collected Studies in Immunity," p. 220.

I should perhaps state specifically that the location of the fertilizin is in the cortex of the egg.

It seems to me probable that the activation of the fertilizin is by no means confined to that bound by the single penetrating sperm, but that activation once set up spreads around the cortex. The supernumerary spermatozoa that fail to enter the egg may also play a part by setting up centers of activation. In this connection Glaser's contention that several spermatozoa at least are necessary for fertilization is of great interest. The nature of the effect of the activated fertilizin on the egg is analogous in some respects to a superficial cytolysis, in this respect agreeing with Loeb's theory. But the "lysin" is contained in the egg, not in the sperm, as Loeb thought; if cytolysis is involved, it is a case of autocytolysis. This may involve increase of permeability, the effects of which R. S. Lillie has especially studied. I mention these possibilities in order to point out that the conception contained in this paper is not in conflict with the well-established work of others.

In conclusion, I may point out that the theory assumes a form of linkage of sperm and egg components by means of an intermediate body that may find a place in the study of heredity. The detailed experiments will be published later.

PART EIGHT

Susceptibility Gradients in Animals

by C. M. CHILD

Child, C. M. 1914. Susceptibility Gradients in Animals. Science 39:73-76. Reprinted by permission of Science.

When Child began to apply his theory of axial gradients to the developing egg, embryology had already escaped far from the trammels of evolutionary dogmatism: Curt Herbst and others had viewed developmental phenomena in the light of physiological studies on tropisms; Roux and Driesch and their many followers, including Harrison and Spemann, had proved the egg and embryo to be amenable to microsurgical manipulation. Driesch had stressed the importance of ferments in development, and Jacques Loeb, often erroneously but always with seminal influence on his contemporaries, had considered development in terms of chemistry and physics as he understood them. Most important of all, Otto Warburg had begun his quantitative studies on the respiration of the echinoderm egg that were to lead to the discoveries of the cytochromes and thereby, within a few decades, to transform not only embryology but the whole of biology. But for all this, it was still the studies by Child that exerted the strongest immediate influence in transforming embryology into a physiological science.

Child was not the first investigator to postulate the existence of gradients; the concept had been introduced by Boveri and discussed by him with clarity in 1910. Child's contribution was his attempt to explain gradients on a metabolic basis. His concept of a gradient along an axis, in which anterior regions were dominant to posterior ones, was first introduced in 1911 (in Die physiologische Isolation von Teilen des Organismus als Auslösungsfaktor der Bildung neuer Lebewesen und der Restitution. Vorträge u. Aufsätze über Entw.-mech., herausg. W. Roux, 1911, Bd. 11, 157 S.) to explain certain regenerative and budding phenomena in various invertebrates. He first discussed extension of the concept to cover embryonic phenomena in an article in Science in 1914; the paper reproduced here was the first which presented his embryological data in detail.

Later studies by other workers, utilizing more refined methods, have failed to confirm Child's hypothesis that dominant regions, those first to disintegrate in Child's experiments after the administration of KCN and other poisons, utilize greater amounts of oxygen than do less dominant regions which are slower to die. Nonetheless, Child's attempted explanations of morphogenetic observations on a metabolic basis were of great weight in stimulating the study of the egg and of the embryo as metabolic systems. In its attempt to relate the part to the whole, the gradient theory no doubt exerted its influence on the organizer theory, with which it overlapped to some degree, as Spemann himself realized. It still today remains one of the few general unifying concepts that attempts to account for over-all pattern in the development of the organism as a whole.

SUSCEPTIBILITY GRADIENTS IN ANIMALS

The writer has called attention in several papers[1] to the existence of axial gradients in rate of metabolism in planarians and other forms and their significance in relation to polarity. During the past summer in the course of other work at Woods Hole the opportunity presented itself to examine various forms belonging to different groups and various embryonic and larval stages for the existence of such gradients.

The method used was that of determining the relative susceptibility of different regions of the body to certain narcotics and poisons, KCN, alcohol and ether being chiefly used. To concentrations of these and various other substances which kill within a few hours without permitting any acclimatization the susceptibility varies in general with the rate of metabolism, or of certain fundamental metabolic processes, *i.e.,* the higher the rate of these processes the greater the susceptibility and the earlier death or cessation of movement occurs.[2] Death in these reagents is usually followed very soon, often almost at once, by rounding, separation or disintegration of the cells, so that the time of death can be approximately determined by visible changes of this kind. Results obtained in this manner can be controlled by removing the animals from the solution at different periods and determining when recovery ceases to occur and experience has shown that these two methods of procedure give essentially similar results. In this way the following forms were examined.

In *Nereis virens* the regional susceptibility of developmental stages from the beginning of cleavage to the late trochophore was determined. In the early cleavage stages the micromeres are more susceptible to KCN 0.005 *m.* than the macromeres. They not only disintegrate before the macromeres when the eggs remain in the solution, but if the eggs are returned to sea water at the proper time the micromeres alone are killed and the macromeres recover and resume division, giving rise to defective larvæ.

At the stage when gastrulation is nearly completed the somatic plate region is apparently the most susceptible region of the embryo, and by return to water at the proper time it is possible to obtain larvæ which do not elongate posteriorly and do not form the three larval segments. If the embryos at this stage are left for a longer time in KCN before return to water, both somatic plate and some or all of the macromeres are killed

---

[1] *Jour. Exp., Zool.,* XII., 1912; *Arch. f. Entwickelungsmech,* XXXV., 1913; XXXVII., 1913.

[2] Child, *Jour. Exp. Zool.,* XIV., 1913.

and the intact portion consists of more or less of the ventral portion of pre-trochal and post-trochal ectoderm with or without a part of the macromeres. Evidently the most susceptible regions at this stage are first the somatic plate, and second, the dorsal part of the pretrochal region and the macromeres.

In the developing egg of another annelid, *Chætopterus pergamentaceus,* the relative susceptibilities of different regions are much the same. In the early stages the animal pole shows the highest susceptibility and in later stages a second region of high susceptibility appears in the somatic plate. In still another polychæte, *Arenicola cristata,* the apical region and somatic plate of the young trochophores are the most susceptible regions. The early cleavage stages of this species were not obtained.

In *Nereis* and *Chætopterus* the region about the animal pole is clearly the region of greatest susceptibility, *i. e.,* of greatest metabolic activity in the early stages of development. Later the activity in this region becomes relatively less in *Nereis* as differentiation of the apical larval region advances and the somatic plate becomes the most active region of the egg. But in *Chætopterus* the apical region retains its susceptibility to some extent at the completion of gastrulation, and this region and the somatic plate appear as distinct regions of high susceptibility. In other words, at the beginning of development an axial metabolic gradient exists with the region of highest rate about the animal pole, but as development proceeds this gradient is altered from its primary simple form by the increase in activity of the cells which give rise to body segments and later by decrease in activity in the animal pole region.

In the egg of the sea urchin *Arbacia* in KCN 0.005 *m.* a distinct susceptibility gradient was observed during cleavage, death and disintegration beginning at one region of the egg and proceeding along an axis, but it was not possible to determine whether the region of highest susceptibility was always the animal pole, though in many cases it certainly was. In the later gastrula and prepluteus stages this simple gradient was complicated by the appearance of high susceptibility in the regions where the arms were beginning to develop.

Since in *Nereis, Chætopterus* and *Arbacia* the different susceptibilities of different regions of the developmental stages make it possible to kill with more or less exactness certain parts of the embryo while other parts may recover and continue development, this method may prove of some value in further investigation of the regulatory capacities of the less active regions when isolated from the influence of the more active.

The adult forms of a number of species from various groups were examined for a susceptibility gradient. In the hydroid *Pennaria tiarella* with KCN 0.0025 *m.* and 0.005 *m.* such a gradient appears very clearly in the body of the hydranth, death and disintegration beginning at the distal end of the manubrium and proceeding proximally. A similar gradient exists in the medusa buds of this species. Besides this it was observed that the full-grown hydranths at or near the tips of stem or branches were in general more susceptible than the more proximal. This difference may be due to external factors such as the lower oxygen or higher CO_2 content of the water about the more proximal hydranths in consequence of the greater number of hydranths in a given area, but it seems more probable, in the light of various data concerning the polarity of plants, that this difference in susceptibility of distal and proximal hydranths is the expression of an axial gradient in the colony.

In several other species of hydroids examined at Woods Hole and at La Jolla, California, among them *Tubularia crocea* and *Corymorpha palma* the gradient in the hydranth body is similar to that in *Pennaria*.

The ctenophore *Mnemiopsis leidyi* shows a distinct gradient in susceptibility along each row of swimming plates. The susceptibility of these animals to KCN is very high and most experiments were made with KCN 0.0000375 *m.*—0.0005 *m.* Rhythmic movement of the plates ceases first at the central end of each row, *i. e.*, the end nearest the apical sense organ, and last at the peripheral end. Before movement has entirely stopped in the apical region the rhythm of the plates in the peripheral half or third of the row becomes different from the central rhythm, being usually more rapid and in some cases irregular or periodic. In two cases a perfectly distinct reversal in direction of the impulse was observed at the peripheral end of a row after movement at the central end had ceased. In this case the impulse started at the extreme peripheral end of the row and traveled some distance in the central direction, finally dying out. This continued for an hour or more before movement at the peripheral end ceased.

This susceptibility gradient is undoubtedly a gradient in the nerve and not in the plates themselves, for the plates do not die in KCN until long after rhythmic movement ceases, and as long as they remain alive direct contact stimulation of single plates produces slight movements of the plate stimulated. However, a slight susceptibility gradient does exist in the plates themselves as is evident from the fact that the plates at the central end of the nerve die first and death proceeds peripherally. The time of death is readily determined, for when they die the plates lose their interference colors and become white and opaque.

As regards the general ectoderm of *Mnemiopsis*, it is difficult to determine the time of death accurately, but observations thus far indicate that the disintegration of the ectoderm proceeds from the apical region.

During the course of my observations on susceptibility gradients Dr. Tashiro called my attention to his discovery of a quantitative gradient in CO_2 production in the claw nerve of the large spider crab, *Libinia canaliculata:* this is a long nerve which readily separates into small strands and is therefore favorable for observation of any structural changes which might occur in connection with death in solutions of narcotics. The nerve is mixed but is believed to consist largely of efferent fibers.

Since there is some evidence in the work of various authors that a gradient of some sort exists in the nerve, the attempt was made to determine whether a gradient would appear in the structural death changes. A number of nerves were observed in various concentrations of KCN from 0.001 *m.* to 0.01 *m.* In these solutions the fibrillæ become after a time irregular in outline and more or less varicose so that the strand appears more or less granular instead of fibrillar like the fresh living nerve. The preparations showed some indications of the progression of the change from the central to the peripheral end of the nerve, but the changes were so slight that the possibility of a subjective factor being concerned could not be neglected. In the attempt to obtain more distinct structural death changes other narcotics were used, and it was found that in ethyl ether the fibrillation almost completely disappeared and the strands became very distinctly granular in appearance in consequence of irregular swelling and varicosity of the fibrils. In 1 per cent ether or somewhat lower concentrations these changes occur, slowly requiring several hours for completion, and a very distinct gradient in their occurrence is visible. The change from fibrillar to granular appearance begins at the two ends of the nerve very soon after it is brought into the solution, and a distinct gradient in this change can be seen extending a few millimeters peripherally from the central end and a shorter distance centrally from the peripheral end. This first change remains limited to the two terminal regions of the nerve and is undoubtedly associated with the stimulation and injury resulting from severing the nerve at these two points.

Later, however, the change begins to progress along the nerve from the central toward the peripheral end, but the change at the peripheral end progresses only very slowly or not at all in the central direction. From this time on a distinct gradient in the change is visible until it has progressed along the whole length of the nerve. Except in the terminal region adjoining the peripheral cut end the death change always progresses in the peripheral direction. The peripheral third of the length may be entirely unchanged at a time when the central third or more has completely lost its fibrillar appearance. When long strands are so arranged that central and peripheral regions are side by side in the same field of the microscope the differences between the two regions are very striking. If the nerve is crushed or injured at any point short gradients appear on both sides of the injury, but do not extend to any great distance before the general change reaches this region in its progress peripherally.

The existence of this centro-peripheral gradient in the death changes of the nerve fiber in narcotics must mean that a gradient of some sort exists in the living nerve and if the action of the narcotics is of the same character here as in other cases we must conclude that this gradient is associated with metabolism and that the rate of metabolism or of certain metabolic processes is in general higher at the central end and decreases peripherally in this nerve.

That metabolic gradients occur very widely if not universally, at least during the earlier stages of development in axiate organisms and structures, is evident from the data of embryology. The so-called law of antero-posterior development must be the expression of an axial metabolic gradient. And as regards plants there is a large body of evidence which indicates that the vegetative tip possesses a higher rate of metabolism than other regions of the same axis. Even in the unicellular body of the ciliate infusoria and in various other cells which show a morphological polarity the writer has observed a susceptibility gradient. In view of the facts it is impossible to doubt that such gradients are in some way closely associated with polarity in organisms, and various lines of experimental evidence which can not be considered here indicate that they constitute the dynamic basis of polarity. There are, moreover, many facts which suggest that the establishment of a gradient of this kind is the first step in individuation in axiate organisms.

PART NINE

1916

The Theory of the Free-Martin

by **FRANK R. LILLIE**

Lillie, Frank R. 1916. The theory of the Free-Martin. Science 43:611-613. Reprinted by permission of Science.

In 1906 Lillie showed that he had been reflecting on the problem of sex differentiation, for in that year he argued that in the zygote (fertilized egg) we must find the primary cause of sexual differentiation and seek an answer to the question as to "how the differentiated conditions are subsequently produced." To him the old concept of a sexually indifferent stage in the life history "is as necessary and fundamental today as it ever appeared to be, and . . . we cannot depart from it without involving ourselves in absolutely hopeless theoretical difficulties." Thus, Lillie clearly and accurately envisaged that the determining conditions set in the egg at fertilization act so as to direct the course of differentiation of sex characters in either the male or female direction and that such characters arise, like other characters, in an orderly sequence in embryogenesis. Thus Lillie was prepared for a chance event that came about on the family farm northwest of Chicago near the village of Wheeling, Illinois. There, in a prize herd of purebred cattle his attention was first drawn to the "free-martin," a term popularly applied from ancient times by experienced cattle breeders to a barren female which is born co-twin to a normal bull calf. The question naturally arose in Lillie's mind as to whether the sterility of the female was a causal consequence of its association with a male co-twin during uterine life. Was this one of nature's experiments that would test Lillie's hunch that mechanisms in the control of sex differentiation can be analyzed?

Lillie's answer to this question is a model of scientific analysis. In it he displayed during exploration, rigorous logic, penetrating insight and creative interpretation, as you will detect in reading his first published paper on the free-martin as reprinted below. The definitive article, "The Free-martin; a study of the action of sex hormones in the foetal life of cattle" was published in 1917. Somewhat later Lillie learned of a similar analysis of two-sexed twins in cattle by Karl Keller and Julius Tandler, published in 1916 in a veterinary journal, the Wiener tierärtliche Wochenschrift, 3. Jahrg., 513-526. These authors reached the same conclusion with respect to the cause of female intersexuality, as Lillie noted in an appraisal of the work of Keller and Tandler in 1923 (Biol. Bull., 44: 47-78).

Lillie's discovery of sex-hormone action in cattle twins marks a turning point in history of the investigation of the nature, origin and action of sex hormones at a time when very little was known about the subject. It started many researches initially designed to test the sex hormonal theory of the free-martin by experimental means. Further, it furnished a sound basis for the concept of selective response of endocrine receptors to hormonal molecules in the vascular circulation of the embryo.

*More recent studies have shown that the modification of sex develop-
ment is not the only change that takes place when the allantoic blood
vessels of dizygotic twins are united so as to permit an interchange of
blood (see facing page). In 1945 Owen made the discovery that such non-
identical cattle twins after birth have identical red-cell antigens, and in
1951 Medawar and co-workers found that skin grafts exchanged between
dizygotic twin calves are in the majority of cases mutually acceptable
whereas skin grafts exchanged between individuals of separate birth are
rapidly destroyed by the homograft reaction. Obviously, the mutual
tolerance of the skin and mixture of blood types have the same origin, i.e.,
through an interchange of blood before birth. Initiated by Burnet's
theory of immunological tolerance, Medawar and co-workers succeeded in
reproducing experimentally by injecting living cell suspensions into
embryos and/or new born animals the same state of tolerance to skin
homografts that comes about by natural accident in cattle twins. In
recognition of their work in the elucidation of the development and
nature of the immune response, Medawar and Burnet shared the Nobel
prize in physiology and medicine for 1960.*

THE THEORY OF THE FREE-MARTIN

The term free-martin is applied to the female of heterosexual twins
of cattle. The recorded experience of breeders from ancient times to the
present has been that such females are usually barren, though cases of
normal fertility are recorded. This presents an unconformable case in
twinning and sex-determination, and it has consequently been the cause
of much speculation.

The appearance of an abstract in SCIENCE[1] of Leon J. Cole's paper
before the American Society of Zoologists on "Twinning in Cattle with
Special Reference to the Free-Martin," is the immediate cause of this
preliminary report of my embryological investigation of the subject. Cole
finds in a study of records of 303 multiple births in cattle that there were
43 cases homosexual male twins, 165 cases heterosexual twins (male and
female), and 88 cases homosexual female, and 7 cases of triplets. This
gives a ratio of about 1♂♂:4♂♀:2♀♀, for the twins instead of the expected
ratio of 1:2:1. Cole then states:

The expectation may be brought more nearly into harmony with the facts
if it is assumed that in addition to ordinary fraternal (dizygotic) twins, there are
numbers of "identical" (monozygotic) twins of both sexes, and that while in the
case of females these are both normal, in the case of a dividing male zygote, to

[1] Vol. XLIII., p. 177, February 4, 1916.

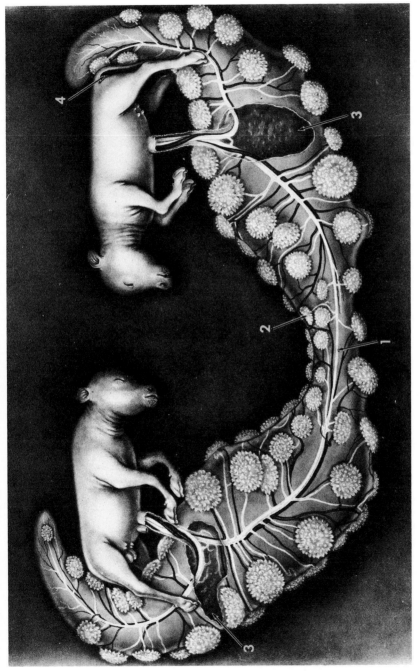

The paper by Lillie reproduced here was not illustrated. The figure shown above was taken from his definitive publication on *The Free-martin; a Study of the Action of Sex Hormones in the Foetal Life of Cattle. Jour. Exp. Zool.*, **23**:371–452 (1917). The original legend reads as follows: **Fig. 4** Twin chorionic vesicle of cow; double injection; case no. 47. ♂ 22.75 cm. ♂ 22.25 cm. ×¼. 1, arterial through trunk; 2, cotyledon with venous connection with both sides; 3, amniotic sacs opened; 4, clitoris of free-martin; note female arrangement of teats; cf. with male.

form two individuals, in one of them the sexual organs remain in the undif-ferentiated stage, so that the animal superficially resembles a female and or-dinarily is recorded as such, although it is barren. The records for monozygotic twins accordingly go to increase the homosexual female and the heterosexual classes, while the homosexual male class in which part of them really belong, does not receive any increment.

Cole thus tentatively adopts the theory, which has been worked out most elaborately by D. Berry Hart, stated also by Bateson, and implied in Spiegelberg's analysis (1861), that the sterile free-martin is really a male co-zygotic with its mate.

Cole's figures represent the only statistical evidence that we have on this subject. Let us follow his suggestion and take from the heterosexual class enough cases to make the homosexual male twins equal in number to the homosexual female pairs; this will be approximately one fourth of the class, leaving the ratio 2:3:2 instead of 1:4:2. Which one of these is the more satisfactory sex ratio I leave others to determine; I wish only to point out the fatal objection, that, according to the hypothesis, the females remaining in the heterosexual class are normal; in other words, on this hypothesis the ratio of normal free-martins (females co-twin with a bull) to sterile ones is 3:1; and the ratio would not be very different on any basis of division of the heterosexual class that would help out the sex ratio. Hitherto there have been no data from which the ratio of normal to sterile free-martins could be computed, and Cole furnishes none. I have records of 21 cases statistically homogeneous, 3 of which are normal and 18 abnormal. That is, the ratio of normal to sterile free-martins is 1:6 instead of 3:1.

This ratio is not more adverse to the normals than might be antici-pated, for breeders' associations will not register free-martins until they are proved capable of breeding, and some breeders hardly believe in the existence of fertile free-martins, so rare are they.

My own records of 41 cases of bovine twins (to date, February 25, 1916), all examined *in utero,* and their classification determined ana-tomically without the possibility of error, give 14♂♂:21♂♀:6♀♀. It will be observed that this agrees with expectation to the extent that the sum of the homosexual classes is (almost) equal to the heterosexual class; and it differs from expectation inasmuch as the ♂♂ class is over twice the ♀♀ class instead of being equal to it, as it should be if males and females are pro-duced in equal numbers in cattle. The material can not be weighted statistically because every uterus containing twins below a certain size from a certain slaughter house is sent to me for examination without be-ing opened. Cole's material shows twice as many female as male pairs, and the heterosexual class is about one third greater than the sum of the two homosexual classes. I strongly suspect that it is weighted statistically; the possibility of this must be admitted, for the records are assembled from a great number of breeders. But, whether this is so or not, if we add the sterile free-martin pairs of my collection to the male side in accordance with Cole's suggestion, we get the ratio 32♂♂:3♂♀:6♀♀, which is absurd. And if we take Cole's figures, divide his heterosexual class into pairs containing sterile females and pairs containing normal females according to the expectation, 6 of the former to 1 of the latter, and add the former to his male class, we get an almost equally absurd result (184♂♂:23♂♀:88♀♀). On the main question our statistical results are sufficiently alike to show that the free-martin can not possibly be interpreted as a male. The theory of Spiegelberg, D. Berry Hart, Bateson and Cole falls on the statistical side alone.

But the real test of the theory must come from the embryological side. If the sterile free-martin and its bull-mate are monozygotic, they should be included within a single chorion, and there should be but a single corpus luteum present. If they are dizygotic, we might expect two separate chorions and two corpora lutea. The monochorial condition would not, however, be a conclusive test of monozygotic origin, for two chorions originally independent might fuse secondarily. The facts as determined from examination of 41 cases are that about 97.5 per cent. of bovine twins are monochorial, but in spite of this nearly all are dizygotic; for in all cases in which the ovaries were present with the uterus a corpus luteum was present in each ovary; in normal single pregnancies in cattle there is never more than one corpus luteum present. There was one homosexual case (males) in which only one ovary was present with the uterus when received, and it contained no corpus luteum. This case was probably monozygotic.

There is space only for a statement of the conclusions drawn from a study of these cases, and of normal pregnancies. In cattle a twin pregnancy is almost always a result of the fertilization of an ovum from each ovary; development begins separately in each horn of the uterus. The rapidly elongating ova meet and fuse in the small body of the uterus at some time between the 10 mm. and the 20 mm. stage. The blood vessels from each side then anastomose in the connecting part of the chorion; a particularly wide arterial anastomosis develops, so that either fetus can be injected from the other. The arterial circulation of each also overlaps the venous territory of the other, so that a constant interchange of blood takes place. If both are males or both are females no harm results from this; but *if one is male and the other female, the reproductive system of the female is largely suppressed, and certain male organs even develop in the female. This is unquestionably to be interpreted as a case of hormone action.* It is not yet determined whether the invariable result of sterilization of the female at the expense of the male is due to more precocious development of the male hormones, or to a certain natural dominance of male over female hormones.

The results are analogous to Steinach's feminization of male rats and masculinization of females by heterosexual transplantation of gonads into castrated infantile specimens. But they are more extensive in many respects on account of the incomparably earlier onset of the hormone action. In the case of the free-martin, nature has performed an experiment of surpassing interest.

Bateson states that sterile free-martins are found also in sheep, but rarely. In the four twin pregnancies of sheep that I have so far had the opportunity to examine, a monochorial condition was found, though the fetuses were dizygotic; but the circulation of each fetus was closed. This appears to be the normal condition in sheep; but if the two circulations should anastomose, we should have the conditions that produce a sterile free-martin in cattle. The possibility of their occurrence in sheep is therefore given.

The fertile free-martin in cattle may be due to cases similar to those normal for sheep. Unfortunately when the first two cases of normal cattle free-martins that I have recorded, came under observation I was not yet aware of the significance of the membrane relations, and the circulation was not studied. But I recorded in my notebook in each case that the connecting part of the two halves of the chorion was narrow, and this is significant. In the third case the two chorions were entirely unfused; this case, therefore, constitutes an *experimentum crucis*. The male was 10.4 cm. long; the female 10.2 cm. The reproductive organs of both were entirely normal. The occurrence of the fertile free-martin is therefore satisfactorily explained.

The sterile free-martin enables us to distinguish between the effects of the zygotic sex-determining factor in mammals, and the hormonic sex-differentiating factors. The female is sterilized at the very beginning of sex-differentiation, or before any morphological evidences are apparent, and male hormones circulate in its blood for a long period thereafter. But in spite of this the reproductive system is for the most part of the female type, though greatly reduced. The gonad is the part most affected; so much so that most authors have interpreted it as testis; a gubernaculum of the male type also develops, but no scrotal sacs. The ducts are distinctly of the female type much reduced, and the phallus and mammary glands are definitely female. The general somatic habitus inclines distinctly toward the male side. Male hormones circulating in the blood of an individual zygotically female have a definitely limited influence, even though the action exists from the beginning of morphological sex-differentiation. A detailed study of this problem will be published at a later date.

PART TEN

1924

Induction of Embryonic Primordia by Implantation of Organizers from a Different Species

by HANS SPEMANN and HILDE MANGOLD

Spemann, H. und Hilde Mangold. 1924. Über Induktion von Embryonalanlagen durch Implantation artfremder Organisatoren. Wilhelm Roux' Arch. Entwicklungsmech. Organ. **100**:599-638. Translated by Viktor Hamburger and printed by permission of Springer-Verlag.

Through an extensive series of exact experiments on the developing newt's egg carried out over a period of almost a quarter of a century Spemann (1869-1941) was gradually led to the discovery of "organizer" effects. The concept may be traced back to his constriction experiments of 1901-1903 in which the blastomeres of the two-celled stage were separated by tightening a human baby's hair around the first cleavage furrow. In some eggs each blastomere developed into a whole embryo small in size (twins), whereas in the majority of eggs one of the blastomeres developed into a perfect embryo and the other one into an unorganized ball of living cells. These differences in results were explained on the basis of variable position of the first cleavage plane with reference to the median plane of the future embryo. In the cases where two normal dwarf embryos developed, the first cleavage plane happened to coincide with the median plane whereas in those cases where only one blastomere gave a whole embryo the first cleavage plane lies at right angles to the median plane, so dividing the egg into dorsal and ventral halves. By constricting eggs during early gastrulation this explanation was proved to be correct. Thus Spemann concluded that as early as the two-celled stage the dorsal half differs qualitatively from the ventral half, the former possessing a quality which enables it to form an embryo whereas the latter lacks such a quality.

In 1918 he reported that small pieces of ectoderm (prospective neural plate and epidermis) exchanged between Triton *embryos of early gastrula stages developed in accord with their new position whereas a piece of the dorsal lip behaved in a different manner, i.e., it developed into an embryolike body with neural tube, notochord and somites when transplanted to new positions. From these contrasting results Spemann made the assumption that the dorsal lip was already determined and he suggested that it might represent a "center of differentiation" from which a process of determination gradually spreads forward to the undetermined ectoderm of the gastrula.*

It is of historical interest to note here that Lewis (1907) using frog embryos had previously reported that a piece of the dorsal lip grafted to a host embryo develops into nerve tube, chorda and muscle. This he interpreted as indicating that the dorsal lip is determined and undergoes self-differentiation.

Although Spemann had noted as early as 1918 that a graft of the dorsal lip to a host embryo tended to result in the formation of an embryo, the question arose in his mind as to how much of its development was due to self-differentiation, and how much to induction. Lewis had assumed that the transplanted dorsal lip self-differentiated. Concepts of induction had already been developing in Spemann's mind as a result of his earlier studies (1901-1912) on the relationships between optic cup and overlying lens ectoderm, and he recognized that the "organizing" effect of the dorsal lip might be related to inductive action by the archenteron roof on the ectoderm overlying it.

The answer to the question was made possible by grafting a dorsal lip of one species of newt to another species differing in amount of dark pigment. In this way the source of cells which contribute to the secondary embryo could be followed in a precise manner. In a postscript to his 1921 paper on heteroplastic transplantation, Spemann, in referring to experiments made by his student, Hilde Mangold, gave the first description of the dorsal lip as an organizing center which he named the "organizer" (Organisator in German) for short. The experiment described in the 1924 article was a crucial one. It showed that both the dorsal lip and host embryo participate in the formation of a secondary embryo but that the graft contributes the major portion of the chorda-mesoderm and the host the major part of the nervous system. The discovery of the organizer and the analysis of its action was one of the most significant events in experimental embryology; it gave reality to the epigenetic concepts of earlier embryologists, demonstrating experimentally that one step in development is a necessary condition for the next, and won for Hans Spemann the Nobel Prize in Physiology and Medicine in 1935.

INDUCTION OF EMBRYONIC PRIMORDIA BY IMPLANTATION
OF ORGANIZERS FROM A DIFFERENT SPECIES

I. INTRODUCTION

In a *Triton* embryo, at the beginning of gastrulation, the different areas are not equivalent with respect to their determination.

It is possible to exchange by transplantation parts of the ectoderm at some distance above the blastopore that in the course of further development would have become neural plate and parts that would have become epidermis, without disturbing normal development by this operation. This is feasible not only between embryos of the same age and of the same species but also between embryos of somewhat different age and even between embryos of different species (Spemann 1918, 1921). For instance, presumptive epidermis of *Triton cristatus* transplanted into the forebrain region of *Triton taeniatus* can become brain; and presumptive brain of *Triton taeniatus* transplanted into the epidermal region of *Triton cristatus* can become epidermis. Both pieces develop according to their new position; however they have the species characteristics with which they are endowed according to their origin. O. Mangold (1922, 1923) has extended these findings and has shown that prospective epidermis can furnish not only neural plate but even organs of mesodermal origin, such as somites and pronephric tubules. It follows from these experimental facts, on the one hand, that the exchangeable pieces are still relatively indifferent with respect to their future fate; and, on the other hand, that influences of some sort must prevail in the different regions of the embryo that determine the later fate of those pieces that are at first indifferent.

A piece from the upper lip of the blastopore behaves quite differently. If it is transplanted into the region that would later become epidermis, it develops according to its origin; in this region, a small secondary embryonic primordium develops, with neural tube, notochord and somites (Spemann 1918). Such a piece therefore resists the determining influences that impinge on it from its new environment, influences that, for instance, would readily make epidermis out of a piece of presumptive neural plate. Therefore, it must already carry within itself the direction of its development; it must be determined. Lewis (1907) had already found this for a somewhat later developmental stage, when he implanted a small piece from the upper and lateral blastopore lip under the epidermis of a somewhat older embryo and saw it develop there into neural tissue and somites.

It suggested itself from the beginning that effects might emanate from these already determined parts of the embryo that would determine the fate of the still indifferent parts. This could be proved by cutting the embryo in half and shifting the halves with respect to each other; in this case, the determined part proved to be decisive for the direction that subsequent development would take. For instance, the animal half of the gastrula was rotated 90° or 180° with respect to the vegetal half; determination then spread from the lower vegetal piece, that contained just the upper lip, to the upper animal piece. Or two gastrula halves of the same side, for instance two right ones, were fused together. As a result, the half blastoporal lips completed themselves from adjacent material of the fused other half, and in this way, whole neural plates were formed (Spemann 1918).

Thus, the concept of the *organization center* emerged; that is, of a region of the embryo that has preceded the other parts in determination and thereupon emanates determination effects of a certain quantity in certain directions. The experiments to be presented here are the beginning of the analysis of the organization center.

Such a more deeply penetrating analysis presupposes the possibility of subdividing the organization center into separate parts and of testing their organizing capacities in an indifferent region of the embryo. This experiment has already been performed, and it was precisely this experiment that gave the first indication that the parts of the embryo are not equivalent at the beginning of gastrulation (1918). However, this intraspecific, homoplastic transplantation did not make it possible to ascertain how the secondary embryonic anlage that originated at the site of the transplant was constructed, that is, which part of it was derived from the material of the implant and which part had been induced by the implant from the material of the host embryo. The identification of these two components is made possible by heteroplastic transplantation, as for instance by implantation of organizers from *Triton cristatus* into indifferent material of *Triton taeniatus*.

This experiment, that followed logically from its presuppositions, was performed during the summers of 1921 and 1922 by Hilde Mangold née Pröscholdt. It gave at once the expected result that has already been reported briefly (Spemann 1921, pp. 551 and 568). In the following, we shall present the basic fact in more detail.

II. EXPERIMENTAL ANALYSIS

Nothing new need be said concerning the experimental technique; it was the same as in previous experiments (Spemann 1920).

Of the species of *Triton* available, *taeniatus* can best tolerate the absence of the egg membrane, from early developmental stages on; and it is the easiest to rear. Hence the organizer that was to be tested for its capacities was always taken from a *cristatus* embryo and usually implanted into the presumptive epidermis of a *taeniatus* embryo. The place of excision was marked by implantation of the piece removed from the *taeniatus* embryo; that is, the pieces were exchanged.

Experiment Triton 1921, Um 8b. The exchange was made between a *cristatus* embryo with distinctly U-shaped blastopore and a *taeniatus* embryo of the same stage. A small circular piece at some distance above the blastopore was removed from the *cristatus* embryo and replaced by a piece of presumptive epidermis of the *taeniatus* embryo. This *taeniatus* implant was found, later on, as a marker in the neural plate of the *cristatus* neurula, between the right neural fold and the midline, and it extended to

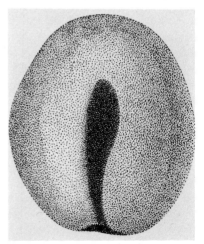

Fig. 1 Um 8 crist. The *cristatus* embryo at the neurula stage. The *taeniatus* transplant is dark and elongated; it is located in the presumptive neural plate. 20×.

the blastopore, slightly tapering toward the posterior end (Fig. 1). One could not see in the living embryo whether it continued into the interior, and the sections, which are poor in this region, did not show this either.

The *cristatus* explant (the "organizer") was inserted on the right side of the *taeniatus* embryo, approximately between the blastopore and the animal pole. It was found in the neurula stage to the right and ventrally, and drawn out in the shape of a narrow strip (Fig. 2). In its vicinity, at first a slight protrusion was observable; a few hours later, neural folds appeared, indicating the contour of a future neural plate. The implant was still distinctly recognizable in the midline of this plate; it extended forward from the blastopore as a long narrow strip, slightly curved, over about two-thirds of the plate (Fig. 3).

This secondary neural plate, that developed in combination with the implanted piece, lagged only a little behind the primary plate in its

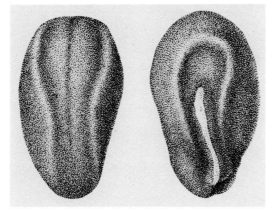

Figs. 2 and 3 Um 8b. The *taeniatus* embryo at the neurula stage, with primary and secondary neural plate; the elongated white *cristatus* implant is in the median plane of the latter. 20×.

development. When the folds of the primary plate were partly closed, those of the secondary plate also came together. Approximately a day later, both neural tubes were closed. The secondary tube begins, together with the primary tube, at the normal blastopore and extends to the right of the primary tube, rostrad, to approximately the level where the optic vesicles of the latter would form. It is poorly developed at its posterior part, yet well enough that the *cristatus* implant was invisible from the outside. The embryo was fixed at this stage and sectioned as nearly perpendicularly to the axial organs as possible.

The sections disclosed the following:

The neural tube of the primary embryonic anlage is closed through the greater part of its length and detached from the epidermis, except at the anterior end where it is still continuous with it, and where its lumen opens to the exterior through a neuropore. The lateral walls are considerably thickened in front; this is perhaps the first indication of the future primary eye vesicles. The notochord is likewise completely detached, except at its posterior end where it is continuous with the unstructured cell mass of the tail blastema. In the mesoderm, four to five somites are separated from the lateral plates, as far as one can judge from cross sections of such an early stage.

Only the anterior part of the neural tube of the secondary embryonic anlage is closed and detached from the epidermis. Here it is well developed; in fact it is developed almost as far as the primary tube at its largest cross-section: its walls are thick and its lumen is drawn out sideways (Fig. 4). Perhaps we can see here the first indication of optic

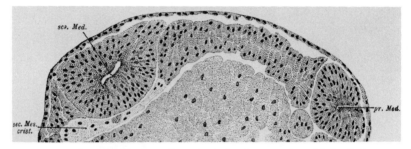

Fig. 4 Um 8b. Cross section through the anterior third of the embryo (cf. Figs. 2 and 3). pr. Med., primary neural tube; sec. Med., secondary neural tube. The implant (light) is in the mesoderm (sec. Mes. crist.). 100×.

vesicles. The central canal approaches the surface at its posterior end, and eventually opens to the outside. Then the neural plate rapidly tapers off; its hindmost portion is only a narrow ectodermal thickening (Figs. 5 and 6).

Although the overwhelming mass of this secondary neural tube is formed by cells of the *taeniatus* host that can be recognized by the finely dispersed pigment, a long, narrow strip of completely unpigmented cells is intercalated in its floor, in sharp contrast to the adjacent regions. This white strip is part of the *cristatus* implant that was clearly recognizable from the outside in the living embryo before the neural folds closed (Fig. 3). The anterior end of this strip is approximately at the point where the thickness of the neural tube decreases rather abruptly; it opens to the outside shortly thereafter. The strip is wedge-shaped, with the pointed edge toward the outside; as a result, only the tapering ends of the cells reach the surface of the embryo (Figs. 5 and 6) or the central canal at the short stretch where they border it.

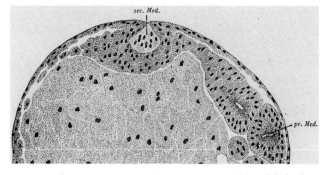

Fig. 5 Um 8b. Cross section through middle third of the embryo (cf. Figs. 2 and 3). pr. Med., primary neural tube; sec. Med., secondary neural tube. The implant (light) is in the secondary neural tube.

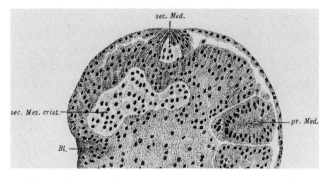

Fig. 6 Um 8b. Cross section in the region of the blastopore (Bl.) (cf. Figs. 2 and 3). pr. Med., primary neural tube; sec. Med., secondary neural tube. The implant (light) has several cells in the secondary neural tube, with its main mass in the mesoderm (sec. Mes. crist.). 100×.

At its posterior end, the *cristatus* strip reaches the blastopore, and it is continuous with a mass of *cristatus* cells that is located between the secondary neural tube and the mesoderm on one side, and the endoderm on the other (Fig. 6). Because of their position one would be inclined to consider these cells as endoderm; but in size they resemble more the mesoderm of the *taeniatus* embryo with which they are associated. At any rate, this cell mass, which extends a bit farther rostrad, has reached its position by invagination around the blastoporal lip. There is yet another mass of *cristatus* cells still farther rostrad. It has the form of a thin plate underlying the anterior part of the induced neural tube, as far as it is closed; at its anterior end and at its sides it coincides approximately with the edge of the tube, and at its posterior end it extends to the ectodermal strip of the implant. This plate is incorporated in the normal *taeniatus* mesoderm (Fig. 4). It is not differentiated further into notochord or somites.

Altogether, a rather substantial part of the implant remained in the ectoderm. This portion was greatly stretched in length; as a result, the circular white disk that was implanted has become a long narrow strip that turns inwards around the blastoporal lip. Shifting of cells in the surrounding epidermis may have played a role in these form changes; the extent to which this occurs would have to be tested by implantation of a marker of indifferent material. A piece from a region near the upper lip of the blastopore could hardly be considered as suitable for this purpose. We know from earlier experiments (Spemann 1918, 1921) that convergence and stretching of the cell material occurs at the posterior part of the neural plate. It is improbable that the cells of the neural plate are entirely passive in this process; rather, they may have an inherent tendency to shift that perhaps has been, together with other characteristics, induced by the underlying endo-mesoderm. This tendency would be retained by the piece in the foreign environment. In this way we might also explain the fact that the piece gains contact with the invaginating region of the normal blastoporal lip, although it was originally far distant from it. Once it has arrived there by active stretching it could be carried along, at least in part, by the local cell shiftings.

Whereas this posterior cell mass is continuous with the cell strip that has remained on the surface, it is separated from the more anterior *cristatus* cell plate by *taeniatus* mesoderm. Therefore, this anterior plate that underlies the neural tube cannot have arrived at its position by invagination around the upper blastoporal lip; it must have been located in the deeper position from the beginning. Undoubtedly it derives from the inner layer of the implant; hence it was originally just under the *cristatus* cells, some of which are now found partly in the neural plate as a narrow strip, and others of which had migrated inside around the blastoporal lip. These displacements carried it along and brought it forward to such an extent that now its posterior margin is approximately level with the anterior end of the *cristatus* cell strip in the neural tube.

Although a piece of presumptive neural plate taken from a region a little anterior to the actual transplant would have become epidermis after transplantation to presumptive epidermis, this implant has resisted the determinative influences of the surroundings and has developed essentially according to its place of origin. Its ectodermal part has become part of the neural plate and the endo-mesodermal part has placed itself beneath it.

Furthermore, not only did the implant assert itself, but it made the indifferent surroundings subservient to it and it has supplemented itself from these surroundings. The host embryo has developed a second neural plate out of its own material, that is continuous with the small strip of *cristatus* cells and underlain by two cell plates of *cristatus* origin. This secondary plate would not have arisen at all without the implant, hence it must have been caused, or induced, by it.

There seems to be no possible doubt about this. However, the question remains open as to the way in which the induction has taken place. In the present case it seems to be particularly plausible to assume a direct influence on the part of the transplant. But even under this assumption, there are still two possibilities open. The ectodermal component of the transplant could have self-differentiated into the strip of neural plate, and could have caused the differentiation of ectoderm anterior and lateral to it progressively to form neural tissue. Or the determination could have emanated from the subjacent parts of the endo-mesoderm and have influenced both the *cristatus* and *taeniatus* components of the overlying ectoderm in the same way. And finally it is conceivable that the subjacent layer is necessary only for the first determination, which thereafter can spread in the ectoderm alone. A decision between these possibilities could be made if it were possible successfully to transplant pure ectoderm and pure endo-mesoderm from the region of the upper lip of the blastopore, and, finally, such ectoderm which had been underlain by the endo-mesoderm. In such experiments, heteroplastic transplantation offers again the inestimable advantage that one can establish afterwards with absolute certainty whether the intended isolation was successful.

In our case, such a separation of the factors under consideration has not been accomplished. Nevertheless it seems noteworthy that the induced neural plate is poorly developed in its posterior part where it is in closest and most extensive contact with the ectodermal part of the transplant; and, in contrast, that it is well developed at its anterior end where it is remote from the *cristatus* cell strip, but underlain by the broad *cristatus* cell plate.

We shall discuss later (p. 174) a second possibility of a fundamentally different nature that is particularly applicable to more completely formed secondary embryonic primordia.

A second experiment, similar to the first, confirms it in all essential points. They both have in common that the implant remains estodermal to a considerable extent, and therefore later forms part of the neural tube. The situation is different in the following experiment.

Experiment Triton 1922, Um 25b. A median piece of the upper blastoporal lip was taken from a *cristatus* embryo at the beginning of gastrulation (sickle-shaped blastopore). It came from directly above the margin of invagination and was implanted into a *taeniatus* gastrula of the same stage in the ventral midline at some distance from the future blastopore. Twenty-two hours later, when the *taeniatus* embryo had completed its gastrulation, the implant had disappeared from the surface, which looked completely smooth and normal. Another 24 hours later, the embryo had two neural plates whose folds were about to close. The secondary neural plate starts from the same blastopore as the primary one; at first it runs parallel to the primary plate, adjacent to its left side, and then it bends sharply to the left (Fig. 7). Shortly thereafter, the embryo was fixed; the sections were cut perpendicular to the posterior part of the axial organs.

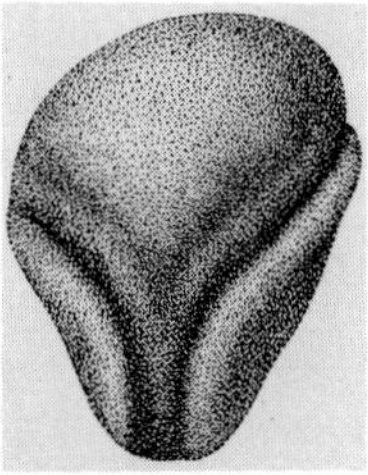

The primary neural tube is completely closed and separated from the epidermis; its optic vesicles are protruding. The notochord is separate down to its posterior end which becomes lost in the indifferent zone. Seven or eight somites are formed.

The secondary neural tube is also closed and separated from the epidermis; anteriorly its walls are broad and its lumen is transverse (probably an indication of optic vesicles). It decreases in thickness posteriorly. In its anterior one-third it is bent sharply to the left and is

Fig. 7 Um 25b. The *taeniatus* embryo at the neurula stage. On the right is the primary and on the left the secondary neural tube. 20×.

therefore at some distance from the primary neural tube: but more posteriorly, at its posterior two-thirds, it approaches the latter and eventually fuses with it; however, the lumina, as far as they are present, remain separate. This secondary neural tube is formed completely by *taeniatus* cells, that is, by material supplied by the host embryo. *Cristatus cells,* that is, material of the organizer, do not participate in its formation.

The implant has moved completely below the surface. Its most voluminous, anterior part is a rather atypical mass located directly under the secondary neural tube (Fig. 8), between it and the large yolk cells of the intestine. Separate somites cannot be seen, but the contour of a notochord can be delineated; in the anterior sections, where the axial organs curve outward it is cut longitudinally, but transversely in the more posterior ones (Fig. 8). Toward its posterior end, the implant tapers off; it forms only the notochord and a few cells that merge with the endoderm (Fig. 9). Thereafter, the notochord disappears also, and

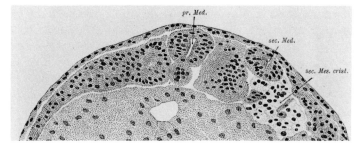

Fig. 8 Um 25b. Cross section in the middle third of the embryo (cf. Fig. 7). In the figure the secondary neural tube is seen to the right of the primary tube. The implant (light) is in the right primary mesoderm (sec. Mes. crist.). 100×.

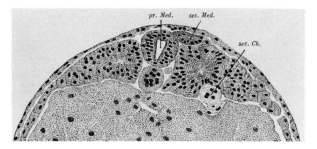

Fig. 9 Um 25b. Cross section in the posterior third of the embryo (cf. Fig. 7). The secondary neural tube is attached to the left side (right in the figure) of the primary tube. The implant (light) forms secondary notochord (sec. Ch.). 100×.

the implant lies entirely in the endoderm and forms the upper covering of a secondary intestinal lumen that extends over a few sections. In its entire posterior part, the implant is separated from the secondary neural tube by interposed mesoderm of the *taeniatus* embryo (Fig. 9). The neural tube extends considerably farther caudad than the implant.

In contrast to the first experiment, the implant in the present case forms a uniform mass; it is not separated into two sections by intervening mesoderm. This must have something to do with the way in which it was shifted to below the surface; however nothing definite can be ascertained concerning this point. The fact that the two embryonic anlagen share the remainder of the blastopore proves that the implant has been invaginated in the normal way around the blastopore. However, it is doubtful whether the implant was entirely passive in this process. It comes from a region whose cells normally participate actively in invagination; and in other instances they have retained this capacity after transplantation. For this reason, the situation becomes complicated.

The implant has formed the entire notochord, also the greater part of mesoderm, which however is not typically segmented, and a small part of the intestinal primordium. It is not clear in the present case whether it has also exerted an inductive effect on the adjacent mesoderm. However, it has certainly evoked the formation of the entire secondary neural tube; but in which way this has occurred remains undecided. A direct influence would be possible in the anterior region where the implant lies directly under the neural tube (Fig. 8); however this explanation is improbable farther back where the implant is displaced by host mesoderm (Fig. 9) or is entirely missing. One would have to assume that this mesoderm has been altered by the organizer and has, in turn, initiated the formation of the neural plate in the overlying ectoderm. However, it could be that the organizer had exerted its entire effect on the ectoderm before it had moved to the interior.

In summary, it is characteristic of this case that implant cells are completely absent in the secondary neural tube, and that the notochord is formed completely by cells of the implant. The same thing is shown, perhaps even more beautifully, in another case (*Triton* 1922, Um 214), in which the notochord formed by the implant, and also the induced neural tube, extend almost over the entire length of the host embryo, and are both near the normal axial organs. But this case again fails to indicate whether the implant can form somites or induce them in host mesoderm. The next case gives information on that point.

Experiment Triton 1922, 131b. The exchange of material was done in advanced gastrulae, after formation of the yolk plug. A large piece of *cristatus,* derived from the median line directly above the blastopore, was interchanged with a piece of *taeniatus* whose origin could not be definitely determined.

The *taeniatus* implant has not participated in the invagination in the *cristatus* embryo; it has caused a peculiar fission (Fig. 10). The neural tube is closed anteriorly; at the point where it meets the *taeniatus* piece, it divides into two halves, one to the left and one to the right. At this point, a bit of endoderm comes to the surface, perhaps as the result of incomplete healing or of a later injury. The cross-sections show a neural tube and notochord in the anterior part back to the point of bifurcation. The two divisions of the neural tube are still distinct for a few sections, but then they become indistinguishable from the surrounding tissue. The same is true, to a greater degree, of the notochord.

The *taeniatus* embryo has reached the neurula stage 20 hours later. The implant is located on the right side, somewhat behind the middle, and next to the right neural fold. Its original anterior half is still on the surface and strongly elevated over the surroundings; its original posterior half is invaginated and appears as a light area underneath the darker cells of the *taeniatus* embryo. The piece is stretched lengthwise and directed from posteriorly, and somewhat above, to anteriorly and somewhat downward. Invagination still continues; a half-hour later, a strip of *cristatus* cells is visible only at the outer margin of invagination. Twenty-five hours later, the neural folds are almost closed; the implant is visible to their right as a long, stretched out pale strip shining through the epidermis. At its posterior end, it continues into an elevation above the surface of the embryo that has the shape of a small blunt horn (Fig. 11). After another 22 hours, the neural tube is note-

Fig. 10 Um 131a. The *cristatus* embryo at the neurula stage. The *taeniatus* implant (dark), in the shape of a triangle with unequal sides, lies in the posterior dorsal half. 20×.

Fig. 11 Um 131b. The *taeniatus* embryo at the neurula stage. The neural folds are closing. The implant (light), in the middle and posterior third, to the right of the dorsal median plane, is visible through the surface layer, and continues into the protuberance.

worthy for its breadth. The implant is still visible at its right side. It apparently participates in the formation of somites; it continues posteriorly into the outgrowth. The embryo was fixed 11½ hours later when a small area of disintegration appeared on the head. The sections were perpendicular to the longitudinal axis.

We shall consider the axial organs, at first disregarding their different origin, and we begin in the middle region, where they show the typical appearance of a duplication (Fig. 14). The neural tube is incompletely duplicated; the upper outer walls and the lower inner walls of the two individual parts merge in such a fashion that their median planes converge dorsally and meet at a right angle ventrally.

There is one notochord underneath each of the two halves. There is an outer row of somites lateral to each notochord, and between them a third row, not quite double in size, that is common to both embryonic anlagen. Also, the intestine shows a double lumen in this region.

We now follow the different organs forwards and backwards from such a middle section.

The left half of the neural tube (at the right on the sections), which already in this middle region is somewhat larger than the right one, becomes relatively larger more and more anteriorly and continues eventually into a normal brain primordium with primary optic vesicles (Fig. 12). Thus the right half becomes reduced to an increasingly more in-

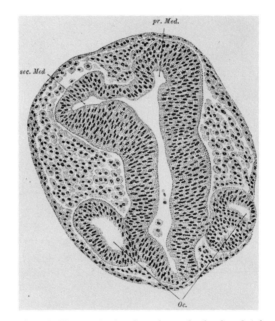

Fig. 12 Um 131b. Section through the head (cf. Fig. 11). Primary and secondary neural tubes are fused and their lumina are continuous. Oc., optic vesicles of the primary neural tube. 100×.

significant appendage and terminates finally without forming optic vesicles. The two tubes continue to have a common lumen; where it seems to be divided into two (as in Fig. 13), we are dealing with a curvature of the tubes resulting in tangential sections through their walls. Toward the posterior region, the two tubes separate from each other; at first their lumina separate (Fig. 15), and then also their walls. As far as one can make out, mesoderm intervenes between them. The larger left tube (at the right in the sections) continues into the normal

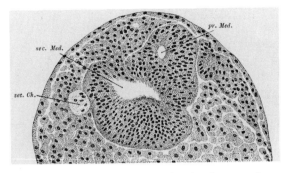

Fig. 13 Um 131b. Cross section in the anterior third of the embryo (cf. Fig. 11). Primary and secondary neural tubes are fused but their lumina are separate. The implant (light) has differentiated into notochord (sec. Ch.). 100×.

tail bud and the smaller right tube into the secondary tail-bud outgrowth. The greater width of the neural tube had already been observed in the living embryo; but in the stage of the open neural plate neither the larger size nor the duplication of the folds, that must have been present, had been noticed.

The left notochord runs medially, in typical fashion, under the left part of the neural tube (Figs. 14 and 15, right). The right notochord

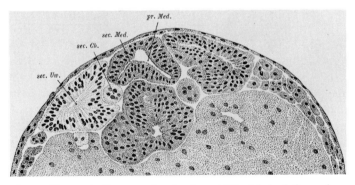

Fig. 14 Um 131b. Cross section in the middle third of the embryo (cf. Fig. 11). Primary and secondary neural tubes are fused and their lumina continuous. The implant (light) forms the secondary somite (sec. Uw.) and the secondary notochord, and in addition the roof of the secondary gut. 100×.

extends even farther forward than the left one (Fig. 13). It is clearly delineated (Fig. 14) up to the point where the secondary tail bud begins (Fig. 15); here its contour becomes indistinct and eventually it disappears entirely.

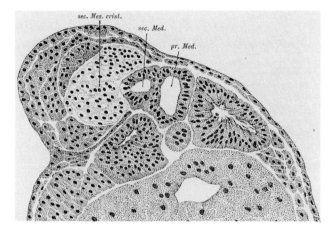

Fig. 15 Um 131b. Cross section at the base of the secondary tail (cf. Fig. 11). The primary and secondary neural tubes are fused; their lumina are separate. The implant (light) is in the floor of the secondary neural tube and forms mesoderm (sec. Mes. crist.) in the secondary tail. 100×.

Of the somites, only the outer left row (Fig. 14, right) is typically developed in its entire length. The outer right row, which is its symmetrical counterpart in the middle region (Fig. 14, left), anteriorly decreases in size considerably. Toward the posterior end it becomes symmetrical within itself, so that the notochord primordium lies approximately in its median plane (Fig. 15). It fades out eventually in the secondary tail bud. The middle row of somites seems, in its middle portion, to belong equally to both sides (Fig. 14). Toward the posterior end, where the right row achieves its own symmetry, the middle row becomes more and more the mirror image of the left row (Fig. 15). The primary plane of symmetry of the duplication therefore no longer bisects the middle row, as is the case in the middle region, but it passes between it and the right row.

Parts of these primordia derive from the *cristatus* cells of the transplant. In the neural tube, there are only a few *cristatus* cells in the median floor of the right half (Fig. 15). Furthermore, the entire right notochord and the entire outer row of somites are formed by *cristatus* cells (Figs. 13-15). In the gut, again, there are only a few such cells, located dorsally, forming the border of a small secondary lumen for a short distance (Fig. 14).

Besides these parts whose *material* derives from the implant, others have received the *stimulus* for their *formation* from the implanted organizer. This is certainly the case with respect to the entire right neural tube. But also the middle row of somites, in its symmetrical portion, has apparently been influenced from both sides, that is, from the normal and the implanted center; and it, in turn, seems to have affected the outer row of *cristatus* somites that are symmetrical to it.

The peculiarity of this case lies in the formation of somites from implanted material and, furthermore, in the interference of the implanted organizer with the normal organization center over a long distance. In the next case, this interference is limited to the anteriormost parts of the two embryonic primordia. Furthermore, the *cristatus* organizer was implanted into the very dark *alpestris* embryo, and the difference in pigmentation is, in part, very sharp.

Experiment Triton 1922, Um 83. The organizer was taken from an early gastrula of *cristatus,* medially, close to the blastopore, and implanted at the animal pole of an *alpestris* embryo in the blastula stage. The *cristatus* embryo disintegrated.

Gastrulation in the *alpestris* embryo begins after 23 hours. The implant is located in the animal half; it is large and curved inwards. Gastrulation is not yet completed after another 23 hours; the implant has disappeared completely into the interior. In its place, a little horn composed of *alpestris* cells protrudes on the dorsal side of the embryo. After another 21 hours, the folds have just begun to form. The little outgrowth is on the right neural fold, at the posterior border of the broad plate. After another 24 hours, the neural folds are in the process of closure; the little horn has disappeared. In the position where it had been visible a small secondary tube branches off the neural tube; it extends obliquely toward the caudal end (Fig. 16). After further development for 24 hours the embryo was preserved and the sections were cut as nearly transverse to the two forks of the neural tube as possible.

Fig. 16 Um 83. The *alpestris* embryo at the neurula stage. Dorsal view. The secondary neural tube branches off laterally from the primary tube and deviates to the right. 20×.

The primary neural tube is closed and separated from the epidermis for almost its entire length (Fig. 18); it is still continuous with the epidermis in the midbrain region where it opens to the outside. The optic vesicles are indicated by compact protrusions of the brain wall.

The primary notochord is delineated in normal fashion for the greatest part of its length (Fig. 18); at the posterior end, it merges with the indifferent tissue of the tail bud.

Of the somites, the left or outer row is normal (Fig. 18, at right); 7

to 8 somites are separate from the lateral plate. The right or inner row (Fig. 18, at left) seems to be somewhat deranged at the anterior end, in front of the bifurcation, as if dammed up.

The secondary neural tube is closed in its middle portion and separated from the epidermis (Fig. 18). It meets the primary tube anteriorly at an acute angle and fuses with it at approximately the level of the future midbrain (Fig. 17); at this point, its lumen opens to the outside.

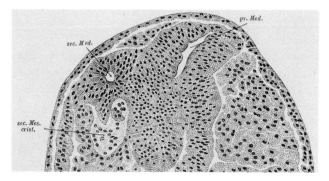

Fig. 17 Um 83. Cross section in the anterior third of the embryo (cf. Fig. 16). In the upper right of the figure may be seen the primary neural tube, from which the secondary tube branches off. The implant (light) is in the mesoderm (sec. Mes. crist). 100×.

Posteriorly, it becomes lost indistinguishably in the surrounding mesoderm of the secondary embryonic anlage, as it would in a normal tail bud.

The notochord is likewise distinctly delineated in the middle portion, (Fig. 18); it lies directly above the wall of the intestine. Anteriorly, it passes without clear demarcation into the mesoderm formed by the implant (Fig. 17), and caudally it merges in the same way with the *alpestris* mesoderm that it has induced.

In the middle region the secondary somites are symmetrically arranged with respect to the secondary notochord and neural tube (Fig. 18). Anteriorly, near the bifurcation point, a mesoderm strip of *cristatus* cells appears between the somites; it connects the lower edges of the somites and separates the notochord from the intestine. In the same region the somites become smaller and indistinct, the left (inner) row earlier than the right (outer) row. Farther back, the somites merge with the unidentifiable tissue in which the notochord and neural tube also lose their identity.

The lumen of the intestine in its middle portion is shifted toward the side of the secondary embryonic anlage, so that it comes to lie in the primary median plane of the duplication (Fig. 18).

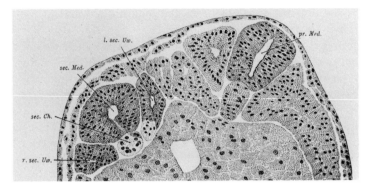

Fig. 18 Um 83. Cross section in the middle part of the embryo (cf. Fig. 16). The primary axial organs are at the upper right of the figure and the secondary axial organs are at the upper left. The implant (light) is in the left secondary somite (l. sec. Uw.) and in the secondary notochord (sec. Ch.). 100×.

In this case, the cell material of the implant participates only in mesodermal structures. The neural tube is composed purely of *alpestris* cells, at least as far as it is delimited from other parts. The notochord, on the other hand, is formed principally of unpigmented cells derived from the *cristatus* implant. But, here and there, distinctly pigmented cells are interspersed along its entire length; they are of the same color as the cells of the neighboring somites (Fig. 18). Since they were never observed in a *cristatus* notochord, they undoubtedly derive from the *alpestris* embryo. Lateral to the notochord, the implant is in an asymmetrical position; in its middle portion it appears in the edges of the *left* somites (Fig. 18, to the right of the notochord), but in its anterior portion, in the *right* somites. In addition, the transplant furnishes the mesoderm strip mentioned above that connects the two sides.

The neural tube and somites of the secondary embryo are definitely induced by the transplant, as far as they are composed of *alpestris* cells.

The pigmentation of the primary and secondary neural tubes is equally deep in both. However, it is surprising how dark the secondary somites are, in comparison to the primary somites (in Fig. 18, however, the difference is exaggerated). It might be assumed that they are formed of different material, that is, of the deeply pigmented cells of the animal half. The experiments of O. Mangold (1922, 1923) have proved that the latter are capable of forming somites. The implant would have carried these cells along with it when it invaginated; this would have been facilitated by the early age of the host embryo (blastula). We shall return to this possibility later. We shall then also discuss the remarkable fact that the implant does not lie in the longitudinal axis of the organs induced by it, but at an acute angle to it.

Experiment Triton 1922, 132. The organizer was taken from a *cristatus* embryo in advanced gastrulation (medium-sized yolk plug). The median region, directly above the blastopore, was transplanted into a *taeniatus* embryo of the same stage. The implant moved inward in the shape of a shallow cup. The *cristatus* embryo, with the exchange implant from *taeniatus,* developed to a larva with primary optic vesicles; it was lost by accident before sectioning. In the neurula stage, the implant had been located medially in the posterior part of the neural plate and extended to the blastopore. Closure of the neural folds was delayed and not quite complete at the caudal end; it was similar to but not quite as abnormal as that in *Triton* 1922, 131b.

Figs. 19 and 20 Um 132. The *taeniatus* embryo at the neurula stage; the secondary neural folds are viewed from the right side (Fig. 19), and from above (Fig. 20). 20×.

In the *taeniatus* embryo, when this is in the neurula stage, 19½ hours after the operation, the implant is no longer visible. In its place are two short neural folds surrounding a groove. They extend obliquely across the ventral side of the embryo, from left posterior to right anterior in front view. Twenty-five hours later the neural folds have approached each other (Fig. 20). The two folds mentioned above and the groove between them are on the left ventral side of the embryo; they are lengthened, and they approach the anterior ends of the host neural folds at an acute angle (Figs. 19 and 20). After another 22 hours, this secondary embryonic primordium has flattened out anteriorly, but posteriorly it projects considerably above the surface. In this region, somites seem to form. Approximately 28 hours later, the embryo has primary optic vesicles, otic pits and a tail bud. In the secondary embryo, at least on the right side, somites can be quite clearly recognized. After another 20 hours, paired otocysts are seen at its anterior end; they are at the same level as those of the primary embryo. The free posterior end has grown somewhat and is bent toward the primary embryo. Four hours later, a pronephric duct is visible in the induced anlage. The embryo was fixed 6 hours later, when a blister appeared on the dorsal surface; the sections were cut transversely.

Immediately before fixation, the living object showed the following features:

The embryo is stretched lengthwise, but its tail is still bent ventrad (Fig. 21). The optic vesicles are strongly expanded, the otic pits distinct, and a large number of somites is formed.
The head is continuously bent to the left, probably due to the secondary embryonic anlage which is on the left side. The latter is rather far ventral, and approximately parallel to the primary axial organs, which it approaches anteriorly at an acute angle. It extends over a considerable part of the length of the primary embryo, from the posterior border of the left optic vesicle to the level of the anus. Its posterior end is lifted up like a tail bud. The central canal of its neural tube is visible through the epidermis, and likewise the lumen of the otic vesicles and of the right somites. The left somites are not recognizable.

Fig. 21 Um 132b. The *taeniatus* embryo shown in Figs. 19 and 20, developed further; viewed from the left side. Surface view of the secondary embryo, with tailbud, neural tube, somites, and otocysts. 20×.

The evaluation of the finer structures is facilitated by the almost complete independence of the normal and the induced embryonic primordia, in contrast to the two previously described cases.

Of the axial organs of the primary embryonic anlage, the neural tube, notochord and somites are entirely normally developed; so is the right pronephros. The left pronephros, however, which faces the secondary primordium, shows a minor irregularity. In the brain primordium, the primary optic vesicles are already transformed into cups, and the lens primordia are recognizable as slight thickenings of the epidermis. The otic pits have closed to form vesicles, but they are not further differentiated, except for the indication of a *ductus endolymphaticus*. The notochord is separated from the adjacent parts throughout almost its entire length. Between 11 and 13 clearly segregated somites can be counted. Neural tube, notochord and somites pass into undifferentiated tissue at the tip of the tail. The primordium of the pronephros consists on each side of two nephrostomes with associated tubules (Figs. 22 and 23). These open into pronephric ducts, in a normal fashion (Figs. 23 and 24). The left duct has a larger diameter anteriorly than has the right one. The pronephric ducts can be traced far posteriorly, but not to their opening to the outside.

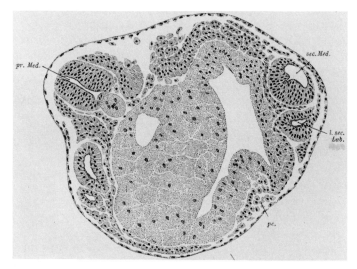

Fig. 22 Um 132b. Cross section at the level of the primary pronephros (cf. Fig. 21). The primary axial organs are at the upper left of the figure and the secondary axial organs at the right. l. sec. Lab., left secondary otocyst; pc., pericardium. 100×.

The secondary embryonic anlage also possesses all the axial organs; they are in part very well formed. The neural tube is closed in its entire length and detached from the epidermis. It is sharply delimited except for its caudal end where it becomes continuous with the undifferentiated mass of the secondary tail bud. In its middle part, the right side is somewhat more strongly developed than the left side (Fig. 24). Toward its anterior end, the diameter increases, and the roof becomes broader and thinner, as in a normal medulla (Fig. 22). At this level, two otocysts are adjacent to it. The right otocyst is shifted forward; it lies at the level of the anterior end (compare the surface view,

Fig. 21), and the left one is slightly more posterior (Fig. 22). They are still attached to the epidermis, and the formation of the endolymphatic duct seems indicated. The notochord extends less far craniad than normally. It is not yet found at the level of the posterior octocyst (Fig. 22); it does not begin until 90 μ behind this section. Otherwise it is well formed, and sharply delimited all the way to its posteriormost part in the tail bud. Somites are formed on both sides; there are more (4 to 6) on the right side facing the primary embryo than on the left side

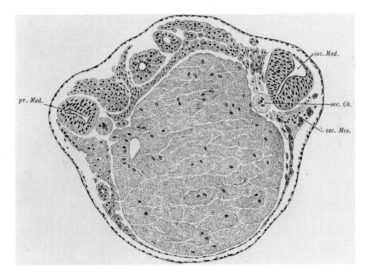

Fig. 23 Um 132b. Cross section in the anterior third of the embryo (cf. Fig. 21). The primary axial organs are at the left of the figure and the secondary axial organs at the right. The implant (light) has differentiated notochord and left secondary somite. 100×.

(2 to 3). On the right side, they extend farther forwards (Fig. 24). A pronephric duct is formed on both sides; again, the left one is longer (about 300 μ) than the right one (about 500 μ) [figures probably erroneously reversed]. Caudally they are not yet separated from the mesoderm, and anteriorly, tubules and funnels are not formed, or not yet. The two adjacent ducts, namely the left one of the primary embryo and the right one of the secondary embryo, are in communication with each other directly behind the second pronephric tubule.

Both embryos share the intestine which is primarily directed toward the primary embryo. It cannot be ascertained with certainty to what extent the secondary embryo has a share in it in all regions. In the pharynx, primordia of visceral pouches may belong to the secondary embryo (Fig. 22); however, they could also belong to the primary embryo and merely be shifted slightly by the secondary embryo. This holds, at any rate, for the heart primordium (Fig. 22 pc, in section through the posterior end of the pericardium). In contrast, a secondary intestinal lumen is distinctly induced beneath the axial organs of the induced anlage, although it can be traced for only a very short distance (about 60 μ; Fig. 24). The anus is somewhat expanded, so that the endoderm is exposed; it is also shifted toward the left side.

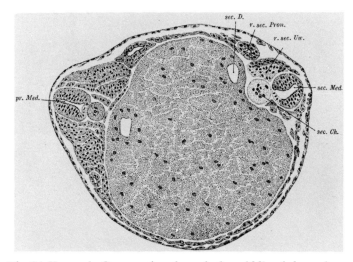

Fig. 24 Um 132b. Cross section through the middle of the embryo (cf. Fig. 21). The primary axial organs are at the left of the figure and the secondary axial organs at the right. r. sec. Pron., right secondary pronephric duct. The implant (light) has formed notochord and part of the right secondary somite. 100×.

The secondary embryonic anlage is again a chimera formed by cells of the host and of the implanted organizer. The two posterior thirds of the neural tube have a ventral strip of *cristatus* cells (Figs. 24 and 25). The notochord is formed entirely of *cristatus* cells. In the somites, the *cristatus* contribution is in the anterior and posterior sections of the left row (Figs. 23 and 25, right) and in the middle part of the right row (Fig. 24, left); there are no somites at all in the middle of the left row (Fig. 24, right). The implant has remained in one place, throughout its length (Figs. 23-25).

All the other structures of the secondary embryo that are not formed by *cristatus* cells have been undoubtedly induced in *taeniatus* material by the organizer.

Hence, in the case the two embryonic anlagen have interfered with

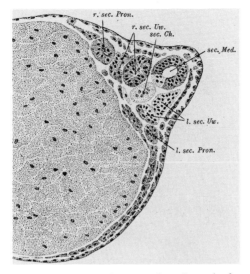

Fig. 25 Um 132b. Cross section through the secondary axial organs, slightly anterior to the secondary tailbud (cf. Fig. 21). The implant (light) is in the floor of the secondary neural tube and in the left secondary somite and has formed notochord. 100×.

each other only to the extent that some of the organ primordia are somewhat more strongly developed on the inner side than on the outer side, and that the pronephric ducts are connected with each other. In other respects, the induced embryonic primordium is entirely independent. This is perhaps one of the main conditions for its complete development.

III. DISCUSSION OF THE RESULTS

1. *Origin and prospective significance of the organizer and site of its implantation.* In all these experiments the organizer was taken from a *cristatus* embryo and inserted into a *taeniatus* embryo, except for one case, where *alpestris* was the host. This combination has proved to be advantageous. The unpigmented *cristatus* cells can be clearly distinguished, over a long period of time, from the pigmented *taeniatus* or *alpestris* cells, and the part supplied by the organizer can thus be sharply delimited from the regions induced by it. Of course, the same would have been true for the implantation of an organizer from the pigmented *taeniatus* or *alpestris* embryo into the unpigmented *cristatus* embryo. This reciprocal experiment would have offered the additional advantage that an organizer could have been implanted into the considerably larger *cristatus* embryo, thus more easily avoiding its

interference with the primary organization center; and, on the other hand, there would have been room for the implantation of several organizers, side by side, and their mutual interference could have been tested. However, several considerable disadvantages cancel out these advantages. For one, the *cristatus* embryos proved to be in general more delicate, as was mentioned above; they seemed, therefore, to be less suitable as host embryos. The larger embryo has probably more difficulty in gastrulation after removal of the vitelline membrane. Furthermore, the neural plate of *cristatus* does not become distinct in early stages, by pigmentation, as is the case in *taeniatus* and *alpestris*. Even after elevation of the neural folds it is much less conspicuous; and for this reason, the small and even less distinct induced neural plates are very difficult to see in the living embryo.

The *region* from which the organizer is taken can easily be ascertained in early gastrulae because the crescent-shaped blastopore gives safe points of orientation. Once the blastopore has become circular, a definite orientation is often no longer possible in the undisturbed embryo. Hence, the piece of host embryo for which the organizer was substituted was implanted in the donor as a marker. This would be an ideal method to determine the normal fate, that is, the prospective significance, of the organizer, if one could be certain that development continues undisturbed despite the operation. As a matter of fact, development is probably somewhat altered (once in a while this can be directly observed), in that gastrulation is impeded. It could be that parts that normally invaginate remain on the surface. The opposite, that is, that more material invaginates than normally, can be excluded almost with certainty. However, this marker is not useless. Even in the most unfavorable case, it will show the position of the organizer with respect to the median plane, whether it was in this plane, or lateral to it; and it will show, furthermore, the *minimal* posterior extent of the organizer. We shall disregard those cases in which a more far-reaching disturbance of development, that is, *spina bifida,* was caused by the implant.

To judge from these markers, or from direct observation, the organizers were all derived from the median plane, closely above the invaginating border of the upper blastoporal lip, or at a short distance from it. They always belonged to the zone of invagination, at least in their posterior part. Accordingly, probably in some cases they would have formed the posteriormost part of the neural plate, but they would always certainly have formed notochord and somites. It cannot be said with the same certainty whether they would have also formed the roof of the intestine. This depends on the lateral extent of the piece, that is, on its width when it was a median piece.

The *age* of the host embryos was variable; it ranged from blastula to advanced gastrula with medium-sized yolk plug. Implantation was always into the animal half of the embryo, but at different places, partly within, and partly outside of the zone of invagination.

Although all this could be determined exactly, the same has not been possible, so far, with respect to the *orientation* of the implanted pieces, since they are exactly circular as is the opening of the micropipette with which they were punched out. This is a disadvantage that will have to be overcome in future experiments. Several different methods suggest themselves, for example, marking the organizer by implanting into it some cells with different pigmentation before it is lifted out; or perhaps an implant with a more characteristic contour can be obtained. Only when the organizer has been implanted in an exactly determined orientation is it possible to establish with certainty the relations between its structure and the direction in which it exerts its effects on its surroundings.

2. *Behavior of the organizer after implantation.* All cases observed have in common the fact that the organizer, which is at first on the surface and level with its surroundings, moves later into the interior, either entirely or in its greater part. The manner in which this occurs differs according to the site of implantation.

If the implant is within the normal zone of invagination, then it passes inwards around the blastoporal lip together with its surroundings. This could be established frequently by direct observation; the piece was seen moving toward the margin of invagination, or immediately in front of it. In other instances, it could be deduced from the result of gastrulation.

Such an invagination of implanted pieces has been observed recently by W. Vogt (1922) and O. Mangold (1922, 1923). In the latter experiments, the implant was indifferent material from the animal hemisphere; it demonstrated its capacity for transformation by becoming mesoderm when carried inside, even though it was presumptive ectoderm. It was also remarkable that an implant taken from a young gastrula seemed to participate more readily in invagination than one from an advanced gastrula (p. 286 ff).

Our experiments cannot be compared directly with these experiments because our implants, derived from the upper blastoporal lip, have brought with them their own invagination tendencies which, depending on the orientation of the piece, might affect the invagination [of the host mesoderm] by either impeding or promoting it. Definite conclusions cannot be expected until it is possible to control the orientation of the implant.

The implant also moves into the interior if it lies outside the zone of invagination. There can be no doubt but that this is caused by forces which the piece brings with it from its region of origin, namely the upper blastoporal lip. Perhaps the first stage in this process is the formation of a depression by the implant; this occasionally appears immediately after implantation and it is frequently still visible on the following day (see p. 164). We have also often observed the gradual disappearance of the implant. The details of this process of independent invagination require more precise investigation. During and after invagination, the implant undergoes a stretching which corresponds approximately in amount to that demonstrated recently by W. Vogt in reimplanted parts of the upper blastoporal lip (cf. v. Ubisch, 1923, Fig. 9). The remarkable protrusion of the piece, which was observed repeatedly (for instance in 1922, 131; cf. p. 157), can probably be ascribed to an obstruction of this invagination which is combined with stretching.

Once arrived in the interior, the implant almost always forms a coherent complex. Only in one case (1921, 8; p. 152) did the mesoderm consist of two portions separated by intercalated host tissue. It was shown that the anterior part probably derived from the deeper layer of the implant.

Even though the process of invagination has to be studied in more detail, the end result is completely clear; it can be read off, directly, from the sections. Depending on its origin and perhaps also on its place of insertion, the implant is brought into the interior more or less completely. That is, part of it remains in the ectoderm and can then be recognized in the neural plate by direct inspection or in sections, where it is found in the wall of the neural tube. Or it is completely sunk into the interior where it forms only mesoderm and perhaps entoderm.

3. *Structure of the secondary embryonic primordium.* The structure of the secondary embryonic primordium is quite complete and can be interpreted most easily when it does not interfere with the primary one. In such cases as that described above (1922, 132), all organ primordia, such as neural tube with otocysts, notochord, somites, pronephros, and perhaps also intestine, can be present and relatively well developed. The only deficiencies are, in the neural tube, the anterior parts of the brain with the optic vesicles; in the pronephros, the tubules and nephrostomes; in the gut, the anus. It does not seem impossible to expect more nearly complete embryos in the course of continued experimentation.

Part of this secondary embryonic primordium always derives from the implant, which can always be sharply distinguished from its surroundings by virtue of its different histological characteristics. The size and position of this component are very variable, depending, undoubtedly, on the size and point of origin of the implant. Host tissue prevails in the neural tube; *cristatus* cells are either absent (e.g. 1922, 25; Figs. 8 and 9, p. 155; 1922, 83, Fig. 18, p. 163), or they form only a narrow strip (e.g. 1921, 8, Fig. 3, p. 149; 1922, 131, Fig. 15, p. 160;

1922, 132, Figs. 24 and 25, pp. 168, 169). This strip is of very different length in the individual cases, but as observed so far, it is always in the median plane; this is of theoretical significance. In contrast, implant tissue predominates in the notochord; in fact, the notochord consisted completely of *cristatus* cells in all cases except one (1922, 83) where small cell groups of the host are interspersed (Fig. 18, p. 163). The somites assume an intermediate position: they can be composed completely of *cristatus* cells (Fig. 14, p. 159), or completely of host cells (Figs. 18 and 25, left); or they can be chimeric, i.e., composed of both (Figs. 18 and 25 right).

The implant as a whole is not rigidly limited to the median plane; this is again of theoretical importance. For instance, in one case (1922, 83) its posterior part extends farther to the left (Fig. 18, right) and its anterior part farther to the right; hence it forms an acute angle with the median plane (pp. 162, 175).

The orientation of these secondary embryonic primordia with respect to the primary axial organs of the host embryo varies considerably. They may be almost parallel to them and nowhere contiguous (1922, 132, p. 164 ff); or they may meet at a more or less acute angle and fuse with them either at the tip, or laterally over a long stretch. To the extent that they are not formed by the *cristatus* cells of the implant, they must have originated from the parts of the host that either were already on the spot, or that came there under the influence of the organizer. This is quite evident for the neural tube; it is formed of cells which otherwise would have formed epidermis of the lateral body wall. The situation is less simple for the more deeply located parts, that is, notochord, somites and pronephros. Sometimes it seems as if they were carved out, as it were, of the lateral plates of the host (e.g. 1922, 132. Figs. 24 and 25). In one case, however (1922, 83; p. 163), the secondary somites were so much more darkly pigmented than the primary ones that the idea suggested itself that they might have been formed by presumptive ectoderm, like the secondary neural tube which they resemble with respect to pigmentation. It would then have to be assumed that the organizer had evoked intensive invagination in the blastula cells of the animal pole where it had been implanted, and had subsequently determined them to form somites. The basis for this possibility is undoubtedly provided by the previously mentioned experiments of O. Mangold. The details of these processes would have to be elucidated by investigations directly aimed at this point.

4. *The causes for the origin of the secondary embryonic anlage.* The causal relationships in the origin of the secondary embryonic anlage are still completely in the dark. The only point that is certain is that somehow an induction by the implant occurs. But even the question of the

stage of development at which this takes place, hence, whether it is a direct, or a more indirect influence, cannot yet be decided.

It is very probable that the inducing action of the implant already begins very early and that it consists at first in inducing its new environment to participate actively in the invagination. That something like this is possible is proved by an earlier experiment (Spemann 1918, pp. 497 ff) in which the bisected blastopore of a medially split gastrula had been fused with material of a different prospective fate and had drawn this latter material into invagination.

The inducing action of the implant could have run its course with this instigation of invagination; everything else could be merely the consequence of this secondary gastrulation. It would then have to be assumed that the general condition imposed on the cells participating in the gastrulation, and by virtue of this process, would in turn provide the stimulus by which further developments are initiated. The different components of the composite chimeric gastrula would then be subjected to this determination process irrespective of their origin. This is actually the case in those chimeras produced by the implantation of indifferent material.

But there is another possibility, namely that after the termination of gastrulation the implant continues to exert determinative influences on its surroundings. For instance, the long, narrow strip of *cristatus* cells in the neural plate could have caused the adjacent cells, which otherwise would have become epidermis, to differentiate likewise into neural plate. And if it should turn out that this is not the correct causal relationship because the development of the neural plate is perhaps evoked by the underlying endo-mesoderm, it is still conceivable that the mesodermal parts of host origin were formed under the influence of the implanted parts.

Both explanations are based on the assumption that the implanted parts have become, by and large, what they would have formed in normal development. According to the first notion, their differentiation would be merely the result of their inherent tendency toward a certain degree of invagination; according to the second notion, the transplants were, in addition, determined with respect to their future differentiation tendency, though perhaps only within the range of a certain degree of variation. These already determined parts would then have the capacity to supplement themselves from the surrounding indifferent parts. It is on this point that the experiments would have to focus that could decide between the two possibilities.

The question of whether decisive facts are already available may be left in abeyance; instead, keeping both possibilities in mind, we shall discuss the factors on which the orientation, the size and the completeness of the secondary embryonic primordia depend.

The first question of interest concerns the *orientation of the secondary primordium* in the host embryo. These are three possibilities: the orientation could be caused entirely by the host embryo, or entirely by the implant, or by a combination of both.

Assuming the first notion to be correct, then the implant would have to be without structure and to behave passively in the process of becoming the substrate [for the neural plate]. Its form and position would be imposed on it entirely by the relations of the host embryo; it would be simply towed along by the cell movements of the latter. Furthermore, the determinative effect would proceed exclusively from this underlying endo-mesoderm; and this effect would be somehow symmetrical with respect to the shape that had been imposed on it from the outside. In this instance, it would probably have to be expected that the secondary primordium would always be similarly oriented with respect to the primary one, and, more specifically, probably parallel to it; but this obviously is not the case. Furthermore, the capacity of the organizer to invaginate autonomously when implanted outside of the normal invagination zone of the host cannot be reconciled with lack of structure within the organizer.

According to the second and third assumptions, the implanted organizer would have a definite structure of its own. On this would depend the direction of invagination and longitudinal stretching and finally, sooner or later, its determinative effect. In this event, the host embryo, in turn, could be either purely passive, or it could participate in the final form and position of the implant by virtue of its own structure or cell movements.

The assumption of an inner structure in the organizer is supported by the fact that the random orientation of the secondary embryonic primordium with respect to the primary one corresponds to the random orientation of the implant. A definite decision will not be possible until the orientation of the organizer can be manipulated at will.

A cooperation of the host embryo seems to be indicated by a peculiarity in the position of the implant to which attention has already been called on p. 164: namely, the longitudinal extent of the implant does not necessarily coincide exactly with the median plane of the secondary embryonic primordium, nor is it necessarily parallel to it; it may form an acute angle with it. This fact would be surprising if the longitudinal stretching of the implant were attributed exclusively to forces residing in it, and if it were assumed at the same time that the implant alone fixes the direction of the determination emanating from it. Under these premises the implant would be expected to stretch exactly in its own sagittal plane and then to supplement itself anteriorly and laterally from adjacent material. It would then be expected to lie exactly in the median plane or at least sagittally in the induced axial organs. The deviation from such a position should probably be attributed to an influence of the host embryo. Either the elongation of the implant is influenced by the cell shifts of the environment, in which event it would then be the resultant of inherent tendencies and extrinsic forces, or the determination itself could be diverted by an inner structure of the host embryo.

These considerations suggest the experiment of destroying the suspected structure of the organizer to test whether the latter can then still have a determinative effect. For instance, a piece of the upper blastoporal lip would have to be crushed, and the attempt would have to be made to place it between the two germ layers of the gastrula by introducing it into the blastocoele of the blastula.

Obviously, the parts of the upper blastoporal lip possess a definite structure by virtue of which they invaginate in a definite direction and perhaps also release stimuli that cause the more indifferent parts to differentiate further in a specific manner. It is irrelevant whether these parts are normally adjacent to the blastoporal lip or brought in contact with it by the experiment. These indifferent parts may also have a directional structure of their own; however this is by no means sufficiently fixed to abolish the influence of the organizer or even to modify it decisively. Depending on the orientation of the implant in the deeper layer of the host embryo, the direction in which its determinative influence pervades the host tissue will differ. For instance, it will pass through the ectoderm in a direction oblique to that of the primary neural plate in cases where the secondary neural plate later forms a more or less acute angle with the primary plate. Whether determination within the induced neural plate, and in the primary as well as the secondary one, is initiated at the posterior or anterior end; that is, whether it progresses cephalad or caudad, as von Ubisch (1923) believes, or whether the entire ectoderm area underlain by organizer is sumultaneously affected cannot yet be decided by definite arguments. It may suffice for now to refer to the noteworthy discussions by von Ubisch.

The *size* of the secondary embryonic anlage may depend on several circumstances. The thought immediately comes to mind that it increases with the size of the implant. In addition, its origin, that is, its prospective significance may be of influence and, in this connection, its shape too. It could make a difference whether the implant is short and wide, or long and narrow. Furthermore, the site of implantation could be of importance; and also the age of the implant, either in itself or in relation to the host embryo. These considerations suggest numerous experiments that are feasible; they promise much further insight, quite apart from the surprises on which one can always count from such experiments. One very important factor will be pointed out shortly.

The *completeness* of the secondary embryonic primordium may depend on factors similar to those that influence its size. Again, either the conditions in the host embryo or those in the organizer could be of primary importance. With respect to the first alternative, there come to mind not only the instances of a very obvious interference of the primordia, where the development of the secondary primordium is impeded by the precocious encounter of its anterior end with that of the primary primordium and by its subsequent fusion with it. It could also be that, despite an apparent independence of the secondary primordium, the completeness of its formation depends on the primary primordium; or, more precisely, the primary organization center could co-determine the mode of action of the implanted secondary center. In this respect, it is noteworthy, for instance, that in experiment 1922, 132 (Fig. 21, p. 165), the two otic vesicles of the secondary primordium are at almost exactly the same level as the primary otocysts, and that the secondary neural tube ends there, blindly. The reason for this could be that the primary organization center caused the ectoderm at this level to form the respective sections of the neural tube and the otocysts. And the reason for the absence of the anterior portion of the secondary neural tube and the optic vesicles could be that the secondary primordium did not extend to the level of the optic vesicles of the primary one. Although, according to this version, the primary organization center would, in the final analysis, also be responsible for the degree of completeness of the secondary primordium, the other assumption could also be correct, namely that the defect is to be traced back to deficiency in the implanted organizer. The latter could have been deficient in certain parts of the organization center which would be necessary for the induction of anterior neural plate with eye primordia.

Quite similar considerations had been made previously in the discussion of peculiar defects in duplications that originate after a somewhat oblique constriction in early developmental stages (cf. Spemann 1918, pp. 534-536). The neural tube of the deficient anterior end can be so seriously defective that it ends blindly at the level of the otocysts, without widening, exactly like the neural tube of the secondary primordium of the experiment just discussed. It is remarkable that here again the four otocysts of the two heads are at the same level. The same possibilities, in principle, were considered as an explanation: the new method [i.e. of heteroplastic transplantation] will perhaps permit an exact decision between these possibilities.

Interferences between the two organization centers, the primary one and the implanted secondary one, are complications that should be avoided for the time being, as far as possible. Once the analysis has progressed, valuable information concerning the finer details of the mode of action of the centers can be expected of them.

Of particular theoretical importance is the question of whether the two embryonic primordia, apart from visible interference, *mutually influence,* or more precisely, limit each other's size. Simple experimental facts show that this is entirely within the realm of possibility. One could have assumed from the beginning that the presumptive neural plate is already determined, in sharp outline, in the ectoderm of the beginning gastrula. This, however, is ruled out by its interchangeability with presumptive epidermis. Then, it could be the size of the organization center which determines the size of the neural plate by the magnitude of its effect. But this is also refuted by the fact that we can remove the ventral half of the embryo without disturbing the organization center and then the size of the neural plate is also reduced to such a degree that it maintains approximately its normal proportion to the reduced whole (Ruud-Spemann, 1923, p. 102 ff). Therefore there must be some retroaction of the whole on the part. We could imagine, for instance, that different primordia require a certain specific degree of saturation which is naturally reached earlier in an embryo of reduced size than in a normal embryo. If something of this sort actually occurs, then we should expect a secondary primordium to exert an inhibitory effect on the first. To test these relationships, more precise measurements would be necessary; these will be tedious but rewarding.

The possibilities that have been discussed presuppose partly one and partly the other of the two basic concepts concerning the mode of induction. It is therefore necessary to find out whether facts are already available to permit a decision in one direction or the other, and to discuss the type of experiments that would have to be designed to bring to light such facts.

It will not be easy to decide by unequivocal experiment whether the process of invagination itself, as the first assumption holds, can create an over-all situation which guides further development in a certain direction. We could try to find out whether passive shifting [of presumptive endo-mesoderm] under the surface has the same effect as active invagination. This could be investigated by implanting endo-mesoderm of a very early gastrula under the ectoderm of another embryo and then observing whether it can produce there the same effect as the endo-mesoderm of a completed gastrula that has already gone through the process of invagination. However, even if the results were clearly positive, the main problem, i.e. the harmonious patterning subsequent to gastrulation, would not be brought much closer to its solution.

As to the other assumption mentioned above, which implies that the implant not only invaginates but also differentiates further by virtue of its inherent development tendencies, a qualifying remark should be made at this time. The possibility was present from the beginning that the implanted piece undergoes pure self-differentiation and develops into exactly the same parts which it would have formed at the place where it came from, and that to form a complete whole it appropriates from the indifferent surroundings the parts that were missing. However, such complete self-differentiation of the organizer almost certainly does not occur, because the implant would then have been too large for the smaller secondary primordium. Insofar as it adapts itself harmoniously to the secondary primordium, its material has been disposed differently than in normal development.

The results of W. Vogt (1922) also argue perhaps against its complete self-differentiation. He found that a piece from the neighborhood of the blastopore becomes ectoderm or endo-mesoderm, depending on whether it remains outside or invaginates inside during the process of gastrulation. The most recent experiments of O. Mangold (1922 and 1923) have shown the same very clearly for the indifferent embryonic areas (i.e. presumptive ectoderm); the experiments of W. Vogt extend this result [namely, lack of rigid self-determination] to the parts near the blastopore.

But complete self-differentiation does not seem to be necessary for the implant to enable it to exert an inducing influence beyond the stimulus for gastrulation. Definitely directed inherent developmental tendency and capacity for regulation are not mutually exclusive. Clarification of this point could be achieved by experiments that would test the effects of different regions of the organization center. If, for instance, a piece taken from its lateral margin should be found later to occupy a lateral position in the embryonic primordium induced by it, then it could be concluded that it was already determined as lateral at the moment of implantation, and that it retained this characteristic after implantation and influenced its surroundings correspondingly. Or, if the degree of completeness of the secondary embryonic primordium should differ according to the exact place of origin of the grafted organizer, this would also indicate differences within the organization center that could hardly have been transmitted to the induced embryonic primordium by stimulation of gastrulation alone.

This much at least is probable: that the possibility exists of a determining effect progressing from cell to cell, not only as suggested by the first assumption, during the period shortly after implantation, when the assumption of an effect on the environment can hardly be escaped, but also during later developmental stages. Among the most recent experiments of O. Mangold (1922, 1923) already mentioned several times, there are some whose continuation could contribute to a decision between the questionable points. If presumptive epidermis, after implantation into the zone of invagination of a beginning gastrula, comes to lie within the somite region, it participates in somite formation. It is not possible to decide when and how the determination of these indifferent cells took place. They could have acquired the characteristics of somites soon after implantation into the upper blastoporal lip, and, on the basis of this first determination, could have participated in all the later destinies of their surroundings. However, this explanation meets with difficulties in the cases where the implant later does not seem to fit smoothly into its environment but forms supernumerary structures. This gives the direct impression that the determining influence emanated from the somite and determined the adjacent indifferent tissue in the same direction. This suggests a new experiment, the implantation of indifferent tissue, such as presumptive epidermis of the beginning gastrula, into an older embryo that has completed gastrulation, so that it reaches its destination without having been part of the blastopore lip. Moreover, the same situation would have prevailed in those cases in which the presumptive epidermis was implanted in the yolk plug, and then moved first into the floor of the archenteron, apparently shifting secondarily into the somite region where it was subjected to determination to form somites (O. Mangold, 1923, p. 258).

If wishful thinking were permissible in questions of research, then we might hope in this case that the second of the previously discussed assumptions would prove to be the correct one. For, if induction should be limited to a stimulus for gastrulation, then the problem of the harmonious equipotential system, which had just seemed to become accessible to experimental analysis, would right from the start confront us again in all its inaccessibility.

Concerning the *means* of the determinative influence, no factual clues are yet available. The experiment proposed above (implantation between the germ layers of crushed organizer that is thus deprived of its structure) could lead us further into this subject.

We would have assumed that the species whose embryos can interact with each other should not be too widely separated in their taxonomic relationship. *Triton cristatus, taeniatus,* and *alpestris,* between which mutual induction is feasible, belong at least to the same genus. However, surprises of great importance seem to be in prospect; Dr. Geinitz in our laboratory has just very recently succeeded (May, 1923) in inducing embryonic primordia in *Triton* by organizers of *Bombinator* and *Rana.* Thus he brought anurans and urodeles into determinative interaction. With this discovery, experimental ideas which seemed to be more dreams than plans (Spemann, 1921, p. 567) have passed into the realm of feasibility.

5. *The organizer and the organizing center.* The concept of the organization center is based on the idea that determination proceeds from cell to cell in the embryo. Such an assumption suggests itself whenever differentiation, that is, the visible consequence of determination, does not start in all parts simultaneously but, beginning at one place, progresses thence in a definite direction. However, pure observation is by

no means sufficient evidence of progressing determination. We might be dealing merely with a chronological sequence in the absence of causal relationship. One way of testing this consists in the interruption of spatial continuity. If such separation does not result in a disturbance, that is, if development that had started on one side of a separating transection continued on the other side, then differentiation in the latter would have been independent, at least from the moment of severance.

A clear example of such a situation in the field of amphibian development is the progressive formation of the blastopore in gastrulation. This begins medially with the formation of the upper blastopore lip; it progresses from there to both sides, and finally reaches the median plane again when the circle is closed at the lower blastopore lip. The observer, quite naturally, gets the impression that the part that is in the process of invagination always draws the adjacent cells of the marginal zone with it. However, if the dorsal half of the embryo including the upper blastopore lip is removed, this does not prevent the formation of the lateral and ventral blastoporal lips, which is not even perceptibly retarded. This holds not only for frontal bisection at the beginning of gastrulation, when determination possibly emanating from the upper lip might already have transgressed the line of transection, but it holds also after frontal ligation in the two-cell stage. Failure of the ventral half to gastrulate would still not have been stringent proof for progressive determination. The fact that gastrulation does occur excludes at least the necessity of assuming such a causal relation.

Braus (1906) followed the same method, in principle, when he analyzed the skeletal development of the pectoral fin of elasmobranch embryos. It is known that the first primordium of fins is a skin fold into which grow muscle buds from the myotomes of the trunk. However, the skeletal rods of the fin differentiate from the mesoderm which fills the skin fold; the rods in the middle form first, then differentiation progresses craniad and caudad. If the tissue that is still indifferent is separated by a cut from the skeletal rods that are already in the process of differentiation, then histological differentiation of pre-cartilage and cartilage proceeds in the former, but organization into separate skeletal rods does not take place. The spatial and temporal progression of this patterning apparently depends on determination that progresses into the indifferent tissue.

We can call this difference in the degree of differentiation at a given moment a differentiation gradient, as does von Ubisch (1923). A gradient is an obvious presupposition for progressive differentiation, although the latter is not a necessary consequence of the former.

This conception of progressive determination leads of necessity back to the conception that there are points in the developing embryo from

which determination emanates. It is therefore not surprising to find
that this idea has been advocated before. For instance, several sentences
in the paper of Boveri on the polarity of the sea urchin egg (1901) hint
at an idea akin to ours. Boveri considers the possibility (*op. cit.,* p. 167)
that in the sea urchin embryo "every region of the blastula is prepared
to form mesoderm or to invaginate and the restriction to one point is
effected by the fact that at this point these processes are more readily
initiated than at all other points. Once differentiation has started here,
then from this point all other regions are determined for their fate
by a process of regulation. The existence of such a preferential region
is explained by the demonstrable differences in the properties of the
cytoplasm in the different regions of the egg." These sentences are
qualified later (*op. cit.,* p. 170) in the sense "that beyond a certain zone
in the animal region of the egg, the cytoplasmic quality which is necessary for gastrulation is not represented at all, or at least not in sufficient
quantity."

Shortly thereafter a similar possibility was considered for the *Triton*
embryo (Spemann, 1903, p. 606).

The facts that were known earlier sufficed only to establish the concept of a starting point for differentiation, but not to demonstrate the
real existence of such centers. To obtain this evidence, it is not enough
to separate the region to be tested, which is believed to be such a center,
from its potential field of activity. It must be brought into contact with
other parts, normally foreign to it, on which it can demonstrate its
capacities. This has apparently been done for the first time in the
embryonic transplantations at the gastrula stage. In these experiments
the organization center was left in its normal position, and indifferent
material was presented to it, so to speak, for further elaboration. A much
more penetrating analysis is made feasible by the transplantation of the
organization center itself, and of its parts, the organizers. The present
investigation makes a first beginning of this analysis. The new possibilities now opened up, particularly in combinations with heteroplastic
transplantation, are not yet foreseeable. Several possible approaches to
further advances have been indicated in the preceding pages.

For the moment, it is of subordinate significance whether the concepts of organizer and organization center will still prove to be useful
when the analysis has advanced further, or whether they are to be replaced by other terms which would be more exact. We can already state
that the concept of the organizer is the fundamental one, and that the
term organization "center" shall be used only to designate the embryonic area in which the organizers are assembled at a given stage,
but *not* to designate a center from which development is being directed.
The designation "organizer" (rather than, perhaps, "determiner") is supposed to express the idea that the effect emanating from these pref-

erential regions is not only determinative in a definite restricted direction, but that it possesses all those enigmatic peculiarities which are known to us only from living organisms.

IV. SUMMARY OF RESULTS

A piece taken from the upper blastopore lip of a gastrulating amphibian embryo exerts an organizing effect on its environment in such a way that, following its transplantation to an indifferent region of another embryo, it there causes the formation of a secondary embryo. Such a piece can therefore be designated as an organizer.

If the organizer is implanted within the normal zone of invagination, then it participates in the gastrulation of the host embryo and, afterwards, shares the blastopore with it; if transplanted outside the zone of invagination, it invaginates autonomously. In this case, part of it may remain on the surface and there participate in the formation of the ectoderm and, specifically, of the neural plate; or it may move altogether into the interior and become endo-mesoderm entirely. In this event it is likely that cells of the host embryo can also be invaginated along with the transplant. Indeed, this might be considered already as a determinative effect of the implant on its environment.

In the host embryo, a secondary embryo originates in connection with the implant; it can show different degrees of differentiation. This depends, in part, on whether it interferes with the primary axial organs, or whether it remains completely independent. In one case in the latter category, a neural tube without brain and eyes, but with otic vesicles, and also notochord, somites, and pronephric ducts developed.

These secondary embryonic primordia are always of mixed origin; they are formed partly of cells of the implant and partly of cells of the host embryo. If, in the experiments under discussion, an organizer of another species is used for induction, then the chimeric composition can be established with certainty and great accuracy. It was demonstrated for most organs, for neural tube, somites, and even for the notochord.

There can be no doubt but that these secondary embryonic primordia have somehow been induced by the organizer; but it cannot yet be decided in what manner this occurs and, above all, when and in what way. The inductive effect could be limited to a stimulation to gastrulation, whereupon all else would follow, as in normal development. In this event, the different parts of the secondary zone of gastrulation would be subjected to the determination without regard to their origin. But the induction by the implant could also continue beyond the stage of gastrulation. In this case, the organizer, by virtue of its intrinsic developmental tendencies, would essentially continue its development along the course which it had already started and it would supplement itself from the adjacent indifferent material. This might also hold for the determination of the neural plate; but it is more likely that the latter is determined by the underlying endo-mesoderm. But the development of the implant could not be pure self-differentiation; otherwise it could not have been harmoniously integrated with the secondary embryonic primordium which is smaller than the primary primordium. Apparently the inducing part, while in action, was subjected to a counter-action by the induced part. Such reciprocal interactions may play a large role, in general, in the development of harmonious equipotential systems.

V. REFERENCES

BOVERI, TH., Über die Polarität des Seeigeleies. Verhandl. d. Phys.-Med. Ges. zu Würzburg. N. F. Bd. 34. 1901.

BRAUS, H., Ist die Bildung des Skelettes von den Muskelanlagen abhängig? Morphol. Jarhb. Bd. 35, S. 38 bis 110. 1906.

LEWIS, W. H., Transplantation of the lips of the blastopore in *Rana palustris*. Americ. Journ. of Anat. Vol. 7. S. 137-143. 1907.

MANGOLD, O., Transplantationsversuche zur Ermittelung der Eigenart der Keimblätter. Verhandl. d. dtsch. zool. Ges. Bd. 27, S. 51-52. 1922.

————, Transplantationsversuche zur Frage der Spezifität und Bildung der Keimblätter bei *Triton*. Arch. f. mikrosk. Anat. u. Entwicklungsmech. Bd. 100. S. 198-301. 1923.

RUUD, G. AND SPEMANN, H., Die Entwicklung isolierter dorsaler und lateraler Gastrulahälften von *Triton taeniatus* und *alpestris,* ihre Regulation und Postgeneration. Arch. f. Entwicklungsmech. d. Organismen. Bd. 52, S. 95-165. 1923.

SPEMANN, H., Über die Determination der ersten Organanlagen des Amphibienembryo I-IV. Ibid. Bd. 43, S. 448-555. 1918.

————, Mikrochirurgische Operationstechnik. *Abderhaldens* Handb. d. biol. Arbeitsmethoden, 2. Aufl., S. 1-30. 1920.

————, Über die Erzeugung tierischer Chimären durch heteroplastische embryonale Transplantation zwischen *Triton cristatus* und *Triton taeniatus*. Arch. f. Entwicklungsmech. d. Organismen Bd. 48, S. 533-570. 1921.

v. UBISCH, L., Das Differenzierungsgefälle des Amphibienkörpers und seine Auswirkungen. Ibid. Bd. 52, S. 641-670. 1923.

VOGT, W., Die Einrollung und Streckung der Urmundlippen bei *Triton* nach Versuchen mit einer neuen Methode embryonaler Transplantation. Verhandl. d. dtsch, zool. Ges. Bd. 27, S. 49-51. 1922.

1939

Tissue Affinity, A Means of Embryonic Morphogenesis

by JOHANNES HOLTFRETER

*from the Zoological Institute
of the University of Munich*

Holtfreter, Johannes. 1939. Gewebeaffinität, ein Mittel der embryonalen Formbildung. Archiv für experimentelle Zellforschung, Vol. 23, pp. 169-209. Original translation by Konrad Keck, amended by Professor Holtfreter. Printed by permission of the author and Gustav Fischer Verlag.

When Wilhelm Roux carried out the studies so important in transforming embryology from a descriptive to an experimental and analytical science, he was performing his work at a time when experimentation was becoming increasingly important in other fields of biology also. During the 1880's experimental investigations in physiology were burgeoning with particular vigor. Among the experimental studies most important in transforming physiological outlooks were those on tropisms and taxes.

Studies on tropisms influenced the development of embryological concepts in a number of ways (see Oppenheimer in Analysis of Development, edited by B. H. Willier, et al., W. B. Saunders Co., Philadelphia, 1955, p. 19). These were of particular interest to Roux, who himself published two papers on the behavior of embryonic cells attempting to analyze their relationships to one another in terms of tropisms and taxes.

Roux's own experiments in this area—as in a number of others—were not very conclusive. It was not until Johannes Holtfreter (1901-   ) performed the experiments reported in the paper reproduced here that the attractions and affinities (and their opposites) between embryonic cells were again seriously reconsidered.

Holtfreter has been one of the most original and productive of the investigators of amphibian development. In the early period of investigation of amphibian embryogenesis he confirmed, by various methods, including the production of exogastrulae, Spemann's concept that contact between archenteron roof and overlying epidermis is a necessary condition for the differentiation of nerve tissue. After it became apparent that non-living organizer could act as an inducer, Holtfreter demonstrated that tissues removed from members of many phyla from tapeworm to man could act as inducing agents; this investigation has borne its fruits in the work of Yamada and others who are currently fractionating mammalian organs in an attempt to pinpoint chemically the effective molecules. After Barth (1941) performed experiments in vitro which suggested that under some conditions prospective epidermis might, after all, differentiate nerve tissue in the absence of chorda-mesoderm, Holtfreter (1944, 1945) extended this analysis in such a way as to raise serious doubts as to whether the transmission of a particular substance from inducer to induced could fully explain the induction of nerve tissue. By simply altering the pH of the medium in which the cells were developing, he could influence the direction of differentiation of prospective epidermis or prospective nervous system. He believed that the medium acts on the surface coat of the egg, and in other investigations he pointed out the significance of the surface coat in directing some of the movements of the cells during migration,

and he emphasized its importance as an integrative agent during develop-
ment.

These represent only a few of his investigations. One of the most
important contributions was an exhaustive description of the differentia-
tion of all the various parts of the young amphibian gastrula in vitro
(1938). The key to his success in studying the development of isolated parts
of the gastrula lay in his adaptation of the method of tissue culture and
to the fact that he devised a satisfactory salt solution which would permit
the normal differentiation of the isolated cells.

These techniques also permitted him to study such recombinations of
cells either of gastrulae or neurulae isolated in vitro as are described
in the paper reproduced here. Further, more exhaustive studies of a similar
nature on cells of the neurula were reported by Townes and Holtfreter in
1955. Comparable experimental dissociation of embryonic cells and study
of their modes of reaggregation is now being carried out on many other
kinds of embryonic material, an area in which the focus of interest and
emphasis centers on the specific properties of interacting cells. Among the
new discoveries are (a) type specific self-sorting of mixed cell populations
(Moscona), (b) specificity of interaction between recombined tissue com-
ponents after isolation from an organ rudiment, e.g., epithelial and
mesenchymal components of a salivary gland of a mouse embryo (Grob-
stein), and (c) self-organization of cells of a functional embryonic organ
(kidney, liver) after isolation and random recombination in the reconsti-
tution of the same type of organ once again, i.e., an organ that is mor-
phologically well organized (Weiss and Taylor). These findings in a
difficult field of endeavor are of particular interest at a time when im-
munological concepts are being called upon in the explanation of develop-
mental phenomena. Further, they are of great importance to the under-
standing of the means by which the cells of the developing organism
establish and maintain a harmony of organization.

It should be remarked here that early in the 1900's H. V. Wilson
performed noteworthy experiments in which dissociated cells of sponges
and other invertebrates reassembled to reconstitute whole organisms. Al-
though these experiments were masterly in execution they failed, because
performed too soon, to excite the imagination of embryologists as did
Holtfreter's later but not dissimilar experiments on amphibian embryos.

TISSUE AFFINITY, A MEANS OF EMBRYONIC MORPHOGENESIS

A systematic organizing process, heredity-bound, is recapitulated each
time an individual develops. By way of materializing it, new and more
specialized agencies come into action successively to bring about new
arrangements and differentiations, an event remindful of the construc-
tion of a building. These agencies obey their own rules, despite their

interdependence and common subordination to the unitarian building plan. Little is known about their nature, but we already know something about their specific accomplishments and their preferred pathways, and we have learned of how, in the course of time, they enhance, supplement, and succeed one another in turn.

Research in developmental physiology since its initiation and orientation by W. Roux has tried to analyze a good number of such agencies, principles or "means" that are at the basis of the formative processes in developing organisms. It remains to be seen whether or not these principles occupy ranks equivalent to each other, and whether an artificial distinction between them will stand up at all to our progressing knowledge. In practice, however, the procedure of separate analyses has proven its value. It has perhaps been unavoidable to deal with the developmental principles of growth, physiological and morphological differentiation, induction, regulation and other phenomena that are manifested in space and time, as though each pursued its own ends. The elucidation of their physico-chemical nature will warrant our interest only after we have sufficiently explored their biological performances. Referring back to the above metaphor: it is not so much the characterization of the laborers but the specifications pertaining to their work, the requirements and rules that they follow while erecting the building, that call for our immediate attention.

The pioneering investigators of developmental physiology were often guided intuitively by considerations of analogy, searching in their own special field for phenomena already known in analogous form in other fields, thus attempting to explain biological phenomena by comparing them with similar ones observed in inorganic systems. Since science depends much on comparing, the heuristic value of such perspectives should not be underestimated. The pioneers were faced by an abundance of unsolved problems. They should not be blamed for the scantiness of their information in this new field, even though they may have been sometimes overconfident in believing that they could explain complicated life processes by pointing glibly to relatively simple processes in non-living matter. After all, their optimistic materialism has turned out to be more fruitful for research than the resigned attitude of a Driesch who in view of the complexity of developmental events felt compelled to renounce causal analysis *a priori*.

In this era of model experiments, that was epitomized by the artificial cell of Pfeffer and the experiments of Bütschli, Rhumbler and others who attempted to imitate protoplasm, investigators were searching in particular for processes of embryonic development comprehensible in rather crude mechanical terms. Even long before, His (1874), in his treatise on the development of the chick, tried to explain the fundamental events in morphogenesis by "unequal growth" of elastic layers of tissue, although he himself performed no experiments on the live embryo. Organ-forming embryonic regions, endowed with specific rates of growth, represented his point of departure. Forces of pushing, pulling and stretching, graded in space and in time, were considered to play an essential role as means of morphogenesis. To illuminate his concepts, His referred to models of clay, paper, or rubber.

Götte (1875) also considered "growth pressure" to be one of the most important morphogenetic factors. It was not until much later that the capacity for autonomous specific form changes and movements was ascribed to the different cells and primordia (Gurwitsch, Rhumbler, Morgan and others). But it remained for Roux (1894, 1896) to establish a sound foundation for these views by demonstrating such capacities in isolated embryonic amphibian cells. Difficulties arose however in deducing, from observations of the dynamic behavior of isolated cells, rules that would help to explain the formative processes of normal development. Let us discuss these experiments in some greater detail and, proceeding from them, pass on to our own experiments.

I. ISOLATION EXPERIMENTS ON EMBRYONIC CELLS

Even before he started his experiments Roux appears to have had the idea that forces of attraction and repulsion prevail between cells, and that these forces cause groups of the same cell type to aggregate and groups of different cell types to separate during the course of development. He seemed thereby to have come across the track of a morphogenetic factor additional to the growth processes already known, a factor that promised to explain certain processes of gastrulation, germ layer segregation, and organ formation. Evidently, in chemistry, analogous forces were engaged in the synthesis and the degradation of complex compounds; and attraction phenomena of a similar kind, interpreted as chemotaxis, had already been recognized as being involved in bringing the gametes together (Pfeffer, 1873).

The results of experiments carried out with embryonic frog cells, isolated in an artificial medium, seemed to validate this concept. Roux studied the changes in form and position of the ameboid cells; he observed that they would either associate in groups and form spherical aggregates or, in other instances, would migrate away and isolate themselves. It appeared that when the wandering cells approached each other, their random movements became directed. Roux believed that mutual attraction rather than chance movements brought such cells together. He therefore spoke of a positive and negative "cytotropism," which he thought to be operating through the action of cell-specific chemical stimulants which diffuse into the environment in a concentration gradient.

Roux failed to give real evidence for the required elective character of the observed aggregations and separations of the cultured cells. It was even questionable whether the cell movements occurring in the "indifferent" culture media used (chicken egg-white; dilute NaCl solution) were to be regarded as normal and not as atypical and due to adverse properties of the medium.

Even though his evidence was by no means convincing, and only little similarity existed between the cellular movements observed in cell cultures and the formative processes of normal development, Roux advanced the dictum of an elective capacity of self-ordering of embryonic cells. In his opinion the embryo has "the tendency to arrange its cells appropriately according to their qualities, and to rearrange them correspondingly after their qualities have changed during development."

Born (1897) concurred with Roux's ideas on the basis of his results obtained in fusion experiments on parts of amphibian embryos. He concludes that "cells derived from the same germ layer unite to form continuous sheets, whereas cells from different germ layers rather tend to separate from each other" (p. 586). He thought the elective behavior was based respectively upon a mutual active seeking out and separation of the primordial parts. In support of this view, Born pointed out that homologous organ fragments that did not fit together at the time of experimental combination would later heal together into a morphologically harmonious and well-proportioned organ.

In view of the numerous unknown factors involved in such fusion experiments with half-embryos the evidence presented by Born does not appear to be very conclusive. As a matter of fact, in none of the innumerable transplantation experiments which have since been performed on amphibian embryos has anybody found reliable proof of an elective cytotropism.

The experiments of Roux were taken up, after a considerable lapse of time, by Vogt (1913), Voigtländer (1932), and Kuhl (1937). None of these authors was able to find evidence for cytotactically controlled, and still less for electively directed movements of the isolated cells. On the contrary, careful observation of individual cells, especially with the help of time-lapse movies (Kuhl), showed that the direction of migrations was random. Ectodermal cells were found to combine with each other just as well as with cells from other germ layers; they even associated with cells taken from different embryonic stages and from different species. It is interesting to note that experiments involving chemical or electrical stimuli gave likewise negative results with the yolky amphibian cells (Kuhl), although similar experiments performed with ameboid Protozoa and with migratory spleen cells in culture produced positive responses (Kathodotropismus, Péterfi and Williams 1934). In other words, none of the many stimuli tested could bring about directiveness of locomotion among the erratically creeping cells.

Consequently the experiments of Roux that originally seemed so promising must be considered to have been methodologically unsuited for their intended purpose. The dynamic behavior of isolated embryonic cells offered no explanation for the directed cell movements occurring during normal development.

Voigtländer and Kuhl went even further and expressed their doubt as to whether the protoplasmic movements, as observed in the culture medium, can be considered normal vital phenomena. From my own experience I would maintain a less sceptical attitude since I have often observed identical ameboid movements in media that permit the culture of such explants for several weeks and which, therefore, can hardly be considered damaging to cells. We think that simply the release of a cell from its normal tissue environment causes it to move restlessly about and to suffer eventually an early death, as was already observed by A. Fischer (1923) and others on isolated cells of fibroblast cultures. If such cells, however, join in time a cell mass of a certain size, they will readily survive the period of solitary migration.

Thus the only result of these experiments valuable for developmental physiology is the finding that amphibian cells—especially from pregastrula stages—roam around restlessly after their dislocation or isolation, until they make contact with a larger group of cells. They then combine with the group to form an aggregate with a minimal, hence spherical, surface. No elective distinction is made between different kinds of cells during this process. But this thigmotaxis is elective insofar as a non-living substrate does not exert the same quieting effect on the ameboid cells as does an organic tissue association. Even though cytotropism, effective at a distance, does not occur, we may go along with Roux in speaking of "Zytarme" [from the Greek meaning cell-junction], meaning a mutual attraction of the living cells *after* they have established contact with one another. This would lead to an intimate but non-elective aggregation. The explanatory value of this phenomenon, however, has its limitations exactly where the isolation experiment was supposed to help, namely, in the analytical interpretation of the directed formative movements beginning at the period of gastrulation.

It is from this junction that our new experiments take their departure. They have shown that there was some truth in Roux's intuitive concepts, even though his and Born's experimental approach did not permit any pertinent conclusions to be drawn. We may list three main reasons to account for the fact that the isolation experiments of Roux and his successors gave such meager results:

1) No strict distinction was made with respect to the origin of the material. Cells were isolated indiscriminately from pre- as well as post-

gastrula stages. It could have been expected, however, that the dynamic response of the cells varies markedly with the stage of the donor embryos.

2) The period of observation was too short (10 to 20 hours). In the normal embryo morphogenetic processes need more time to become clearly recognizable. This was all the more to be expected under the experimental culture conditions.

3) Even during normal development it is not individual cells but whole groups of them—not clearly demarcated from one another—that change their relative positions with kneading movements. In order to detect directed movements, larger cell complexes of homogeneous or mixed composition should have been studied rather than individual cells.

This is what we have done in a variety of experiments on material from embryos of several urodele and anuran species. From the results of these experiments we shall select in a summarizing manner only those that are relevant to the problem of cytotropism. More detailed reports on this material will appear soon in Roux' Archiv. In those reports as well as in some of our earlier papers (1934, 1938a, b) photomicrographs of sectioned material are given as documentation for those processes that we shall illustrate here with slightly schematic drawings.

II. ISOLATION AND RECOMBINATION EXPERIMENTS ON GASTRULA MATERIAL

We too shall begin our isolation experiments with pregastrula stages of amphibian embryos, such as the late blastula; we shall note carefully the origin of the material and follow the fate of the isolated tissue over several days. The cultures are maintained in dilute Ringer's or Tyrode's solution in glass dishes. Let us first observe the behavior of pure endodermal material.

(a) Isolation of pure endoderm. Endoderm which has been excised from the vegetal floor of a blastula or early gastrula consists of large yolky cells which soon increase their surfaces of contact with each other. Within one hour the irregular aggregate becomes a smooth-walled, solid sphere consisting of polyhedrally arranged cells. Within the next 24 hours—sometimes later—no apparent change occurs. If during this time two endodermal spheres are placed in apposition, they will exhibit the same tendency for union that was observed earlier with individual cells (Fig. 1b). The two spheres first join to form a double structure (Fig. 1c) which after approximately one day rounds up to assume the shape of a single sphere (Fig. 1d).

This demonstrates that the ameboid sliding motions of such endoderm cells are maintained for quite some time, and that during this period the cell aggregates retain the capacity for morphological regulation. A similar reconstitution into a spherical shape also takes place when

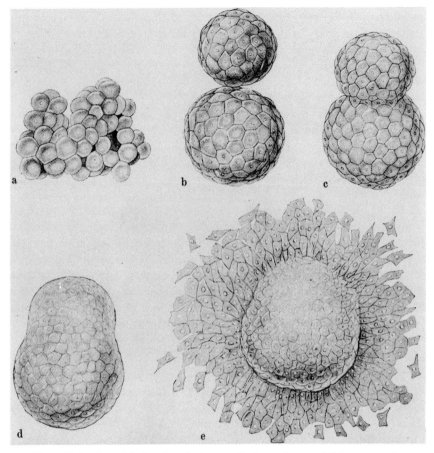

Fig. 1 Behavior of isolated endoderm cells from the amphibian gastrula.
(a) The cells shortly after isolation; (b) two aggregates rounded into
spheres are placed adjacent to one another; (c) (d) fusion of the two
aggregates to form a single sphere; (e) flattening of the sphere and
spreading out of the flattened cells.

several spheres are combined, or when a sphere is divided into two
halves.

Approximately 20 hours after isolation, a fundamental change
takes place in the dynamic behavior of the endoderm cells. Up until
then the isolated cells had been nearly spherical in shape, with
conical pseudopodia extruding from all sides. When contacting each
other the cells tended to become closely associated and thus gave rise
to an aggregate with minimum surface. Now the whole mass begins to
flatten out shield-like on the bottom of the glass dish, its periphery
spreading out like a membrane. Instead of the earlier rounding up, there
now appears the tendency in each individual cell, and hence in the

whole mass, to increase their surfaces (Fig. 1e). The spreading proceeds radially without favoring any particular axis. Some cells may isolate themselves at the periphery and migrate out a short distance. Within the flattened and two-dimensional cells the centrally located nucleus becomes visible as a clear space among the yolk platelets. Instead of the former lobe-shaped pseudopodia that freely protrude from the cell surface, pointed and occasionally branched processes are now extended over the glass surface. The mode of locomotion changes from an ameboid rolling to a slow sliding motion resembling that of the cells in conventional tissue cultures.

We are obviously dealing here with an autonomous process since in this isolate neither heterologous neighboring tissue nor any other environmental factors are present which could be responsible for the dynamic conversion of the endodermal mass. Endogenous factors must have caused the change in surface tension of these cells. The inorganic substrate is no longer avoided but it is, on the contrary, actively sought out. Even though the cells are generally retained within the peripheral sheet their migratory tendency may none the less lead to their individual self-isolation. The "Zytarme," in Roux's terminology, seems to have changed over to "Zytochorismus," a mutual repulsion [from the Greek meaning cell-separation]. In the present case this change occurs within a homogeneous mass of cells and not, as should have been expected from the concepts of Roux and Born, between cells of different quality. But upon closer examination the term "Zytochorismus" does not quite fit the present situation. It is not so much a mutual repulsion between cells but a tendency to autonomous migration and spreading that has led to the isolation of individual elements, since the cells can return to the central mass as easily as they separated from it. Therefore the dynamic behavior of the cells with respect to each other might rather be designated as indifferent. The original association, once it has been established, is merely tolerated. At any rate, a very firm mutual attraction can no longer be postulated to exist because then the observed self-isolation of the cells could not have occurred.

If such isolates of pure endoderm are cultured for a sufficiently long time, i.e., some 15 to 20 days, the peripheral membrane develops into a sheet of intestinal epithelium while the central mass, though remaining compact, nevertheless also assumes the cytological structures of intestinal cells. In view of this attested adequacy of the culture medium it seems justified to assume that the ameboid movements of the free cells observed in this medium may be considered just as vital as the creeping movements of the cells after they became flattened.

The results of these experiments have significance for the explanation of normal development. It was found that the surface spreading takes place at exactly the stage during which, in the intact embryo, the floor of the invaginated trunk endoderm shifts dorsad where the lateral walls fuse to form the closed intestinal tube. The morphogenetic movements of the endoderm in an explant and in the gastrula and neurula are therefore fundamentally of the same nature.

Still another conclusion may be drawn from this and similar experiments. It has been mentioned above that the environment could not have exerted an initiating effect upon the dynamic conversion of the endoderm. Yet we have to assume that the environment does play a role in the orientation of the spreading movements. Whereas the explanted endoderm spreads centrifugally in all directions along the glass surface, certain laterally and dorsally directed movements occur during the normal formation of the intestinal tube (Vogt 1929). In the embryo rearrangement takes place in three dimensions; in culture it is only in the horizontal plane. When, however, the explanted endoderm has been furnished with the core of a tissue substrate, it will glide over this surface and form an envelope of epithelium facing out. Such inverted intestinal vesicles covered by a peripheral epithelium and enclosing a core of connective tissue have been obtained previously in cultures of intestinal fragments of the chick embryo (Maximow 1925, Fischer 1927, Törö 1930 and others).

Thus the gut primordium merely possesses the tendency to spread indiscriminately over a suitable surface. If, within the intact embryo, the movements of the endoderm become oriented in certain directions, this feature must be due to the particular three-dimensional topography of free surfaces over which the cell material is permitted to glide.

(b) Isolation of endoderm and ectoderm combined. This second experiment deals with the study of the behavior of the endoderm in combination with pure ectoderm. In practice this can be done by excising from an early gastrula the mediocaudal region opposite the blastopore containing presumptive ectoderm and the underlying endoderm. In this operation the accidental inclusion of ventral mesoderm should be avoided.

At first the two types of cells are only loosely interconnected (Fig. 2a). The dislocated white endoderm cells form an irregular heap within the cup of the inward curling ectoderm. If the amount of ectoderm is insufficient to enclose all of the endoderm there soon arises the configuration shown in Figure 2b. The ectoderm has proceeded to encase the rounded-up endoderm, acorn-fashion. The two components establish intimate mutual contact indicating that despite the difference of the tissues the principle of "Zytarme" has been operating.

After approximately one and a half days the aggregate begins to change shape (Fig. 2c). The border zone between the two parts becomes constricted and, within another day, it narrows down to a "wasp waist" (Fig. 2d). Gradually all the endoderm flows out of the ectodermal sac;

the connecting bridge becomes more attenuated until finally the two parts are cleanly and completely isolated from each other (Fig. 2e). If the endoderm mass, now almost spherical, makes contact with a suitable substrate, it can, as described above, spread out and differentiate into intestinal epithelium. If, however, it remains floating freely in the medium, no epithelial sheet is formed, and the whole mass gives rise to a structure of non-polarized but cytologically differentiated intestinal

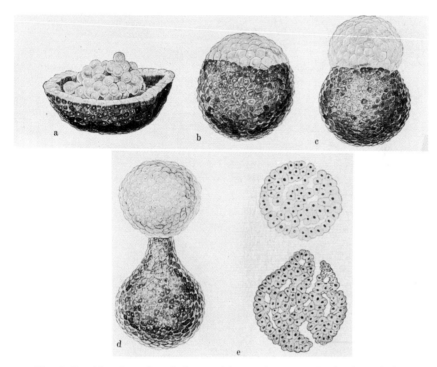

Fig. 2 Combination of endoderm with ectoderm. (a) Beginning of the experiment; (b) the two components have joined together to form a solid sphere; (c) beginning, and (d) almost completed self-isolation of the components. (e) The segregated parts are seen in section to consist of chaotically arranged gut or epidermis cells.

cells, perforated by irregular spaces containing secretion fluid. Isolated pure ectoderm forms a texture very similar to that of pure endoderm (Fig. 2e).

This experiment demonstrates for the first time the process which Roux and his successors tried vainly to find, namely, a definitely active self-separation ("Zytochorismus") of heterologous cell groups that were previously closely associated by "Zytarme." The separation came about neither by differential growth, nor by budding, nor by external push or pull; it was achieved by means of autonomous ameboid shiftings of the cell masses without a significant contribution of growth and cell proliferation. Vogt coined the appropriate term "Gestaltungsbewegungen" (morphogenetic movements) for this type of formative events which are so characteristic of gastrulation.

At first glance the result of the present experiment does not seem to invite further conclusions related to normal development. The rounding off of separate spheres of ectoderm and endoderm appears to be quite atypical. And yet this experiment reveals the existence of tendencies which are probably of great importance for normal development as well. Further experiments have indicated that a whole system of such attraction and repulsion phenomena is operating between various cell types during development and that information on this system will yield valuable information concerning the shiftings and segregations of tissues during organogenesis. Before attempting to relate these findings to normal development let us consider the phenomena themselves in more detail.

It seems advantageous to us to introduce a more fitting term for the forces that are instrumental in these processes of attraction and repulsion. Henceforth we shall apply the term *affinity,* which partly substitutes for the terms of Roux and which may serve as a reminder for the existence of analogous phenomena in chemistry. Affinity may be either positive or negative, it may be graded in its intensity, and may approach the point of neutrality. These gradations may change during development, increasing or decreasing between two cell generations, or they may repeat themselves in cycles. It can hardly be denied that there exists a far-reaching similarity between the phenomena occurring here in tissue associations and the cytotactic relationships between free gametes, such as have been extensively studied under the designation "relative sexuality" by M. Hartmann and his students.

To answer the question as to whether organismic affinity is merely a collective term for a series of subfunctions would require further investigations on an advanced level. Stimulated by the suggestions of Roux and by the experiments with gametes, one feels inclined to relate affinity to the progressively diversified chemodifferentiation of the tissue primordia. Probably the simultaneous interplay of physical forces is equally, if not even more significantly, involved in these phenomena.

(c) Fusion experiments between endodermal and ectodermal isolates. The increasing tendency of endoderm and ectoderm to separate, reported above, can be demonstrated in still other ways. We have mentioned that balls of endoderm may be made to fuse with one another within one or even two days after isolation. In later stages, however, fusion is possible only if the balls are provided with a new wound surface, or if the endoderm is derived from the inside of an early larva. Here a second phenomenon is involved, the arising of a polar property at the outer, nude surface of the peripheral cells; this reduces the ameboid mobility of the cortical layer, and hence its capability of adhesion. We do not wish here to enter any further into the problem of cell polarity, but merely point out that two balls of endoderm placed into contact with each other can exhibit positive affinity as late as two days after isolation, and that these homogeneous aggregates, once fused into a single sphere, never become constricted as do the endoderm-ectoderm composites.

If we now carry out the same combination between endodermal and ectodermal isolates after different intervals of cultivation, we obtain the following results. For example, if in a combination of these two tissues, taken from an early gastrula, the endoderm has been kept in salt solution for one day but the ectoderm is freshly isolated, a complete fusion between them will still take place. But when both isolates are one day old and their outer surfaces brought into contact, no adhesion whatsoever will occur. Only after a new wound surface has been provided will both partners combine though they still will not form a single sphere. The area of fusion will remain still smaller when both tissues are kept isolated for two days and the ectoderm is cut freshly at the site of contact. An isolated piece of ectoderm 3 or 4 days old will not adhere to endoderm, even when the latter is still very young and when some of the outer cells of both partners have been removed.

This experiment shows once more, apart from the problem of polarity which introduces additional complexities here, that in the course of time a negative affinity arises between endoderm and ectoderm. It is manifested by the degree of fusion which the two partners establish when confronted with one another after various periods of time. The shapes of the fused pieces correspond timewise to the constriction phases described above.

It would be feasible to determine by means of additional combinations which of the two cell types plays the more active role. On the basis of the present findings it may already be concluded that although the increasing "antagonism" is mutual, yet it seems to develop earlier in the ectoderm than in the endoderm.

That these phenomena of affinity are quite tissue specific is demonstrated by the following experiment:

(d) Combined isolation of endoderm and prospective connective tissue. We again combine endoderm and ectoderm, but with a thin layer of mesoderm between them. The simplest way to accomplish this is to excise from the gastrula a latero-caudal piece of the marginal zone. In contrast to the previously used caudal sector, this piece contains more elements of the lateral plate giving rise to connective tissue. Indeed, an isolate from the ventral belly region of a neurula would serve the purpose equally well.

As before, the complex mass of cells cultured in physiological salt solution rounds up in a short time into a sphere. Some portion of the endoderm may remain uncovered by the ectoderm because of the insufficient surface area of the latter (Fig. 3a). Here again, one to two days later a protrusion of the endoderm and the formation of a waist-like constriction are observed (Fig. 3b). However, instead of progressing

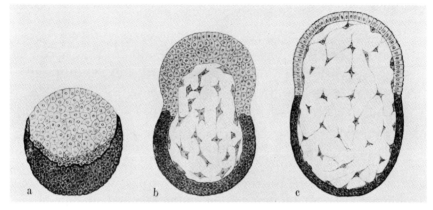

Fig. 3 Combination of endoderm and ectoderm with a layer of prospective connective tissue interposed. Sections. (a) Close union of the cells; (b) protrusion of the endoderm; (c) spreading of the ectoderm and endoderm to form a common epithelial wall around an internal cavity filled with mesenchyme.

further, the constriction regresses in many instances. A vesicle is formed, the interior of which is filled with mesenchyme cells forming a loose network because of the accumulation of secreted cellular fluid. In this instance, endoderm and ectoderm do not remain solid masses of cells but form the epithelial wall of the vesicle (Fig. 3c). The endoderm tends to form a single-celled layer while the ectoderm commonly becomes a layer two cells thick. The two epithelia are neatly delimited from one another and only touch along a ring-like borderline which sometimes appears as a slight fissure. Due to the presence of a common mesenchymal substratum self-isolation of the epithelia does not take place, even if the explants are cultured for an indefinite period of time.

It may be concluded from this experiment that endoderm as well as ectoderm retains permanently a positive affinity for connective tissue. As to intensity, these affinities seem to be even stronger than those between homologous cell material of the same age, since if endoderm and mesoderm are combined after they have been isolated for some time, they still fuse at those advanced stages, which are no longer favorable for homologous combinations.

(e) Endoderm enclosed in an epidermal vesicle. We again combine ectoderm, endoderm and mesoderm. In this arrangement, however, the ectoderm is made to cover completely the other cell types, with the meso-derm lying unilaterally between ectoderm and endoderm (Fig. 4a). The initially tight union of the solid mass of cells loosens up during the fol-lowing days. It is remarkable that even under these conditions complete

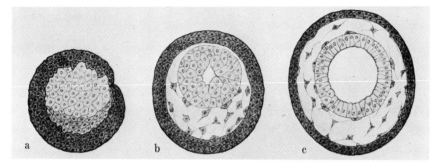

Fig. 4 Endoderm surrounded by ectoderm and mesenchyme separates away from the ectoderm and forms an intestinal vesicle the lumen of which arises by way of secondary cavitation.

detachment of the endoderm from the ectoderm takes place and that a cleft arises between them (Fig. 4b). This takes place autonomously. It is at a later time that this space is invaded and widened by connective tis-sue.

An epithelial spreading of endo- and ectoderm is facilitated by the hydrodynamic conditions within the vesicle. While the ectoderm pro-duces the external envelope, the inner, initially solid mass of endoderm forms a lumen which ordinarily enlarges due to the accumulation of a secreted liquid, until a single-layered cyst of intestinal epithelium is formed (Fig. 4c).

Thus, here again a self-separation of endoderm from ectoderm is obtained, although, in this case, the endoderm is delaminated into the inside of an epidermal vesicle and both tissues become subsequently cemented together by mesenchyme. The phenomenon of epithelial po-larity asserts itself. Under the present conditions, when the endoderm is shielded from the external medium by an epidermal envelope, it de-velops into an internal cyst with its epithelium facing the central lumen and not the outside as occurred in the previous experiment when the endoderm was lying at the outer periphery of the vesicle. The present arrangement of the three germ layers with respect to one another cannot be regarded as abnormal; in fact it is diagrammatically representative of the normal relationships.

(f) Isolation of combined mesoderm and ectoderm. It is still neces-sary to investigate the dynamic behavior of ectoderm toward pure mesoderm. We saw that mesoderm, as connective tissue, acts as a binding substance for epithelia and that association with it, once established, is never relinquished. At an earlier stage, however, conditions are slightly different; the affinity first develops in the opposite direction, since the phase of mutual close contact is preceded by a phase during which the ectoderm tends to separate from mesoderm. We can best investigate these relations by choosing a larger amount of mesoderm, for instance, a part of the dorsal marginal zone from an axolotl gastrula. This region provides chiefly chorda and somites, but also almost always regulates to give

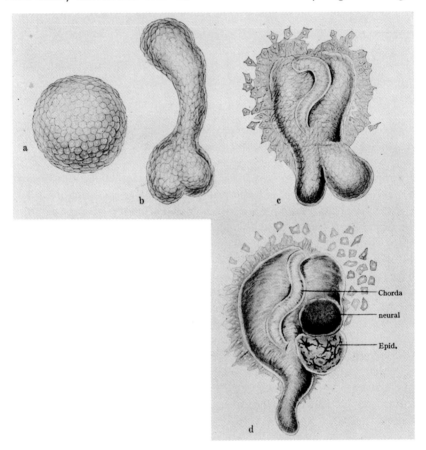

Fig. 5 Form changes in a fragment isolated from the region of the dorsal blastopore. (a) The aggregate rounds up into a sphere; (b) it elongates and forms a hump; (c) the isolate contracts, becomes attached to the glass surface, and begins to separate off a sphere of ectoderm. It segregates notochord and musculature, which is beginning to proliferate peripherally. (d) The ectoderm, which has re-established contact with the rest of the explant, has differentiated into epidermis and neural tissue, and the three axial tisues have grown out to form a tail.

rise to a small portion of ectoderm. Endoderm is absent here. Such explants display a great diversity of form changes and not until a comparison is made of many specimens can the general characteristics of the
events be formulated.

At first such an isolate rounds up into a sphere just as does any other
isolated fragment of the early embryo (Fig. 5a). Toward the end of the
next day it begins to elongate and, after another day, it often takes on
the shape of a femur (Fig. 5b). Tissue segregation is not yet apparent,
except for a small protruding hump at the lower end of the structure,
the histological character of which is not yet clear. On the third day,
the upper end has become attached to the glass surface and in doing so
contracts and flattens into a shield-like shape (Fig. 5c). The mesodermal
character of this part is already indicated by the advancing pseudopodia
at the periphery. On the upper surface of this layer a notochord begins
to shape up vaguely. The hump of the preceding stage has become set
off more distinctly as an almost spherical protuberance which, one day
later, can be identified as ectoderm. Its initially pronounced constriction
from mesoderm never leads to separation but regresses later on; still later
the ectoderm reestablishes a broad contact area with the rest of the explant and differentiates into epidermis or even neural tissue (Fig. 5d).

The subsequent behavior of the tissues need not be of special concern
to us in this connection. The chorda becomes more and more prominent
as a tortuous rod. The mesoderm gives rise to dorsal musculature and re-
leases at the periphery free myoblasts and connective tissue cells. It is
sprouting forth the attenuated cone of a tail which contains, concealed
inside, an extension of notochord and neural tube. The ectoderm which
at first appears as a homogeneous hump later segregates into epidermis
and neural tissue, a process which will be treated in greater detail later
on.

The following morphogenetic sequence is characteristic for all such
explants of the dorsal marginal zone: 1) general rounding up into a
sphere, 2) stretching of the total mass, 3) contraction and flattening of
the mesoderm that adheres to the bottom of the dish and a simultaneous
incomplete detachment of the ectoderm, 4) further spreading and axial
growth of the mesoderm and its partition into muscle and chorda, 5)
reassociation of the ectoderm with mesoderm over a widening area of
contact and its eventual segregation into epidermis and neural tissue.

During the initial phases, the general changes of shape are produced by
means of morphogenetic cell movements whereas the formative principles
of cell differentiation, cell proliferation and migrations become significantly engaged only at later stages. When observing such isolates from the
dorsal blastoporal region one is reminded of the form changes during
the development of a fruiting body in Myxomycetes, that dramatic
process which A. Arndt has once demonstrated so impressively in a

time-lapse movie. In both instances the material, like a plastic dough, displays all sorts of elongations, transformations, segregations, recombinations, and final differentiations. But whereas in the case of this lower fungus we are dealing with a multinucleate plasmodium, in an embryonic fragment we encounter the remarkable fact that the mass translocations are produced by a multitude of individual cells which nevertheless behave like an organic unity.

Among these processes, the changing dynamic relationship between ectoderm and mesoderm is of special interest, since we recognize therein an expression of affinity relations. At first this behavior resembles, even in its time sequence, the process of constriction in the combination of ectoderm and endoderm. Later on, however, the affinity reverts from a negative to a positive sense, a condition that had existed at the beginning of the experiment. That ectoderm which becomes epidermis will always remain on the surface, while the ectoderm that has been induced to form neural tissue actively penetrates, as neural tube, into the deeper mesoderm layers. To what extent affinity relations play a role in this process will not be discussed further here.

(g) Significance of affinity for the processes of gastrulation. Let us now examine these experimental findings with respect to their significance in developmental physiology. In the first place it should be understood that the phenomena described above are not artifacts introduced by unfavorable culture conditions. The same phenomena have been repeatedly observed under a variety of experimental conditions, as, for instance, when isolates are implanted into the coelom of older larvae, a milieu that may be regarded as eminently suitable for endoderm and mesoderm. We may therefore assume that similar processes, although they cannot be so easily detected, take place within the framework of the whole organism.

We have already pointed out that the epithelial spreading movement of the intestinal primordium is principally the same in both the explant and the gastrula and that the substratum affects the direction of spreading. We also noted that the upward shifting of the invaginated endoderm to form a tube is a natural consequence, on the one hand, of the autonomous and nondirectional spreading tendency of the entoderm, and on the other, of its specific position in a cavity that is only open in a certain direction. The wrapping experiment (p. 200) shows furthermore that an inner lumen of the intestine can be formed subsequently, by way of delamination within an endodermal mass that has been screened against the outer medium by an epidermal envelope. In such a case the pressure of the internal liquid may contribute to a flattening of the endoderm cells into an epithelium.

Ordinarily, connective tissue represents the natural gliding surface and later the substrate of the endoderm. The fact that these associated germ layers, mesoderm and endoderm, comprise a system of such mechanical stability is not due to their accidental, passive apposition but rather depends on their active, permanent combining tendencies. By the way, other mesodermal tissues show the same positive relationship to the endoderm as does connective tissue.

The incompatibility of ectoderm with mesoderm, which is only temporary, and with endoderm, which is increasing, seems to play an important role in the steering of invagination processes. On an earlier occasion we have described a similar process of separation on a large scale, namely, in total exogastrulation (Holtfreter 1933). There, too, a complete stripping off and self-isolation of the ectoderm took place when the endoderm became thinned out to a connecting stalk; however, if some mesoderm was present in the stalk the pinching off process remained incomplete.

Indeed, the normal process of invagination comprises an isolation of ectoderm from endomesoderm during which the connecting zone gradually diminishes. However, there this process does not lead to a moving away of the endomesoderm into the outer medium as in an exogastrula, but to its incorporation within the ectodermal vault. The problem of why invagination and not evagination takes place normally has not yet been clarified. The most likely factors contributing to this result are a mechanical counter-pressure of the vitelline membrane, osmotic conditions and finally an active "tendency" for invagination which first begins at the head-gut region. However, it seems to us important that the second process characteristic of gastrulation, viz., the progressive constriction of the ectoderm, can be carried out independently of invagination. That in this process the epibolic spreading of the ectoderm does not exert an active pushing effect, but rather follows the receding material, was shown in the case of exogastrulation and also in our combination experiment in which an ectodermal epiboly was absent. Furthermore, mesodermal invagination along with a constricting blastoporal rim were observed in embryos that were practically free of ectoderm (Holtfreter 1933, p. 781). It seems to follow that normal gastrulation likewise operates by way of an active moving apart of heterologous tissues. That the connecting zone, in the form of the blastoporal rim, is narrowing down to the anal opening would then be due to the topographical arrangement of the primordial regions. It appears that the driving principle behind the streaming apart of heterologous cell masses has to be sought in a change of affinity between the tissues to a negative state. Let us consider some additional details.

In the intact embryo the ectoderm is everywhere separated from endoderm by a zone of mesoderm, which is, however, very narrow in the ventro-caudal sector, the future anal region, where the mesoderm disappears rapidly during invagination so that ectoderm and endoderm come to border directly on each other. Their epithelial contiguity in the proctodeal borderzone is stable only because in the meantime some mesoderm has shifted underneath and holds them together. In the other regions of the embryo it is probably the temporary incompatibility between ectoderm and mesoderm, observed above in the explants that is instrumental in the involution movements. In addition one must take into account the inherent capability of the mesoderm to stretch itself axially, which it can do independently of any contact with heterologous neighboring tissues; this in itself must lead to a decrease of contact border with the ectoderm. After the mesoderm has moved off the surface of the gastrula and has come to underlie the ectoderm, the phase of attachment between these two layers begins. The strength of adhesion increases progressively, and it becomes particularly pronounced between chorda-somites and neural plate. In a late gastrula the underlying mesoderm can be peeled off easily from the ectoderm; in a late neurula however, this requires much more patient skill, and in the larval stage it cannot be done without severely damaging the cells. If this strong adhesion had already prevailed during the gastrula stage, the gliding movements of the invaginating mesoderm would surely have been arrested.

While, in the dissection of an advanced neurula, many of the mesoderm cells remain stuck to the epidermis, this does not happen in the liver region. In this mesoderm-free region the endoderm is contacting directly the ectoderm (Vogt 1929). This localized non-adhesion between superimposed endoderm and ectoderm may very well be ascribed to the emergence of a negative affinity between them: the advanced neurula corresponds in time to the phase in our combination experiment when the constriction between the two tissue types was almost complete.

Certain phenomena met with in the blastoporal region can also be explained on the basis of the above experiments. It may happen sometimes that beyond the neurula stage a considerable portion of the endoderm remains protruding in the anal region as a yolk plug. Such plugs never fuse with the adjacent epidermis and therefore do not cause an obstruction of the anal opening. They are later either constricted off or become overgrown by the advancing skin. Once the intestinal primordium has invaginated, a mesodermal layer develops everywhere between it and the ectoderm; this binds them together mechanically and causes both of them to elaborate an epithelium whose surface is oriented toward a liquid medium.

Special conditions prevail in the mouth and gill regions that shall not be discussed here in detail. Thus the head endoderm retains adhesiveness toward the ectoderm much longer than does the rest of the endoderm. It is by this means that the inductive origin of the various ectodermal mouth structures becomes possible.

III. ISOLATION AND COMBINATION EXPERIMENTS WITH NEURULA MATERIAL

The preceding experiments and their interpretation have helped us in gaining new insight into the morphogenetic processes, especially those occurring during the period of gastrulation. Now another series of isolation experiments shall be presented which deal with the dynamic relations between epidermis, neural components and mesoderm. They may serve to explain some of the important processes of neurulation.

The most striking feature of a neurula is the appearance of the neural plate, which narrows progressively, involutes into a tube and separates from the epidermis. This is not the place to offer a comprehensive causal analysis of these morphogenetic processes. We shall merely present a few impressive experimental results which will show that in this process also, local growth by cell proliferation, or outer factors such as pressure, push or pull of neighboring tissues are only insignificantly involved, whereas the formative capacities inherent in the cell material proper and physiological influences of the environment are of much greater importance.

(a) The morphogenetic capacities inherent in the neural plate. The histological capacity for self-differentiation of isolated pieces of the neural plate has been demonstrated frequently in transplantation or isolation experiments. In connection with our problem it seems important to examine, first of all, to what extent the amount of neighboring tissues can be reduced without deranging the typical process of neural plate development. Later on we plan to examine in some complex isolates the specific influence of various neighboring tissues upon the neural formative processes. Let us first confine our attention to the brain region.

It is known that the subjacent cephalic endomesoderm does not merely exert a single inductive stimulus on the prospective neural material but that it continues participating in the modeling of its shape. The initial stimulus, however, accomplishes very much, if not the essential part. One arrives at the same conclusion if one considers the amazingly complex effects of a dead abnormal inductor, although it does not take part materially in the modeling of the neural tissue which it induced. A variety of brain structures, even symmetrical ones with typical eyes and other sense organs, can be formed in such a case although the contact influence may have lasted only for some 40 hours (Holtfreter 1934b, p. 234).

Once it has become induced, the ectoderm itself acquires the capacities for an extensive, though certainly not entirely typical morphogenesis. It has been hitherto tacitly assumed that in this process mesenchyme and epidermis play merely a protecting and supporting role. This matter, however, shall become the very problem of our subsequent studies. First, it will be shown that typical form changes take place in a fragment of the neural plate that had been isolated without its subjacent inductors but was supplied with an abundance of epidermis.

The explant shown in Figure 6 was excised from the cephalic region of a fully developed neurula; it consists in part of the lateral portion of the neural plate and, to a larger extent, of the adjacent epidermis. Located between them is the neural crest, the source of origin of mesenchyme, pigment cells and also of ganglia and cartilage.

In a short time the epidermis turns upwards and wraps itself around the neural material whereas the latter contracts and sinks in to form a groove (Fig. 6b). The over-all shape thus resembles a very thick-walled bowl. This shape, since it deviates from a sphere, indicates that although the capacity for ameboid movements of the cells and their inclina-

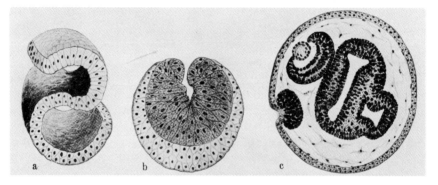

Fig. 6 Isolation of a portion of head neural plate together with a larger piece of adjacent prospective epidermis. (a) Beginning of the experiment: above, neural material, involuted concavely; below, epidermis. (b) The components have tightly united and the neural plate has sunk in to form a groove. (c) Differentiation of a brain with an eye and a nasal pit inside the epidermal vesicle.

tion to establish maximal contact with each other are still present, neural material already possesses formative tendencies of its own. Even under such abnormal conditions it attempts to sink into the depth. Neither a pull by underlying mesoderm, nor lateral pushing by the epidermis can be responsible for this, since mesoderm is absent and the epidermis is initially present only on one side; furthermore this epidermis is deflected in its movements because it attempts to envelop the whole isolate. Yet the involution of the neural primordium takes place nearly concentrically. Moreover, since involution is also observed in pieces completely devoid of epidermis, it must be considered an autonomous process.

On the following day involution is complete and the neural material is fully enclosed by the epidermis. The process of involution usually leads to the formation of a central lumen. Mesenchyme and pigment cells develop from the neural crest; the epidermal vesicle expands and becomes transparent making it possible to see the inner neural mass. The latter develops into a brain diverticulum associated with a typically shaped eye which in turn induces the formation of a lens. Even an olfactory pit may develop in such an isolate. As is brought out by the slightly schematized illustration of Fig. 6c, all the neural material with the exception of the olfactory pit is separated from the epidermis by a layer of mesenchyme. As in a normal brain there arises as fibrous marginal layer and a proximal nucleated layer. If one disregards the obviously fragmentary character of this brain one must admit that its development has proceeded quite typically in the absence of head mesoderm. This is true for the eye and nose as well.

This experiment may serve as a control for a second one which will again raise the question of affinity and may bring us closer to solving the question of the influence of mesenchyme and epidermis upon the configuration of the neural differentiations.

(b) Self-isolation of neural tissue from epidermis. Again we excise from the lateral head region of a neurula a purely ectodermal strip which this time, however, contains relatively more neural plate and less pro-

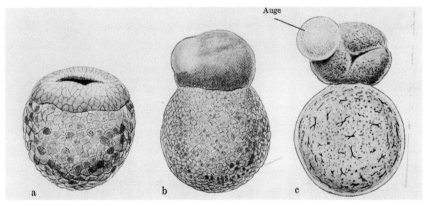

Fig. 7 Isolation of a portion of head neural plate together with a smaller piece of adjacent prospective epidermis. (a) The conjoined cells have formed a spherical mass, and there is a neural groove. (b) Beginning, (c) progressing constriction.

spective epidermis. As in the previous experiment such a piece immediately bends in such a way that the neural material curves concavely and the epidermis convexly. Both components contract simultaneously and then merge into a compact mass showing a blackish depression (Fig. 7a). This groove disappears at older stages becoming under these conditions covered with neural cells instead of epidermis. Thus the involution of the neural tissue can take place without the assistance of adjacent tissues. If the epidermal component is relatively small, the neural tissue never becomes completely covered by it.

In the course of time a constriction develops, quite similar to that between ectoderm and endoderm with the difference however that here even connective tissue cannot prevent an outward movement of the neural mass. As in the preceding example this mesenchyme stems from the neural crest, i.e., it is of ectodermal and not mesodermal derivation.

One to two days after isolation, the material, now recognizable as neural tissue, begins to slide out of the epidermal envelope (Fig. 7b). The connecting bridge between them becomes narrower with time (Fig. 7c) until complete self-isolation of the neural mass has taken place (Fig. 8a). As the constriction progresses, the exit hole in the epidermis closes.

The brain fragment remains considerably more compact when entirely isolated than when cultured within an epidermal vesicle. Just the

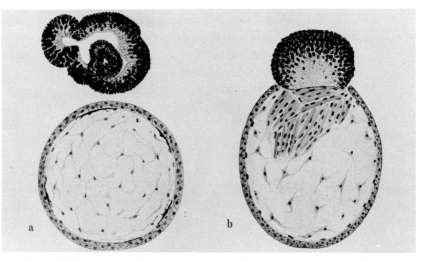

Fig. 8 (a) An uncovered eye has protruded from the isolated neural portion; melanophores and mesenchyme are present within the epidermal vesicle. (b) The neural mass adjacent to the musculature is mushroom-shaped and is not constricted off.

same, an inner, rather slitlike lumen may be formed. However, the nuclei of the neuroblasts are now located at the periphery so that at least a partial inversion of the stratified structure must be assumed. As in the case of the gut epithelium, this inversion of polarity must be ascribed to the absence of enveloping tissues. As regards cytological differentiation, the neural tissue may become quite normal.

In a region remote from the epidermis, an eye has evaginated from the brain fragment. In the living explant it can be distinguished from the other neural parts by its lighter tinge and smooth surface, and in section it appears as a simple hemispherical protrusion from the neural layer.

An identical hemispherical eye protrusion from a solid mass of brain is obtained if, in a whole neurula, all of the epidermis is removed so that the neural tissue is forced to differentiate in a superficial position. These observations prove that the primary eye vesicle is not formed due to mechanical intervention of any neighboring tissues but that its evagination results from active formative tendencies within the eye material itself. Here we find on a smaller scale the same phenomenon of constriction that is exhibited between the whole neural mass and the skin vesicle. Our subsequent experimental results indicate that we are dealing again with the emergence of physiological differences between brain material and eye primordium and thus once more with a show of affinity that causes them to move apart. In an uncovered brain, however, complete isolation of a spherical eye never occurs. Here the significance of the mesenchyme in the development of the eye enters the picture.

The difference between such an exposed eye and one that has formed within a mesenchymal mass, as in our preceding experiment, is very striking. The naked eye primordium does not differentiate into tapetum, multilayered retina, rods and cones, and it fails to fold inward into an eye cup. Differentiation is arrested at the stage of the primary eye vesicle. Therefore, the embedding of the eye primordium in mesenchyme seems to be necessary for the development of all of these organo- and histotypical structures.

In this experiment, all the mesectoderm has remained inside the epidermal vesicle. We find here mainly mesenchyme and pigment cells, but occasionally also small ganglia with outgrowing nerve fibers. The self-isolation of the parts is completed cleanly just as it is in the case of endoderm.

One could argue against the assumption of an active self-separation of the neural mass by postulating that its expulsion may have been caused by a pressure of the expanding mesenchyme. However, this is not supported by a number of other experimental results. It is possible, for instance, to obtain the formation of neural tissue in the almost complete absence of mesoderm by implanting a dead inductor into an ectodermal vesicle. The enclosed neural mass always becomes separated from the ectoderm by a space and, if there is merely a narrow opening to the external medium, it will force itself through it. Correspondingly, negative results are obtained in fusion experiments between ectoderm and neural material that had been kept isolated for a prolonged time.

Thus, even in the absence of mesenchyme, a repulsive action can originate solely in the epidermis. But the mesectoderm also has an inherent tendency to emancipate itself from the neural material which was its former neighbor tissue. For instance, if a piece of neural plate including neural crest is transplanted into the ventral lymphatic spaces of an older host larva, the neural portion develops into a sphere of neural tissue. Mesenchyme and pigment cells, however, derived from the neural crest, migrate away and become widely dispersed in the host tissue. This can be especially clearly demonstrated in xenoplastic combinations (Holtfreter 1929, Bytinsky-Salz 1938). In particular, the cells of the dermis derived from an implant of a foreign species or genus migrate actively underneath the host epidermis; similarly melano- and xanthophores seek out this neighborhood and spread there in their typical manner. A similar "epidermophilic" behavior is shown by the primordial buds of the lateral sensory line (Harrison 1904, Holtfreter 1935).

Thus although these three derivatives of the neural crest sever their connection with neural material, they nevertheless retain the tendency to associate with the epidermis. As is shown by the xenoplastic combinations, the tissue-specific affinities are not confined to tissues of the same species.

From the experiment illustrated in Figure 8b it may be likewise concluded that the extrusion of the neural mass from the skin vesicle cannot be explained as being due to pressure conditions. In this case the isolate included some of the underlying somite material in addition to the ectodermal parts. This material has a much stronger binding power for neural tissue than has mesenchyme. Here too the exposed neural tissue tends to separate from the remaining parts, but is held fast by the muscle mass; it protrudes outward in the shape of a mushroom, its nuclei again located peripherally and the nerve fibers proximally.

Even if there were a pressure exerted by the inner mesenchyme of the skin vesicle, we have never observed this force to be able to cause an isolation of musculature or other mesoderm or endoderm. Thus this segregation phenomenon must be considered peculiar to neural tissue, suggesting that this tissue is not strongly anchored in purely ectodermal mesenchyme.

Likewise, a possibly existing constricting action of the epidermis cannot have played a primary role in this instance, since if this were the case it should also have brought about a separation of the neural material in the experiment with musculature. There, however, the condition as illustrated remains permanent.

Hence we reach the conclusion that the segregation of the ectodermal derivatives must be attributed to the development of a negative affinity between them. This accompanies differentiation since, if prior to the inductive action of the subjacent mesoderm, we isolate a piece—half neural and half epidermal—from exactly the same region, the whole piece retains an epidermal character and no constriction takes place. The relative size of the components is immaterial for the result. The prospective neural mass may be very large and the epidermal portion very small, or vice versa, a further indication that crude mechanical forces such as push and pull cannot play any role.

Finally, still another experimental modification is shown in Figure 9a which illustrates quite strikingly the elective character of tissue affinities.

(c) Positive affinity of eye primordium for connective tissue. The isolate in the present experiment was excised from the median rather than the lateral head region of a neurula; it comprised the primordia of brain-eye and the adjacent frontal epidermis. Although here again the entire brain material slipped out of the epidermal vesicle, the eye remained inside and differentiated into all its typical structures. In the end only the optic nerve retained a connection with the isolated neural mass (Fig. 9).

Why is the eye excluded from the process of isolation? Is it mere coincidence that it remains within the mesenchyme? The fact that there are many similar cases speaks against this supposition. It appears, rather,

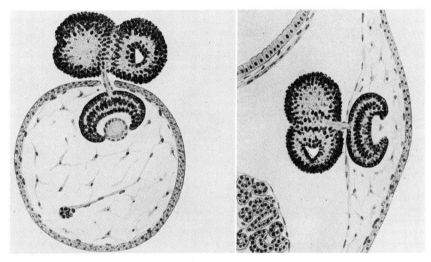

Fig. 9 While the brain material has isolated itself, the eye has remained within the epidermal vesicle.

Fig. 10 Implantation of head neural plate into the abdominal cavity. The eye rudiment has evaginated into the abdominal body wall; the brain portion remains free in the coelomic fluid.

that the eye, in contrast to the brain, has a pronounced preference for mesectoderm. We consider the following experimental findings as a direct proof for this latter view.

We isolate the same piece of neural plate, but this time without any adjacent epidermis and substrate, and then push it through a small slit into the abdominal cavity of an older amphibian larva. There it floats freely between the viscera and the coelomic wall and continues differentiating during the following days. When the host larva bearing the implant is examined microscopically, the following picture is obtained.

If the implant has developed into neural tissue only, it is never found to have established tissue connection with the mesoderm of the host. Such pieces behave exactly like those cultured in physiological saline. Their neural involution may proceed until a tube is formed, or may not pass beyond the neural groove stage. The fibrous layer is always situated centrally, as we have already shown previously in an illustration (Holtfreter 1929, p. 443).

Quite different, however, is the behavior in many cases of the eyes that have evaginated from these brain fragments. They alone, in a remarkably high percentage of cases, establish tissue contact with the coelomic wall, as shown in Figure 10, and they may even become deeply embedded in the host mesenchyme. The attached brain portion always projects freely into the coelom.

Only some definite action on the part of the eye primordium itself can have been responsible for its embedding in mesenchyme. The following course of events must be envisaged. At first, the implant, while temporarily lying still, adhered lightly to the coelomic wall. Then the eye primordium, in contrast to the neural tissue, penetrated the peritoneal lining on its own and invaded the mesenchyme. This process can be explained only on the basis of a specific, positive affinity of the optic material to connective tissue, and not by any pull, pressure or suction on the part of the living substrate.

Thus, in the preceding experimental set-up, it was the result of directed tissue-specific movements of the material rather than of mere chance that the eye became incorporated in the skin vesicle whereas the brain portion emigrated.

The eye gains a remarkable advantage by becoming embedded in the connective tissue of the host. Instead of remaining in the stage of a primary optic vesicle, as do the uncovered eyes in the coelom, it continues its development quite typically, even folding into a cup. A lens is absent because the host epidermis was much too old to form a lens in response to the eye stimulus. It should be mentioned that here the eye has invaded mesenchyme which is of mesodermal and not of ectodermal origin, as it was in the foregoing experiments and as it is predominantly in normal development. Therefore, the age and local origin of the mesenchymatic matrix seem to be immaterial for the embedding process.

Before drawing general conclusions from these observations we should like to introduce a final series of tissue combinations, that will again demonstrate the specificity of these attraction and repulsion phenomena.

(d) Positive affinity of the neural material for mesoderm. From the behavior of neural tissue in the experiment illustrated in Figure 8b it is already evident that this material is attracted by the somite musculature and that it remains permanently combined with it. In this case it had formed a mushroom-shaped cushion because it was only locally attached and it was laterally impeded by the epidermis. If a larger piece of trunk neural plate is isolated from a neurula free of epidermis but including a small portion of the underlying somite primordium, the following result is obtained.

The isolate assumes a nearly spherical shape, and the neural material glides around the mesoderm. In this case rolling in to form a neural tube, such as occurs in pure isolates or in the presence of epidermis, does not take place. A firm adherence to the substrate seems to suppress this inherent tendency. When the somite portion is very small, the neural plate cells spreading over its surface may enclose it entirely and thus form a thick mantle of neural tissue, the fibers of which lie proximally and the cell nuclei distally (Fig. 11a). A neural lumen is absent in this type of

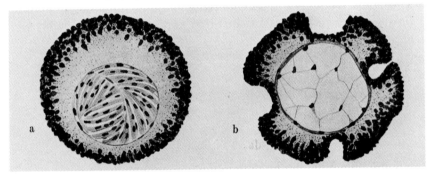

Fig. 11 Polarizing effect of the underlying tissue on neural material. (a) Naked neural tissue adjacent to musculature does not develop a lumen. (b) When adjacent to chorda, the neural layer forms groove-like depressions.

combination. No separation of the two tissues takes place even at later stages.

The tendency for close adhesion of the neural tissue to chorda is even more pronounced. Very striking examples are obtained when, for instance, a fragment of the chorda primordium is isolated from a neurula together with a piece of neural plate, or when a piece of chorda is wrapped in a thin layer of gastrula ectoderm, which is then induced to form neural tissue. Figure 11b illustrates such a case in which chorda is wholly surrounded by a layer of neural cells. This layer does not represent a smooth surfaced, solid cushion as in combination with muscle, but it has formed several groove-like depressions and occasionally even closed lumina.

Thus, whereas neural plate cells in combination with somites tend to accumulate into a thick mass, they tend, in contact with chorda, to spread into as thin a layer as possible. Accordingly, when the chorda surface at their disposal is abundant, the neural cells may adopt an almost epithelial-like arrangement. Local grooves or lumina appear within this layer only when the cells remain piled up because of a limitation of the surface over which they could spread.

In the last two experiments we came upon phenomena that have already been considered elsewhere. Thus Bautzmann (1928) pointed out that the formation of the median groove of the open neural plate might be attributed to a special effect of attraction exerted by the underlying chorda, a view which is supported by considering the firmness with which these two germ layers cling together. Lehmann (1926, 1929) and many subsequent authors have called attention to the peculiar mass distribution and shape of the neural plate material that takes place in response to contact with these inductors. Thus, the part of the neural tube in contact with chorda was always found to be thinned out, whereas it became thickened in its wall that was adjacent to somites. These re-

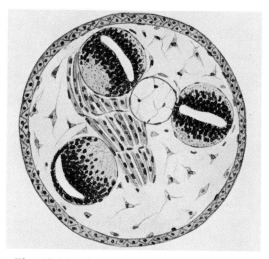

Fig. 12 Morphogenetic influence of chorda and musculature on neural tube, surrounded by epidermis.

lationships are schematically illustrated in Figure 12, assuming in this case that the neural material is surrounded by both mesenchyme and epidermis.

(e) Influence of the inductors upon the shape and arrangement of neural tissue. In the cross-section shown in Figure 12, three neural tubes are depicted which differ from one another by their material arrangement of neural tissue. The neural tube on the lower left, having contact with muscle only, has a distally located transverse lumen. Its basal thickening and the location of the fibrous layer toward the contact surface is in accord with the behavior of neural material that rests directly on muscle in the absence of ectoderm. However, in the present example, the existence of a mantle of mesenchyme and epidermis has permitted the prospective neural material to execute the movements of involution and to form a tube or a cyst.

Somewhat different environmental factors have had a formative influence on the morphogenesis of the neural tube to the right, which rests on chorda. Its surface spreading was prevented and thus a rounded tube was formed with a single lumen perpendicular to the chorda. The basal layer of the neural tube is thin, whereas its lateral walls are symmetrically thickened.

Finally, the uppermost neural tube is unilaterally in contact with muscle and basally with chorda. Both of these tissues have exerted a polarizing influence, since the basal layer is thin, and the wall adjacent to muscle is thickened, whereas the side wall away from muscle is not quite as thin as it would have been if under the unilateral influence of muscle tissue alone. A bilaterally symmetric thickening of both side walls would have occurred only if, as in a normal embryo, the tube had been in contact with somites on two sides.

Let us summarize as follows an evaluation of these last experimental results with respect to their bearing on the problem of affinity.

(1) The mesoderm (chorda and somites), in contrast to the epidermis, exerts a strong attraction on neural plate material, a condition that is retained at least until their histological differentiation has taken place. In this respect chorda is more effective than muscle primordium.

(2) This phenomenon is linked with a tissue-specific polarizing influence of the mesoderm upon the mass distribution of the prospective neural tissue. The contact area is thinned by chorda and thickened by muscle.

(3) In order to form a closed tube the cells of the neural plate while being attracted by mesoderm must be provided with an external supporting matrix. This support, mainly mechanical in nature, is provided in this case by mesenchyme and epidermis. The lack of affinity of both of these tissues for the older neural tissue is probably a contributing factor for the latter to form a rounded cyst or tube, i.e., once the neural material is trapped by these tissues, it tends to reduce its contact surface with them to a minimum.

(f) Significance of affinity for the process of neurulation. In the preceding paragraph it was shown that an insight may be gained into the causal mechanism of the process of gastrulation from the autonomous formative tendencies of the explants and from the dynamic behavior that is exhibited by the germ layers in various combinations with one another. In a neurula the distribution and segregation of meso- and endoderm is completed in rough outlines. Here we are more concerned with the formative processes of the outer germ layer. An attempt will now be made to synthesize the experimental results on neurula material and to relate them to normal organogenesis.

On the basis of the few data presented here in rough outline, a general rule can already be established, namely, that when a morphological segregation occurs in a hitherto undivided cell layer, there is also a change in affinity between the new derivatives. Let us follow the course of events while confining ourselves to the ectoderm and its derivatives.

The gastrula ectoderm is still morphologically and potentially homogeneous, and if fragments from various regions of it are combined together, they show a uniformly positive affinity with one another. In this quality, however, the ectoderm does not differ from the other organ primordia, since, as we have previously seen, all of them at this stage can unite indiscriminately with one another. If the ectoderm remains histologically undetermined owing to the absence of inductive stimuli, it also retains its dynamic homogeneity, a fact which ought not to be taken for granted. If, however, the underlying mesoderm has induced local differences in the developmental capacities of the ectoderm, they will manifest themselves dynamically together with the first appearance of structural differences, if not earlier. The prospective neural plate of an early neurula which is outwardly not yet demarcated will, when isolated, rapidly bend inward, thus behaving like epidermis of the same or even older stages. But when the same material is isolated at a slightly older stage, when the neural folds have become delineated, its edges will bend upward, concavely; and this involution will occur the faster and the more vigorously the later the stage of operation. This concave curling, resulting from a latent state of tension of the neural plate, signalizes the coming of further mass rearrangements of the isolated material which will proceed in the same direction. Even without any support from neighboring tissues, an isolated older neural plate is capable of a concave infolding that leads to the formation of a closed cyst or tube. On the other hand, isolated epidermis, especially if connective tissue is left attached to it, will always curve convexly to form a vesicle.

During the period of involution the neural material loses its capacity to adhere to the ectoderm that is differentiating into epidermis. At the same time it tends to become repellent toward the neural crest derivatives, such as mesenchyme and pigment cells, whereas the latter now tend to combine with epidermis. The active outbulging of the optic vesicle seems to be an expression of a physiological difference arising between it and the brain primordium that forces them to separate from one another. The detachment and complete evagination of the eye are then enhanced by a positive affinity between eye and neighboring mesenchyme. In contact with the epidermis the eye induces a lens with which it will henceforth remain intimately associated. Thus the lens is withdrawn from its generating germ layer. This event does not result from a hypothetical "suction" exerted by the eye primordium, but from an active constriction process similar to that of the evagination of the eye, since it may take place even without the inductive action of an optic vesicle or of any other morphologically defined inductor. Hence it seems that the emancipation of the lens is caused by a physiological estrangement to the epidermis. The lens acquires a positive affinity not only to the eye but also to the nasal pit and ear vesicle.

The following scheme may summarize this intriguing system of affinities of the ectodermal derivatives which comprises sequentially mutual estrangements between parent tissue and its filial primordia and newly arising elective bonds between filial primordia, and other tissue derivatives of second or third order. The positive or negative relations between the tissue types are represented by + or — signs:

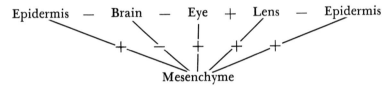

This scheme does not support the viewpoint advocated by Born (1897) that derivatives of the same germ layer attract while those from different germ layers repel each other. The system of relationships is much more complicated. In fact it is precisely the switch from a positive to a negative affinity between organ primordium and parent tissue which becomes the cause of the emancipation and morphogenesis of the derivative. A positive affinity may exist among the derivatives of the same germ layer, as well as among organ primordia of different germ layers. On the other hand, cells of the very same tissue layer may exhibit only a very slight tendency for mutual connections, as for example the mesenchyme. A homogeneous aggregate of either endodermal or epidermal cells, when cultured in the complete absence of a substrate, breaks apart during differentiation into its individual elements. The bonds that hold these homologous cells together are thus much weaker than those which connect them with the mesoderm. Generally speaking then, one finds rather more incidences of positive than of negative affinity between different tissue types.

The initiating stimuli for the introduction of local differences in the ectoderm are derived from the mesodermal and, in part, from the endodermal sublayer. Beginning at the early neurula stage, the prospective chorda, the somites, and the cephalic endomesoderm exert a pronounced attraction for the ectoderm. This leads to an intimate contact between them, which is a prerequisite for the occurrence of induction effects. Varying with the inductive specificity of the underlying tissues, the various neural, mesectodermal and epidermal districts are then physiologically demarcated within the ectoderm. With this stimulation the most important step has been taken, since from then on the newly emerging affinity interrelationships enable the ectodermal primordia to carry out a good number of important morphogenetic processes quite independently of any further cooperation with the inductors. However, under normal conditions, the subjacent heterologous tissues do continue to influence the formative processes and the material disposition of the induced ectodermal derivatives. As an example of this we demonstrated the specifying action which chorda and somites exert upon the distribution of the cellular mass of the neural tube. These secondary formative influences depend likewise on an intimate contact between the modelling agency and the responding pliable material. Correspondingly, the lens primordium requires a prolonged contact with the optic cup in order to acquire and retain its typical structure.

Important though the arising of negative affinities turns out to be for the local segregation of organ primordia from their parent tissue, positive affinities, whether retained or newly acquired, are just as indispensable for the pursuance of an organotypical development. The harmonious intertwining of these phases is assured by the initial disposition of the organ-forming areas of the embryo, as well as by the age- and tissue-specific character of the reactions that are predetermined within the material itself.

There is no need to dwell upon the obvious fact that purely mechanical environmental factors are also engaged in influencing the formative processes of early embryogenesis. This became apparent enough from the explantation experiments alone. But such influences play merely the role of non-specific factors in the realization of these processes and are replaceable to a great extent by non-living structures. In comparison with the physiologically transmitted stimuli, the crude forces of push and pull are of a very minor importance. The blastopore as well as neural tube, optic vesicle, or other organ primordia are not at all molded into shape by extraneous pushing or compressing agencies nor by a pulling from the interior; rather they form themselves by means of active translocations of cell areas that are set in motion by changes of their physiological states. The environment may then guide these autonomous movements in certain directions, and it may thus participate in determining the axiality and over-all shape of the primordial mass. However, the specific morphogenetic tendency inherent in the formative material itself remains the truly organizing principle. We are still far from grasping the physico-chemical processes involved in this "self-mobilization."

In view of the prominence which the study of growth processes has attained in the current work on tissue cultures, it seems timely to emphasize once more that growth is not of primary significance in early embryogenesis. Even the genesis of the disparate organs is mainly achieved by means of morphogenetic cell movements; such as have been strikingly exemplified by the gastrulating pieces of embryos. Only later, when the ameboid mobility of the cells is decreased as a result of differentiation, do the dough-like mass transports of entire cell complexes come to an end. Then locally regulated growth by cell division, by individual cell migration, or by the deposition of intra- and extracellular material takes over as the leading formative principle.

VI. CYTOTROPISM AND AFFINITY

Finally the phenomena of affinity, as treated in this paper, will be contrasted with Roux's cytotropism which provided the starting point for our considerations.

According to Roux, a mutual, dynamic influence between cells may occur in two ways: 1) between freely motile, individual cells (the term cytotaxis would be more appropriate here than cytotropism since we are dealing with the locomotion of free elements), and 2) between cells in cell aggregates (directional movement). The stimulating agents in both cases were supposed to be identical, namely, specific substances emitted by the cells that diffuse away in a concentration gradient and act selectively to bring about either attraction or repulsion. Accordingly the stimulus would act over a certain distance, not only between isolated cells but also amongst the cells in firm aggregates.

Roux's contention of having demonstrated an elective cytotaxis between isolated blastomeres must be considered as disproved on the basis of the aforementioned investigations of Voigtländer (1932) and Kuhl (1937). Nor did the experiments performed by these authors on cell combinations of early embryonic stages yield any evidence for a "self-ordering power" of the cells according to their different qualities.

To what extent these negative findings are also applicable to the cells of more advanced embryonic stages remained undecided. Subsequent investigations dealt with much older, already differentiated single cells of the organism (germ cells, ameboid blood elements). There indeed instances of a chemotactic or cytotactic cellular responsiveness were found. In this connection, attention must also be drawn to the dissociation experiments on sponges, first carried out by Morgan (1900, 1907) and later by Galtsoff (1925). They have shown that harmoniously organized individual sponges can be reconstituted from a mass of completely disorganized isolated cells. More interesting still: when the dissociated cells from one species were mixed with those from another species, only the cells from one and the same species would unite and form a new organism. In this case an actual self-ordering of the free cells seems to have taken place, which suggests that a tissue-specific cytotactic affinity has operated here as the organizing power. Further-more, in sponges cell affinity seems to be species-specific, which is cer-tainly not the case in amphibians while they are in early embryonic stages.

In an organism, however, it is the mode of movement and the forma-tive changes of integrated cell complexes, rather than the behavior of individual cells, that call for an exploration. Do the cytotropic actions at a distance postulated by Roux exist also between cell complexes as a means of morphogenesis?

The affirmative opinion of Born on this question has not been shared by any of the later experimentalists working on amphibians. How-ever, when tissues from warm-blooded animals were cultured in the usual media consisting of blood plasma and embryonic extract, growth processes were observed that appeared to be based upon cytotropism. This is the well-known bridge phenomenon of growth which often oc-curred when two explants were placed rather closely together in the same drop of the plasma medium. This phenomenon could be interpreted as the expression of a chemotropic distant action of the explants on one another. Thus a series of experiments on such confrontation cultures has been carried out by Centanni and his co-workers with the aim of ascertaining the elective nature of the stimulus. The results were am-biguous. Tissues of the same as well as of different kinds were able to grow toward each other while in other experiments repulsive effects seemed apparent. Although it was difficult to systematize such findings, Juhásc (1929) believed that they had demonstrated the existence of tissue-specific growth substances acting at a distance; he termed them "cyto-blastines."

These interpretations are no longer convincing as a result of investiga-tions by Weiss (1929, 1934). According to him the bridge of cells between two explants can be explained on a purely mechanical basis. As a con-sequence of dehydration, the plasma around each explant is assumed to undergo local condensation which causes the micelles of the colloidal medium to become oriented along the lines of stress. Since cells proliferate preferentially along such micellar guiding structures, the connecting strand of cells may simply be explained on the basis that a pronounced system of parallel guiding tracks has formed in the zone between the explants. According to this viewpoint, the diversity of experimental results of Juhásc might readily be explained by postulating variations in the dehydrating capacity of the different kinds of tissue.

The concept of cytotropism has found favorable support especially among neurologists since it seemed to provide an explanation for the directed growth of nerves if it is assumed that attracting stimuli emanate from the future effector organ. Some investigators (Kappers, Child and others) considered a difference in electrical potential to be important while others (Cajal, Tello) assumed that specific chemical substances may act as stimulators.

Indeed, several authors interpreted the behavior of the outgrowing axons toward other cells in the explant in terms of chemotropism. There was for instance the observation that when nerve fibers grow into a fibroblast culture in the same plasma medium the path of some of them became apparently deviated in such a way as to make contact with a mesenchyme cell. This was considered proof for the existence of chemotropic relations between the cellular elements (Grigorjeff 1931), even though the nerve fibers would as often as not take no notice of the neighboring cells.

The interpretation of these findings has been rejected by Weiss (1934) on the strength of his counterarguments referred to above. On the basis of further extensive tests in plasma cultures in which neural tissue was confronted with other kinds of tissue, or with extracts of crushed tissues or chemical agents applied to one side, he concluded that the outgrowing nerve fiber does not respond to chemotactic stimulation, and that the direction of its growth is determined primarily, if not exclusively, by mechanical factors.

In commenting on this notion, one could argue, of course, that the conditions in explantation experiments by no means correspond to those prevailing in the organism, and that therefore a negative outcome of such experiments does not permit definitive conclusions as to the processes that occur in normal development. However, such considerations lie beyond the scope of our present topic. What is important here is to point out that on the basis of these investigations of Weiss, which thus far have remained unchallenged, cytotropism has not been experimentally demonstrated for animal tissues. Nevertheless, the notion that side by side with the mechanical factors, there occur intercellular correlations in the nature of physiological stimuli and that they may act as important formative principles, is not put on trial by this view.

To return to our present experiments, let us summarize their principal results, especially in their relation to the foregoing considerations.

In our isolation and combination experiments, carried out on embryonic amphibian material, the question of a chemotropic distant effect between cells has not even been touched upon. All the phenomena here described occurred while the various kinds of cells and tissues were in direct mutual contact. What was actually observed was an orderly union as well as non-unions and self-isolations. The events proceeded in an age- and tissue-specific manner, removed from the embryo as a whole, in a purely protective, indifferent medium and without the participation of a physically structured substrate. We, therefore, called them autonomous events and ascribed them to mutual cell-specific stimulation which we interpreted as an expression of affinities. Their chemical or physical nature was left undiscussed.

These stimulatory affinities share with the hypothetical cytotropism the capacity to bring about gradations of attraction and repulsion between cells, which lead to directional changes in their form and position, even though no action beyond that of direct cell contact has yet been proved.

As a means of the self-ordering of embryonic regions these phenomena are of great significance. They lead to the anatomical segregation of physiologically different organ primordia and to their recombination with other parts of the embryo. They provide a unified explanation for local migration and constriction movements in whole cell complexes, starting with those in gastrulation and being continued during organogenesis. The processes of induction and subsequent formative influences would not be possible without a positive affinity between the reacting material and the inductor. In view of the transparency of the situation and the ready availability of the material there should be no difficulty to explore the problem of affinity by means of further experiments and thus obtain new, well-documented support for a theory of development.

REFERENCES

BORN, G., Über Verwachsungsversuche mit Amphibienlarven. Arch. Entw. mechanik **4** (1897).

BYTINSKY-SALZ, H., Chromatophorenstudien II. Arch. f. exp. Zellforschg. **22**, H. 1 (1938).

FISCHER, A., Contributions to the biology of tissue cells. I. The relation of cell crowding to tissue growth in vitro. Journ, exp. Med. **38** (1923).

————, Gewebezüchtung. München, Müller u. Steinicke, 1927.

GALTSOFF, Regeneration after dissociation (an experimental study on sponges). Journ. of exp. Zool. **42** (1925).

GÖTTE, Die Entwicklungsgeschichte der Unke. Leipzig, 1875.

GRIGORJEFF, L. M., Differenzierung des Nervengewebes ausserhalb des Organismus. Arch. f. exper. Zellforschg. **11** (1931).

HARRISON, R. G., Experimentelle Untersuchungen über die Entwicklung der Sinnesorgane der Seitenlinie bie den Amphibien. Arch. mikrosk. Anat. **63** (1904).

HIS, W., Unsere Körperform, Briefe an einen befreundeten Naturforscher. Leipzig, F. C. W. Vogel. 1874.

HOLTFRETER, J., Über die Aufzucht isolierter Teile des Amphibienkeimes I. Roux' Arch. **117** (1929).

————, Die totale Exogastrulation, eine Selbstablösung des Ektoderms vom Entomesoderm. Roux' Arch. **129** (1933).

————, Formative Reize in der Embryonalentwicklung der Amphibien, dargestellt an Explantationsversuchen. Arch. f. exp. Zellforsch. **15** (1934a).

————, Nachweis der Induktionsfähigkeit abgetöteter Keimteile. Roux' Arch. **128** (1934b).

————, Morphologische Beeinflussung von Urodelenektoderm bei xenoplastischer Transplantation. Roux' Arch. **113** (1935).

————, Differenzierungspotenzen isolierter Teile der Urodelengastrula. Roux' Arch. **138** (1938a).

HOLTFRETER, J., Differenzierungspotenzen isolierter Teile der Anurengastrula. Roux' Arch. **138** (1938b).

JUHÁSC, A., Wachstumspolarität bei Gewebezüchtungen in vitro und ihre Beziehungen zur Tuberkuloseimmunität. Arch. f. exp. Zellforsch. **6** (1928).

KUHL, W. Untersuchungen über das Verhalten künstlich getrennter Furchungszellen und Zellaggregate einiger Amphibienarten mit Hilfe des Zeitrafferfilms. Roux' Arch. **136** (1937).

LEHMANN, F. E., Entwicklungsstörungen in der Medullaranlage von Triton, erzeugt durch Unterlagerungsdefekte. Roux' Arch. **108** (1926).

————, Die Bedeutung der Unterlagerung für die Entwicklung der Medullarplatte von Triton. Roux' Arch. **113** (1928).

MAXIMOW, A., Tissue-culture of young mammalian embryos. Publication 361 of the Carnegie Inst. of Washington (1925).

MORGAN, T. H., Regeneration in Bipalium. Arch. Entw.mechanik **9** (1900).

PÉTERFI, T., u. St. C. Williams, Elektrische Reizversuche an gezüchteten Gewebezellen. II. Versuche an verschiedenen Gewebekulturen. Arch. f. exp. Zellforsch. **16** (1931).

PFEFFER, Physiologische Untersuchungen. Leipzig 1873.

ROUX, W., Über den „Cytotropismus" der Furchungszellen des Grasfrosches (Rana fusca). Arch Ent.mechanik **1** (1894).

————, Über die Selbstordnung (Cytotaxis) sich „berührender" Furchungszellen des Froscheies durch Zellzusammenfügung und Zellengleiten. Arch. Entw.-mechanik **3** (1896).

TÖRÖ, E., Das organoide Wachstum der Darmkulturen. Arch. exp. Zellforsch. **9** (1930).

VOGT, W., Über Zellbewegungen und Zelldegeneration bei der Gastrulation von Triton cristatus. I. Anat. H. **48** (1913).

————, Gestaltungsanalyse am Amphibienkeim mit örtlicher Vitalfärbung. II. Teil: Gastrulation und Mesodermbildung bei Urodelen und Anuren. Roux' Arch. **120** (1929).

VOIGTLÄNDER, G., Neue Untersuchungen über den „Cytotropismus" der Furchungszellen. Roux' Arch. **127** (1932).

WEISS, P., Erzwingung elementarer Strukturverschiedenheiten an in vitro wachsenden Geweben. Roux' Arch. **116** (1929).

————, In vitro experiments on the factors determining the course of the outgrowing nerve fiber. Journ. of exp. Zool. **63** (1934).